BRUCE ROBERTS
BOATBUILDING

STEEL . GLASS . WOOD
ALUMINIUM

By R. Bruce Roberts-Goodson AM SNAME

BRUCE ROBERTS
BOATBUILDING

ISBN 1 898307 06 7

First Edition 1994

R. Bruce Roberts-Goodson AM SNAME
13 Preston Grove,
Faversham Kent ME13 8JZ
Tel. & Fax. (0795) 534 204
From outside UK + 44 795 534 204

Published by

Capall Bann Publishing
Freshfields
Chieveley
Berks
RG16 8TF
Tel. & Fax. 0635 248711

CONTENTS:

INTRODUCTION AND ACKNOWLEDGEMENTS

When preparing the copy for this book, my object was to provide sufficient information on the various boat building techniques. Choose the method of construction best suited to your abilities and personal preferences.

I wish to thank the many builders without whose cooperation this book would not have been possible. To those builders who have allowed me to photograph the various stages of their building programme, to those who have contributed ideas and solutions to problems and to those who have contributed photographs of their projects. I extend my sincere appreciation for their generous cooperation.

R. Bruce Roberts-Goodson   AM SNAME

Photograph by Michael Harvey
Cover design by Daryth Bastin

ii

CHAPTER ONE
THE BUILDING SITE

Consider the transportation and launching of your completed boat when looking for a suitable building site. We have seen it all; boats built on the top of mountains and launched by large military type helicopters; boats built behind houses and then lifted over the house with a crane; boats built in the highlands of New Guinea and launched after bulldozing a road to the sea; boats built on the beach in Belize; boats built in Kansas USA and hauled by road to the sea; a boat built in the Arctic Circle where the supply ship arrived only once a year, and a 35' wooden boat built in a living room, requiring the removal of the end wall of the house, to get the boat out!

We can think of hundreds of examples where the building conditions would have prevented the faint hearted from ever starting the project. If you are unable to find a more desirable building site as outlined below, do not despair, seek out the best available site and get your project under way. Finding a suitable building site, will be an important consideration when deciding which material and building method you should choose for your boat building project. Some materials require an enclosed, well ventilated building with some form of temperature control, while you can use other materials in the open air. Many builders have successfully built steel boats outside. The builder would have enjoyed the project more, if he had arranged some form of cover over and around the boat. You should find a boat building location as close to your home as possible. It is always easier to get started, when you do not have too far to travel.

The solution to finding a place to build, can include the renting of an older unused building. It is surprising just how many of these buildings are available in most areas. Don't be discouraged by the high prices quoted in the "Industrial Property to rent" columns of your local newspaper. These high priced newly built buildings may not be for you. There are older buildings that may be rented at low cost, such as unused railway sheds, wharf buildings, farmer's barns and other similar structures.

Another solution is to build your own shelter. If you have a suitably sized yard and friendly neighbours,

"Temporary" shed — Total cost $1150. Built by Chris Deselles for his ROBERTS 38.

For the less severe climates this type of building cover is adequate.

then this is the ideal solution. You may need to obtain a permit for the temporary structure in your own yard. For those who live in an apartment, you may wish to consider renting a suitable house for the duration of the boat building project.

If you decide to build your own boat building shed, then the most economical method is to use 2" x 4" [50 x 100] timber framing covered with builders plastic sheeting. This plastic may be purchased at most hardware super stores. Obtain a better quality plastic, so it will last the duration of your boat building project.

Under no circumstances should you build a fibreglass boat in the open. We have seen some attempts at this, and it is always a rush to get everything done before the next rain shower or spell of bad weather. Exposing some forms of core material to sunlight, will expand or contract the foam, and may distort the whole hull structure.

If you intend to build using the Wood/Epoxy or other similar wooden boat building technique, you will require a suitable shelter. You do not need a shelter when building in steel. However even when you build in this medium, we advise some type of covering. A considerable amount of non steel materials needed to complete a steel hull and these are usually susceptible to the elements.

You will often choose to build a steel boat using prime coated plate. Damage to the prime coating can occur if left to the elements during the construction stage. If you choose untreated steel, then you may build outside. You can remove by sand or grit blasting the amount of rust your hull will accumulate during any reasonable length of time building the hull and deck. Some of our plans include provision for a shelter built into the setting up of the hull.

One of the best building sites is the local boat yard, where it is often possible to rent space for building your boat. Make sure that the yard has liberal policies regarding where you obtain your materials and occasional professional help. Make sure you are not required to purchase your building supplies and services from any one source. As the length of time you will take to build your boat can vary from a few months to several years, you should make sure you consider all factors before committing yourself to a building site.

Temporary shed — 2" x 4" and plastic, costs about $200.00.

CHAPTER TWO
FIBREGLASS - THE MATERIALS

Before considering the individual fibreglass boat building techniques, you will need a reasonable knowledge of the materials you use to build your boat. Fibreglass is an easy medium for the boat builder to handle. The more informed you are about the various types of resins and glass materials and their particular uses, the easier it will be for you to build your boat.

Fibreglass, is known by different names in various areas. In English speaking Europe it is called Fibreglass; in the USA it is known as fibreglass. Some people refer to the finished product as FRP that stands for Fibreglass reinforced plastic. In other areas the term is GRP standing for glass reinforced plastic. The fibreglass or more correctly glass fibre is only one component of the finished material. The other main ingredient is the resin.

TYPES OF GLASS FIBRE.

The glass component is available in three main classes, E glass, which is the original glass material and R and S glass, which are more recently developed versions. Usually you will be working with the less expensive E glass, while R and S glass are usually reserved for the more specialised applications.

Other materials such as Kevlar and Carbon fibre are sometimes used as the reinforcing component of the fibreglass laminate. When your boat building project does call for R or S glass, carbon fibre, kevlar or other similar materials, you can obtain excellent information from the manufacturers of the product concerned.

Most readers of this book will be concerned with building a strong, practical boat, so unless you are considering a specialised race boat or similar application, you can concentrate on E glass and use the more traditional fibreglass boat building materials.

MAT

C.S.M. are the initials for Chopped Strand Mat. This material is of glass fibre strands and is available in

C.S.M. — MAT

varying types and weights. The mat available includes 3/4 ounce per square foot [225 grams per square metre], 1 ounce per square foot [300 grams per square metre], 1 1/2 ounce per square foot [450 grams per square metre] plus 2 oz. [600 g/m 2] and 3 oz. [900 g/m 2]. The last two examples are the way you will most often see the weights expressed, by designers or manufacturers of the material. In our own material lists we simply say 1 1/2 oz. mat [450 g/m 2] and so forth.

Held with an emulsion binder, the strands make up the mat. This binder will dissolve when the resin is applied, without causing any adverse reaction to the resin. The construction of the mat is often described as random discontinuous fibres. The mat is also available with a powder binder. Continuous filament, is another form of mat that is, as the name suggests, made of random continuous glass fibre.

The author (R) discusses production techniques with foreman boatbuilder Len Freestone.

CONTINUOUS ROVING.

Supplied in "cheeses," this material, which resemble a coil of light rope and used with a fibreglass depositor machine. The reduction in cost of the equipment required to apply this material, has made it worth considering its use if you are building a single large boat or several smaller craft.

Run through a "Chopper gun," the continuous roving mixes the chopped glass fibres with the resin at the gun; simultaneously sprays the mixture of glass and resin on to the hull mould surface. The result is a quickly applied chopped strand mat. This technique is more suitable for female moulding. If you are considering a female mould or laying up your hull using "Panel Construction" methods, then continuous roving may be of great interest to you. Many builders use the gun as a resin depositor only. This allows mixing and depositing of the resin by mechanical means, with greater time and some material savings.

It takes an experienced and careful operator to get a perfectly even coat of the mat and resin to the mould. For male moulding, evenness of the application is most important, so the continuous roving will not be suitable for this method. You may wish to use a "Chopper gun" set up as a resin depositor only.

WOVEN ROVING.

This material is the real meat of your fibreglass laminate. Called WR, this material as manufactured, consists of continuous strands of roving woven into a loose cloth type structure and sold in various weights per square yard or square metre. This is a little confusing to those working with imperial measurements, because when working out the basic laminate; you have to divide the weight of the woven roving by nine to bring it to square feet, and then add the various mat and roving quantities together; to arrive at the weight per square foot, of the glass content required for your project. For those working in the metric system, you will be pleased to know that quoted in grams per metre, woven roving uses the same basis as the weight definitions for the mat.

Woven roving is available from 8 oz. per square yard [270 g/m 2] to 27 oz per square yard [900 g/m 2], with a variety of intermediate weights. Sold in a variety of weave patterns, Woven Roving is available as, bidirectional, unidirectional, biaxial, triaxial, double bias and specially stitched, etc. The designer of your boat will generally specify the type of woven roving he wishes you to use in the various parts of your boat building project. Woven roving should never be laminated one to the other, without a layer of the chopped strand mat between the roving.

COMBINATION FABRICS.

Special reinforcing glass materials combined with the mat are available. This makes one easy to install fabric, which is applied more quickly and evenly than separate layers of the mat and roving. You can check with your local fibreglass supplier to see which of these materials are available in your area.

FIBREGLASS CLOTH.

The difference between this material and woven roving, is in the cloth. Made up of twisted fibres, each strand is then woven into the finished material. In woven roving, the fibres are simply laid side by side and then woven to complete the fabric.

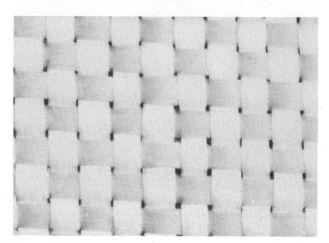

Woven Rovings

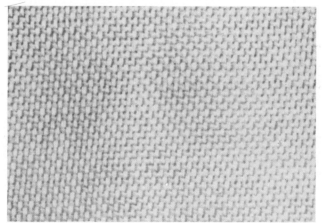

Fiberglass Cloth. The difference between this and rovings is that each strand is made up of twisted fibers and then woven into cloth.

4

Fibreglass cloth is available in a variety of weights per square yard, similar to woven roving, so that 8 oz cloth is only equal in weight to one ounce mat, however the cloth is stronger. For those working in metric measurements, the comparison is simpler; all the fibreglass fabrics are quoted in grams per metre.

Fibreglass cloth can be used when you have an inordinate amount of fairing compound on your hull. One or two layers of 10 oz. [1 g/m 2] cloth will help to even out the surface and keep the filler in place. This material is also used as a sheathing material for plywood hulls and superstructures. When used for sheathing, fibreglass cloth is best applied using Epoxy resins, instead of the Polyester resin used in normal fibreglass construction.

KEVLAR

This material has been available for several years, and is widely used in the construction of high performance boats where special strengthening is required. Kevlar is best used, where keeping the weight to a minimum, combined with special strength requirements, make its use desirable. Kevlar should be included in your laminate, only when specified by the designer. Do not decide to use any of the more exotic fabrics associated with fibreglass construction, without first consulting the designer of your boat.

CARBON FIBRE

The most commonly used reinforcement materials are the roving and mat as previously described; the more expensive and specialised fabrics such as carbon fibre and kevlar do have their place when used where special strength requirements can only be achieved by using these fabrics.

The search for superior materials continues, particularly for use in the aerospace industry. The most significant of these more recent developments is the use of the carbon which is a readily available element and it has many useful properties. Most organic materials are freely available and very low in cost. Certain types of carbon fibre can be manmade in vast quantities so it would appear that this is the material of the future. The larger scale production at competitive prices is a matter of time and research.

Not withstanding the above, we feel that carbon fibre would need to come a long way down the price

Carbon fibre and R glass rovings are used where specialised strength requirements make the additional cost wothwhile

scale before we could recommend it for general purpose use in boat building. Used for producing free standing masts, Carbon fibre is also used in hull laminates where the combination of high strength and minimum weight is required.

It is our recommendation that you do not use any unspecified materials in your fibreglass boat building process. If you have a through understanding of the newer materials and a deep enough pocket to pay the higher prices; consult the designer of your boat, before making any changes to the laminate as shown in your plans.

FOAM CORE

Foam cores are best used in hull construction, although sometimes they can be successfully used in deck structures. The best known foam is Airex Tm. which like all the best of the foam core materials, is manufactured from P.V.C. Airex is made in large buns that look something like a huge loaf of bread, sawn into sheets of varying thicknesses, including 3/8" [10 mm], 1/2" [12 mm], 5/8" [15 mm], 3/4" [20 mm] and 1" [25 mm]. Manufactured in different densities, foam core as used for most boat building applications has a density of 5 pounds per cubic foot.

The foam core can be smooth both sides, or scored with a special pattern of cuts to allow it to be bent without heating. Several years ago it was necessary to preheat this type of material, special scoring plus developments in manufacturing, make it possible to use it without any pre treatment being required.

There are several manufacturers of foam core namely; those marketed under the names of Klegecell, Divinycell, Polimex and of course the well-known Airex. You should check to see which material is locally available. Make sure it is the P.V.C. variety, and it is the correct density for your particular project. If you are using foam core for decks, you should ensure that it is of a suitable type, and will not warp due to the heat generated when the hot sun beats down on your deck. Our recommendation is to use foam core for hulls, and balsa core for deck and cabin structures.

BALSA CORE

Balsa core is available in two main forms; the most commonly used is end grain balsa. This material consists of small blocks of end grain balsa attached to a light netting scrim to make up sheets of about 36" x 24" [1 metre x .75 metre]. The end grain balsa has a high compressive strength, and is ideal as a core material for decks and the bottom of power boat hulls.

BALSA

DuraKore is a product marketed by Baltek, the largest manufacturers of balsa core products. DuraKore is a composite material, consisting of balsa skinned with hardwood veneers. DuraKore comes in 8' x 4' [2.4 m x 1.2 m] sheets. DuraKore

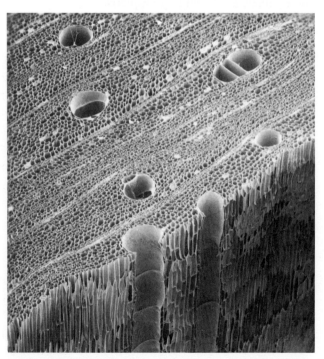

Close up of end grain and radial surface of BALSACORE. Photo 30X.

is usually sawn into planks. The planks are then end-finger jointed to the required length. When using DuraKore, the hull is planked similar to a strip plank timber hull, and then the core is covered on both sides with fibreglass to form a sandwich structure.

NOMEX - HONEY COMB CORES

These cores are almost exclusively used in race boat applications and are difficult to use. The edge of the honeycomb offers only a small bonding area, and Epoxy resins are essential if your select Nomex as your core material. If there is any water penetration of the skin, then the honey comb chambers will hold a considerable amount of water, making your boat heavy, and doing untold damage to the structure. If you are used to building specialised race boat hulls, then you will be familiar with this material, if not, leave it to the experts.

POLYESTER RESIN.

There are several types of polyester resins available and each has its own particular application. Some resins are specifically designed for the bulk of the laminating, while others are added to and modified to make up exterior and interior gelcoats. Most of the resin types you will be using, have been available for long enough, and tested sufficiently for you to use them with confidence. Technical information and instructions for usage, will be available from your local resin supplier.

ORTHO OR ISO

These polyester resins are still the most commonly used, but vinyl esters are growing in popularity for both new construction and repair work. Although the more recently developed resins may look good on paper, you should assure yourself that you are choosing the material best suited for your project. Some materials are fine for primary bonding, including laying up the basic hull and superstructure. These materials are not so successful when it comes to secondary bonding, such as joining one section of pre moulded fibreglass to another, or bonding other materials such as plywood to your hull.

Unwaxed Resin

Where it is anticipated that a considerable time span will elapse, between starting, and completion of the particular section being moulded, you should use the unwaxed resin. It takes up to a few days for this resin to finally cure. The surface will remain tacky, thus facilitating the bonding of the subsequent layers. You should complete all of your layers, without more than thirty-six hours between laminations.

Waxed Laminating Resin

This material, as the name implies, has had wax added to provide a smooth, non tacky surface, which will not pick up dirt etc. This resin is used for moulding in any area where the work is to be completed within a short period, and used also where you wish to later sand the surface, to get an improved finish. You may purchase your waxed resin with the wax already added, or you may prefer to purchase a wax solution, and add it to the unwaxed resin.

EXTERIOR GELCOAT

There are several types of this material, each having their own particular function. The most often used, is the one for female moulding. This gelcoat comes in various colours and is unwaxed. It may be pre promoted and will need some catalyst added before being applied to the mould surface.

The gelcoat forms a barrier between the general laminate and the outside elements. The type of gelcoat you choose, and the way you apply it, will certainly affect your finished boat. Spray or brush this material on to the mould surface. If you are building a male moulded boat, you may well replace the gelcoat with urethane or epoxy based exterior paint system.

INTERIOR GELCOAT

This material is designed for brushing on the interior surfaces of your fibreglass hull. By the way, when we speak of the hull, we often refer to the entire hull deck and superstructure. Interior gelcoat gives a durable smooth finish to your work. Also known as resin coat, this material is available in many attractive colours, but white is preferred for the interior finish. Interior gelcoat flows well as it contains thickening agents and brushes on well without leaving brush marks.

FUEL AND WATER TANK RESIN

Special resins are available to coat the interior

surfaces of fuel and water tanks and these resins insure that a suitable barrier is set up between the liquid and your fibreglass laminate. If you used regular laminating resins in your water tanks, the water would have an unpleasant taste. You may have to flush out the water tanks several times to get rid of any uncured catalyst, as this could also effect the taste of your drinking water.

POLYURETHANE PAINTS

Generally preferred, this type of paint finish is used for external hull protection when the male moulding building techniques are employed. International Paints make excellent coatings of this type and their products provide attractive and long lasting protection for your boat.

ACCELERATOR

Supplied with the accelerator or promoter, most resins have this material already added. These resins are called, pre promoted resins. If your resin has not been pre promoted, you will need to add the correct amount of the accelerator. Extra amounts of the accelerator can be added to most resins, if you require a quicker setting time than the recommended amount would normally allow. Do not add excessive amounts of the accelerator to any resin mix, because it may reach a level where your laminate will set too quickly.

CATALYST

This is the additive that makes the resin go hard; it is the curing agent. The catalyst is a peroxide material and comes in different forms, the most common being a clear liquid. This material should always be stored in plastic containers and can be quite dangerous if indiscriminately used. Spillage should be avoided and any material that does escape should be immediately cleaned up, taking care not to get the catalyst on your skin, as this material can give you a nasty burn.

RESIN PUTTY - FILLERS

You will use sizeable quantities of fillers and putty on your fibreglass boat building project. Female moulded, and to a greater extent, male moulded boats, require a generous amount of the material, we commonly call "BOG." There are several materials that can form the dry ingredients for the resin putty mixture. These include, aerosil, cabisol, micro balloons, carbon, and of course my favourite, industrial talcum powder. Check with your local fibreglass supplier and the designer of your boat, as to the recommended materials, for the project in hand.

INDUSTRIAL TALCUM POWDER

Of all the powders that can be used as the solid component of fillers and fairing materials, the cheapest is talcum powder that comes in bags similar to a bag of cement. Talcum powder can be used to make an inexpensive resin putty, commonly known as "BOG." which has many uses when building a fibreglass boat, and it is especially useful when building a male moulded hull or superstructure. Talcum powder should be of a fine grade and must be stored in a dry place.

RESIN PUTTY - "BOG"

This do-it-yourself material can be made for a fraction of what you would pay, if you bought this type of putty from your local resin supplier. To make your own "BOG" the procedure is as follows. Place a small amount of pre promoted resin in a disposable container and add a dash of accelerator. Stir thoroughly and slowly while adding the talcum powder until you have a "BOG" of the desired consistency. You will soon learn the amounts to make up at once. This material if stored in a covered container, will keep for up to two or three weeks. When you wish to use the material, you simply dip out a quantity and place it on a mixing board. You now add a dash of catalyst, this does not have to be measured, as you will soon gauge the amount required to make the bog set in the desired time. This material has many uses as you will soon discover.

PREGELL

Use this material to thicken the resin, when you are laminating in a location where the resin of normal viscosity would sag and run out of the part, before the curing process could get under way. Pregell usually contains aerosil and other thickening agents. Pregell is sometimes added to gelcoats; generally only experienced builders should use the pregell material.

FIRE RETARDANT RESINS

Designed for either general laminating or gel-

coating, these resins are required in areas where there is a higher than usual fire risk, for example in the area of the galley and the engine room. As fire retardant resins are generally more expensive than regular laminating resins, most builders tend to only use them where necessary.

ACETONE

WARNING! This is a highly volatile chemical, used for cleaning your tools and brushes and if used correctly, it will save you considerable expense. If not cleaned properly, your brushes and rollers will soon become clogged up with cured resin and have to be replaced after each laminating session. Acetone should be stored in a sealed metal container and measured out in small quantities; say 2" [50 mm] in the bottom of a plastic container in which you should throughly wash the brushes and tools. The dirty acetone is then properly disposed of and the tools washed again in clean acetone. If you store the brushes in clean acetone overnight, make sure you use a sealed container, as the acetone has a high evaporation rate and you could find your brushes ruined, if the container dries out. You can use acetone to thin the resin. Used to thin the brushing variety of exterior gelcoat, when it is a little too thick for brushing, a small amount of acetone will make it easier to get a good finish. **HANDLE ACETONE WITH UTMOST CARE.**

STYRENE

This is one of the main ingredients used to manufacture laminating and general purpose resins. Use styrene to thin the resin when necessary. Sometimes you may wish to add styrene to replace the amount of the material that has evaporated from your resin mix when working in a draughty or other unsuitable environment. It is best to avoid the unsuitable conditions, if this is possible. Some resins are more prone to losing part of the styrene content than others. This will be apparent by the resin becoming prematurely thick, before setting would normally take place, due to the normal curing process. Avoid resins that show unfavourable tendencies, such as excessive styrene evaporation. Don't forget to wear the correct mask and other protective clothing, when handling materials containing styrene. **HANDLE STYRENE WITH CARE.**

PRE-PREG REINFORCEMENTS

It is now over twenty years since the aerospace industry switched to this type of fibreglass laminating. For many reasons, pre-pregs have not made much of an impression on the use of the more traditional fibreglass boat building techniques. These materials have to be stored at zero degrees and of course that means expensive and reliable storage facilities will be required. These cold storage arrangements are usually not available at most boat building facilities. Before you use the pre-preg material, it has to be brought to room temperature.

Curing this material requires a special oven that can reach 200 degrees Fahrenheit [93 C], and of course the ovens have to be large enough to contain the part being manufactured. Pre-pregs have all sorts of behaviour patterns that are different from the usual fibreglass materials. Regarding the cost, pre-preg fibreglass materials are expensive, far too expensive for general use. The technology associated with Pre-pregs is continually evolving and if you are interested in learning more about these very specialised materials; start your search at your local fibreglass supplier who will direct you to where the latest information is readily available.

CHAPTER THREE
FIBREGLASS - SAFETY EQUIPMENTT

You will need a range of safety equipment, including breathing masks, to prevent you from inhaling noxious fumes and dust particles. You will also require a variety of clothing items to protect your outer body from harmful burns and contact with the materials that can cause skin rashes and similar unpleasant and more serious illnesses. Sometimes, prolonged exposure to resins and other fibre glassing materials can, over a long period, make you sensitive to any contact with the materials.

Your hearing will also need protection and there is a good selection of protective equipment available. Hoods are becoming more popular as a protective device, to totally isolate you above the shoulders. Some hoods have built in filters and most are designed not to restrict your vision. Remember that restricted vision is a health hazard. Proper care and protection, can ensure you suffer no ill effects from using fibreglass materials.

RESPIRATORS AND BREATHING MASKS

The most important piece of safety equipment for working with fibreglass, will be a respirator or mask, which will protect you from a variety of airborne hazards. You will need protection from simple dust through to potential cancer causing dust and vapours. Protect yourself against the vapours from styrene and paint finishes. These items of safety equipment range from the simple paper mask, through to separate air supply units, which totally isolate you from the surrounding environment. You should discuss the various options with your fibreglass supplier, who will advise you of the options available for each particular use and workplace situation. Designed to avoid a particular dangerous workplace condition or range of hazards most masks have some form of filter arrangement.

Some respirators do not work when used over a beard or for that matter stubble. If you are not clean shaven, then look towards the all over hood type protection.

The 3M corporation has recently designed a respirator as part of the Easi-Care 7800S series. This unit is a light weight half mask respirator with swept back cylinders for better vision and balance, a diaphragm for communicating and a special strap arrangement to reduce pressure points. This unit is worth your investigation.

A well-run building workplace can take the pressure off the safety equipment by providing a clean environment. Keep rubbish and trash off the floor. As created, stow trimmings immediately. Make sure you have adequate ventilation. Keeping a clean workplace will go a long way to keeping you healthier. You will reduce fire risks and keep your insurance man happy.

HAND PROTECTION

Your hands are involved in most of the work; you should take extra care that they are well protected. Using gloves or barrier creams will be the choice and each has its good and less satisfactory points. Never work with bare hands. Not only resins, but also timber and glass materials can cause problems when worked without protecting your hands. Sometimes it will take gloves and barrier creams to give satisfactory protection. Again seek the advice of your local fibreglass supplier; he will generally only give the best available advice. When working around fibreglass, keep your hands away from your orifices, eyes, mouth and nose etc.

EYE PROTECTION

Some hoods and respirators also incorporate eye protection. For certain jobs, separate goggles are important. You will need to choose between goggles and safety glasses. Eye protection from the sides is important. When grinding fibreglass and other associated materials, it is amazing the various trajectories the ground particles can take. For jobs such as grinding, you might find a face shield more comfortable while providing better protection.

EAR AND HEARING PROTECTION

If you are working in conditions where the noise level is in the 80 plus decibel range, you must consider using ear plugs or earmuffs. Foam plugs provide a good sound masking, but you may prefer the earmuff option. Do not forget the cumulative effect of a radio playing over the sound of a grinder or saw. One professional boatbuilder insists that the foam earplugs have florescent cords, so the foreman can see from a distance, the plugs are being worn when necessary.

BODY PROTECTION

For the best body protection, you will need an all over body suit that is usually of the disposable variety. Suits have improved in the past few years and most now feel more comfortable to wear while still providing the necessary protection. How you feel about wearing a suit may depend on the climate. Some hot climates call for creative arrangement such as the tissue paper suits worn by some boat builders.

FOOTWEAR

Your feet are the easiest areas to protect. Most fibre glass workers wear sneakers. Disposable over booties are necessary for some jobs but generally sneakers, especially the ones with high sides, will give you the necessary protection. Do not forget, if you are working in an area where you are likely to be handling heavy equipment and may be liable to drop some heavy item on your foot, then suitably reinforced boots will be required.

Picture shows builder measuring hardener (catalyst) for resin.

CHAPTER FOUR
FIBREGLASS - THE TOOLS.

You will purchase most of the tools you require, at the same source as your other fibreglass supplies. You will need an assortment of brushes, paint rollers, scrapers, squeegees, plastic containers and measuring devices. A few of the items you can make yourself or scrounge, are for example, plastic ice cream containers that make ideal mixing vessels for working quantities of the resin. Screeding and mixing devices can be made by you the builder.

PAINT SCRAPERS

You will need an assortment of cheap paint scrapers. Usually the cheaper ones have more flexible blades and these are for handling the resin putty "Bog" and fairing up various areas of filler. Order a selection of widths, say 1" [25], 2" [50], 4" [100], and 6" [150], and one or two with rounded ends that can be used for creating fillets. There will be many uses for your selection of paint scrapers. The scrapers can be washed in acetone after scraping off the residue of hardened bog, which will gradually build up on the blades. Keep your scrapers as clean as possible.

DISK SANDERS

Do not skimp on the quality of this tool, buy the absolute best you can afford. The right size is about 7" [175]. Choose a low or duel speed disc sander that will be happy running at 4,000 RPM. The sander should be equipped with an 8" [200] circular foam pad; such as "Ferro pads" or a similar unit. You will use the stick on type sanding discs; of the open coat aluminum oxide 8" [200] type. You will need a selection of varying grits. This outfit will be often used during the construction of your boat. Again I stress, always buy the best quality sander you can find, the cheaper variety, sold for home handyman use, will soon fail.

Fiberglass boatbuilding tools – trowel, steel rollers, Surform, mohair roller, knife, plastic buckets, brushes and sander with foam pad attachment.

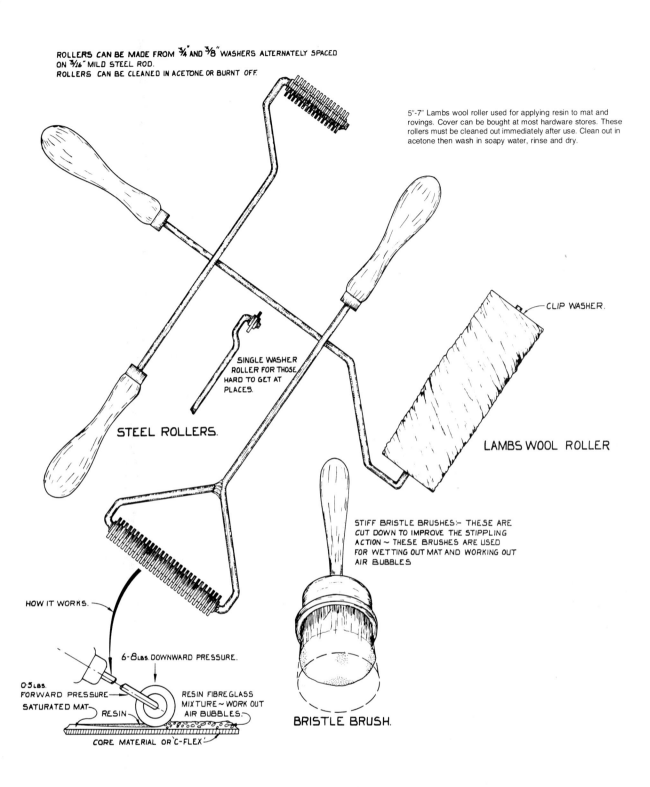

ROLLERS CAN BE MADE FROM ¾" AND ⅜" WASHERS ALTERNATELY SPACED ON ³∕₁₆" MILD STEEL ROD.
ROLLERS CAN BE CLEANED IN ACETONE OR BURNT OFF.

5"-7" Lambs wool roller used for applying resin to mat and rovings. Cover can be bought at most hardware stores. These rollers must be cleaned out immediately after use. Clean out in acetone then wash in soapy water, rinse and dry.

CLIP WASHER.

SINGLE WASHER ROLLER FOR THOSE HARD TO GET AT PLACES.

STEEL ROLLERS.

LAMBS WOOL ROLLER

STIFF BRISTLE BRUSHES:- THESE ARE CUT DOWN TO IMPROVE THE STIPPLING ACTION ~ THESE BRUSHES ARE USED FOR WETTING OUT MAT AND WORKING OUT AIR BUBBLES

HOW IT WORKS.

6-8 LBS. DOWNWARD PRESSURE.

0·5 LBS. FORWARD PRESSURE
SATURATED MAT
RESIN
RESIN FIBREGLASS MIXTURE ~ WORK OUT AIR BUBBLES.
CORE MATERIAL OR 'C-FLEX.'

BRISTLE BRUSH.

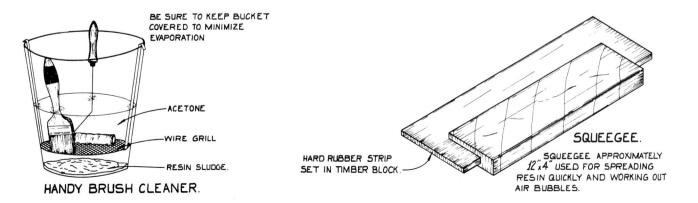

BE SURE TO KEEP BUCKET COVERED TO MINIMIZE EVAPORATION

ACETONE
WIRE GRILL
RESIN SLUDGE.

HANDY BRUSH CLEANER.

HARD RUBBER STRIP SET IN TIMBER BLOCK.

SQUEEGEE.
SQUEEGEE APPROXIMATELY 12"x4" USED FOR SPREADING RESIN QUICKLY AND WORKING OUT AIR BUBBLES.

OTHER SANDING DEVICES

You will need a selection of sanding blocks and boards. One useful board is a piece of plywood 4'-6" [1.37 M] x 6" [150 MM] x 1/2" [12 MM] thick. This board will be equipped with handles and will accept the stick on sandpaper. The board is handled with long sweeping strokes that follow the contour of the hull and will tend to even out any unfair areas. There is a variety of power sanders with all types of actions, ask your fibreglass supplier for details. Always use any new sanding tool on a test area, before committing its use to large areas of your boat.

BRUSHES

All the brushes you purchase should have unpainted handles and you will require several 3" [75] and a few 1" [25] and 2" [50]. The 3" [75] width will be ideal for most laminating operations.

MOHAIR ROLLERS

You should purchase as complete units, one 3" [75] and one 5" [125] mohair roller, both with unpainted handles. Also, equip yourself with several replacement sleeves. After use, always remove the sleeve from the roller and thoroughly wash the sleeve in acetone and allow to dry. Make sure you always use mohair rollers, as other types sold for painting, will soon fall apart when used with the various fibreglass resins.

PLASTIC BUCKETS AND CONTAINERS

Save all of your suitably sized plastic containers and have your friends save theirs too. Use these for mixing your resin. You may also purchase some small plastic buckets. Half gallons [2 lit.] and one gallon [4 lit.] will be the best size for your purpose. The hardened resins will crack out of these after use. It is a good idea to use one specially calibrated and marked bucket for measuring out the specified quantities of the resin; this will save you the bother of actually weighing every batch.

JIGSAW

When building any boat, there is a considerable amount of trimming required and an electric jigsaw will be suitable for this purpose. Use only high grade metal cutting blades and the unit will handle the fibreglass laminate without the blades becoming

blunt too readily. Equipped with the correct blades, use the jigsaw unit for cutting out the plywood bulkheads, plywood sole etc., so again remember to purchase a good quality unit. Use high quality blades suitable for the purpose when cutting plywood.

SURFORM

This neat little tool that should be purchased in its plane form, has many uses during the building of your boat. Flat and rounded blades will be required, and are readily available from most hardware stores.

ELECTRIC DRILL

This piece of equipment is not only used for drilling holes, but with the addition of a set of hole saws and other attachments, it will see plenty of use during the construction programme. Purchase a good quality unit.

STEEL ROLLERS

When used for rolling the mat and roving, the rollers remove any air bubbles trapped in the laminate. The steel rollers also roll the material to a smooth finish. A range of sizes of steel rollers is required including some very small ones for getting in the corners. Check with your supplier regarding the various sizes and types.

SCALES

A set of kitchen scales that weigh up to ten pounds will be ideal for weighing out the resins and you will find these at your local hardware store.

SCREEDS

You will need a variety of screeds, most of which are made from flexible plastic. You can make your own or purchase special ones from your supplier. A special screed is made from an old wood saw with the teeth ground off; this is ideal for screeding large areas, such as the main sections of the hull.

VACUUM BAGGING EQUIPMENT

You may wish to use vacuum bagging when installing the core materials, used during the construction of your hull and deck. Details of the equipment required, will be covered in a special section, dealing with vacuum bagging techniques.

MISCELLANEOUS ITEMS

You will need several other items such as scissors to cut the fibreglass mat and woven roving; sharp scissors are required. Also needed is a paddle mixer, used with your electric drill running at slow speeds. A table on which to lay out the mat and roving with a device to hold the roll at one end is a necessity. Also, required is a measuring glass for the catalyst and a selection of woodworking tools, clamps, and ladders etc.

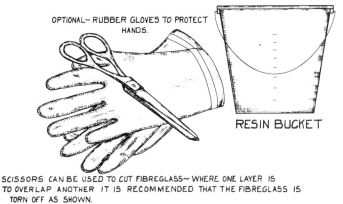

OPTIONAL~ RUBBER GLOVES TO PROTECT HANDS.

RESIN BUCKET

SCISSORS CAN BE USED TO CUT FIBREGLASS~ WHERE ONE LAYER IS TO OVERLAP ANOTHER IT IS RECOMMENDED THAT THE FIBREGLASS IS TORN OFF AS SHOWN.

2 GALLON BUCKET MARK IN POUNDS WEIGHT OF RESIN CLEARLY ON SIDE OF BUCKET.

MEASURING GLASS FOR CORRECT AMOUNT OF HARDNER (CATALYST) IN MILLILITRES

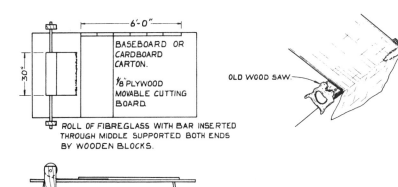

6'-0"

BASEBOARD OR CARDBOARD CARTON.

⅛" PLYWOOD MOVABLE CUTTING BOARD.

30"

ROLL OF FIBREGLASS WITH BAR INSERTED THROUGH MIDDLE SUPPORTED BOTH ENDS BY WOODEN BLOCKS.

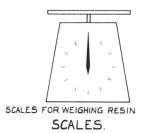

OLD WOOD SAW.

SCALES FOR WEIGHING RESIN

SCALES.

A convenient surface for laying out mat and rovings is essential.

CHAPTER FIVE
FIBREGLASS - BUILDING A MALE MOULD

With the development of Computer lofting, it has become possible for the designer to supply the builder with very accurate full size patterns. Usually included with the full size patterns, are the frames, stem, expanded transom, deck beams, cabin top beams and miscellaneous items, which can be made straight from the patterns. Before computer assisted design and lofting; drawing the lines plan and lofting the boat full size, was a long and expensive process, which took around 250 man hours to complete. Now it is possible to reduce this time to less than one tenth, so we invest more time elsewhere in the designing process.

Having the personal knowledge of several thousand 18' to 70' [5.48 M to 21 M] boats being successfully built from full size patterns, I can say with absolute confidence; you should try to obtain a plan with full size patterns. You will save many man hours and the boat will be shaped as the designer intended it to be.

FULL SIZE PATTERNS

For masochists and those who either want to build a boat from archive material, where patterns are not available, or for those who are unfortunate enough to deal with a designer who is unable or unwilling to provide full size patterns, you may be forced to undertake the job of completely lofting your chosen design full size. There are several books available which cover the subject fully; I will leave it to you to research lofting, if you are forced to draw your future boat full size and draw your own patterns.

If you are going to loft full size, make sure you do the complete lofting job. Do not take shortcuts by lofting frames only, without drawing out all the water lines, buttock lines etc., all full size. If you take short cuts with your lofting, you will regret it, when you start to assemble and fair your hull.

If you are fortunate enough to receive full size patterns with your plans, please use the patterns. On no account should you try to "Improve" the patterns by re lofting the lines. There may be a slight movement in paper patterns due to the changes caused by variation in climate and temperature. This movement is usually evenly distributed through out the patterns. Provided you are working under

TRANSFERRING ON TO TIMBER (TAKING OFF)

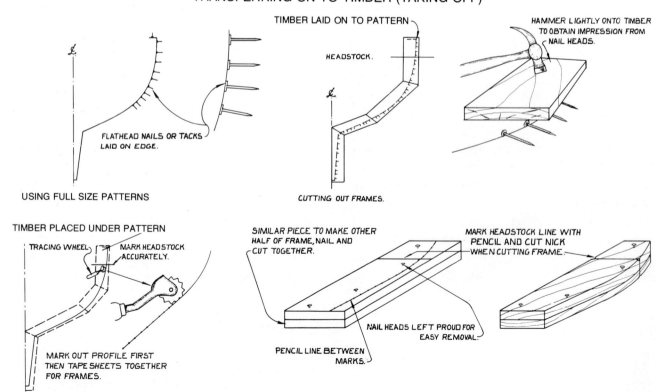

reasonable conditions these variations will not be large enough to effect the finished product. When ready to use the patterns, you should pick a day when you believe the temperature, humidity and other weather factors will remain constant, at least for that day. Prepare to transfer the patterns to a plywood floor or "take off" the frame shapes and other various items as shown on your patterns. If you want the ultimate accuracy and are prepared to pay extra, then you could ask your designer to supply the patterns plotted on mylar film.

LAYING OUT THE PATTERNS

Most full size patterns are plotted or traced on 24" [610] or 30" [760] or perhaps 36" [1 metre] wide paper or mylar film. These sections are laid side by side wallpaper fashion; to reveal the complete set of frames, stem pattern and other elements of your boat that are supplied full size.

You will find the patterns generally show one side, or half the shape of the frame. As most boats are symmetrical, your patterns will show only one side of the boat. Usually frames 0,1,2,3,4 and 5 are shown on the right side and frames 6,7,8,9 and 10 are on the left side of your assembled patterns. Some designs may also have half frames, for example 1.5, 2.5 and so forth. You will need the radius of the expanded transom so you can later form the transom to its correct rounded shape. Study your patterns with the lines plan. The lines plan will contain frame spacing and other important measurements that you will need when setting up your hull framework.

When laying out the patterns, you will need a space that is wider than the beam of your boat. The best way to lay out the patterns is to make up a plywood floor that is equal in size to the patterns, and a small amount all round. The various sheets should be taped down in position, making sure the centre line, headstock or base line and waterline all match up as shown on the patterns. Your patterns may also have small cross reference points; these must be correctly lined up to give an accurate set of full size patterns. Once you have the patterns laid down in position, there are several ways to transfer the lines or the frames and the stem. You will need to mark the lines on to the timber, so you can cut out the shapes as shown in your plans. Illustrations show some methods; your plans may suggest others.

MAKING THE FRAMES

When you are making up the frames, or moulds as they are sometimes called, it is best to make up the two halves of the frame at once. This is achieved by nailing the two pieces of timber together, usually 1" by 8" [25 x 200] or similar sized material and of suitable length to cover the section of the frame you are making. The two pieces are tacked together and the pattern marked out on one side. Clearly mark the waterline, sheer line and headstock line where they occur, on any one frame section. After you have joined up, faired and clearly marked the line of the outer edge of the frame you are making; then carefully cut the frame section out on the band saw or using a jig saw that is up to the job. Make sure you cut the frame piece square off the marked surface; the two sides of the frame will not match.

Once you have assembled the pieces of the frame to make up one half, which consists of two layers; these should be joined on one side with gussets. Next remove the nails holding the frame halves together and lay out the frame as you would open an oyster and bingo you have the entire frame.

Before you attempt to assemble the complete frame, measure directly from the patterns, the width of each frame at the headstock line; sheer line and waterline and make a check mark on the opposite side of the frame patterns including the frame number. Now you have three reference points to make sure the other half of the frame is laid out symmetrically. Problems can arise if you try to use the offsets when taking the measurements off the patterns. Please use the patterns exclusively.

Now you can lay out the complete frame by installing the headstock or baseline board, and gusset the keel together; add bracing and strengthening members to the frame as shown in your plans. Your frame must pass the test of both sides matching the master pattern. You now have one completed frame ready for installation on the strong back, bedlogs or setting up rails. After you have marked out all the frames, stem and the backbone and they have been cut out and assembled, the next job is to prepare your strong back or bedlogs.

SETTING UP THE FRAMES

Usually the bedlogs or strong back are made from 6" x 2" [150 x 50] or similar sized timber depending on the size of the vessel. Your plans should give some guidance on the scantlings and assembly methods for the setting up base. The size of the strong back, which is the width and length, will be decided by the shape and size of your hull. The

Well constructed strongback.

forward end of the strong back should be of sufficient width to adequately support the forward most frames, but not so wide, as to prevent the frames from fitting over the width of the rails or strong back. The same applies to the aft end, which will be wider than the forward section. The width of the strong back should be planned to adequately support the width of the hull. As the widest part of the hull is normally around or just aft of the centre, it will be easy to arrange adequate support in this area. Sometimes it is best to build the strong back coffin shaped, to offer the best support to the hull, at all its various widths. The setting up height is quite important. The hull will be upside down and there must be room for you to have access under the sheer and into the interior of the hull. Yourhull must not be so low as to allow the bow to touch the floor. I have seen some setups miscalculated and consequently a hole was required to accommodate the bow of the boat. Obviously this is not a very workmanlike way to begin your building program, so make sure your bedlogs, strong back or setting up rails are at the correct height.

Once the strong back is completed, it should be checked for level in all directions. The use of chocks and wedges can correct any misalignment. Make sure any blocking or wedging is done so it will

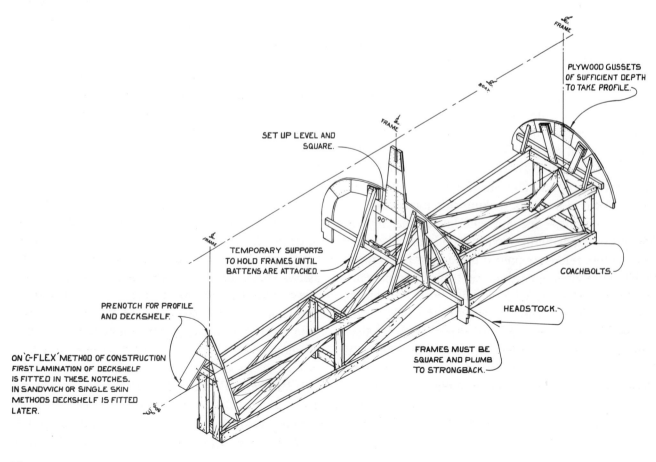

remain permanently in position until the hull is completed. If you are working on an earth floor you may wish to install concrete pads. The strong back and the whole mould structure must be capable of sustaining the weight of the completed hull, until the laminating and fairing is completed and the hull turned over.

Once you are satisfied that the strong back or support rails are level in all planes and securely in position; install a string line down the centre line of your strong back, and mark out the station spacing on the rails on both sides of the strong back. All station marks should be marked square off the centre string line so both sides are square off the centre. Nailing 2" x 1" [50 x 25] cleats across the strong back or bedlogs, at each station point, may be the best way to accurately position the frames. Make sure you consider which side of the station mark your frame is to be positioned. Make sure the frames are installed square off the centre line and level across the headstock line. It will be necessary to attach each frame to the strong back. You may attach the headstock to the upper rail or the bedlog, by through bolting, coach screws or skew nailing. Access to the strong back or bedlogs may decide your method of attachment. Remember you will not want the strong back to come loose and be waving about during the turning over process.

Use adequate braces and temporary supports to hold the frames in the correct position, until they are all installed. Make sure they are all square relative one to the other and that the individual spacings remain constant throughout. Normally the frames are erected so the forward edge of the forward frames, those ahead of station 5, are in line with the station mark. The aft edge, of the aft frames should be in line with the station mark. Frame 5 can be positioned so the centre of the frame is on the mark. The reason for this positioning of the frames in relation to the stations marks, is so that when the battens are installed, they will touch only the forward edge of the forward frames and the aft edge of the aft frames. This eliminates the need to bevel the frames. As this is the mould you are building and not part of the hull, it is not necessary to consider the frames and battens as a permanent structure, but as a mould former. Consequently, a considerable amount of time can be saved by not having to bevel these frames. Provided the frames are installed as outlined above, you will find that the battens will lay around the frames in a smooth and fair manner, without the necessity of pre bevelling.

Frames being installed on strongback by Glen Cook.

INSTALLING THE STEM

The next step is to install the stem and backbone. Install these items in the slots that have been previously cut to receive them. The stem will need temporary support at its most forward point. Take check measurements to make sure the stem is in the correct position, relative to the sheer line and the centre line of the hull. The biggest mistake you can make, is to have the stem not exactly on the centre line of the hull. Check everything against the centre string line; use plumb-bobs, a large square and tape or ruler to make absolutely sure everything is correctly located, and square off the centre line.

KEEL AND SKEG

A word about the keels and skegs on sailboat hulls. You may attach the keel webs to the frames by screwing the gusset that will hold the main part of the frame to the keel web; do this in a way that allows you to unscrew the keel section, and you can remove the keel section of the mould separately. Sometimes the keel section will be reluctant to leave the mould; so by making provision to allow the hull to be removed without the keel, you will overcome this potential problem. Skegs can be built separately and attached to the mould with a screwed gusset. The hull can be removed without the skeg that stays with the mould.

THE BATTENS

You should now have your battens on hand and these may be scarfed into full length, to match the length of your hull. You may join them on the job using plywood fairing strips, as described later in this chapter. It is wise to obtain battens of the correct width and thickness; they will not bend to a fair shape on your hull. For sailboats between twenty-five feet [7.5 M] and sixty-five feet [20 M] the best size battens are 1 3/4" x 5/8" [44 mm x 15 mm]. For power boats you may use larger battens on the bottom only, 4" x 3/4" [100 x 20] will usually lay in place without giving you any problems.

Once the frames, stem and backbone are in place, you may now install a few battens to check the fairness of the structure to this point. If you have used the computer generated full size patterns and cut and assembled the frames with due care, you will find the framework very fair and accurate. The main thing is to have a fair hull so you may shim and trim frames as necessary, to make sure the battens lay in a fair curve. From now on, your eye will be your guide. You will soon develop an eye that can spot an unfair lump or hollow in your mould. If you do not spot the lumps and hollows now, there will be those who will be happy to point these out to you, at a later stage.

INSTALLING THE BATTENS

You may start the battening up process at any part of the hull mould, but make sure that the battens are progressively installed on either side. If you batten up say twelve inches [310] on one side of the hull, then make sure you next install the battens in the

Reverse transom on ROBERTS mold built by William E. Bunn.

same area, on the opposite side of the mould. This will prevent any pulling or deforming of the structure due to the strain of having battens in one area and not having battens to balance the opposite side. At this time you should be particularly careful, to make sure, that the stem remains straight and true, right on the centre line. After installing a few battens over the entire area of the hull, you will find the mould will take on a more rigid form; it will be easier to maintain the correct shape. During the early stages of installing the battens, you will be giving consideration to building and installing the transom. There are several ways to build this item. One way is to form a transom as we have shown in the photos and sketches shown here. Most of the latest plans include the developed shape for the transom, this with the known radius, will offer another way to easily form up the transom as the designer intended. We have noticed that some designers who specialize in plans for amateur builders have taken to designing boats with flat transoms. A flat transom is an exceedingly ugly thing and not at all necessary. It is so simple to have at least a small amount of round, camber or curvature in the transom of your boat. Flat transoms always look concave or hollow, so please don't do it. Always build some curve into the transom.

As the battening of the mould former proceeds, keep a careful check to make sure there are no low or high points in the structure. If you find several battens wish to go past a frame without touching it; or can only be made to touch the frame by pushing inwards and deforming the batten out of a fair curve; then let the battens lay as they may, and pack out the frame to suit. If you find one frame is particularly high and needs some trimming to make the battens lay fair, then dress a little off that frame.

If you have been careful in following the patterns, making the frames, and setting up your mould former, then the battens will go on without any problems. If some errors have crept into the structure at this stage, now it is time to make sure you eliminate any unfairness in your hull. If the battens have run past a frame without touching it, then fasten the battens to the other frames first. Now go back to the frame that is low and spile in a piece of plywood or timber, to add a piece on to the frame, to provide support for the battens. The battens can then be nailed into position.

Note the method used for installing battens on chine hulls.

Excellent example of well-formed transom on ROBERTS 57 built by Lorne Bentley.

Note how battens installed one side only have pulled the stern out of line. Always batten both sides of mould together, especially at bow (stem) and stern.

FORMING A TRANSOM THE BRUCE ROBERTS WAY
WORK WITH YOUR PLAN
SKETCHES REPRESENT ANY BRUCE ROBERTS PLAN
STEP 1

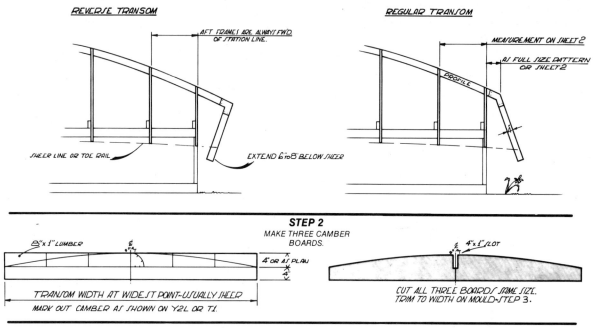

REVERSE TRANSOM

REGULAR TRANSOM

AFT FRAMES ARE ALWAYS FWD. OF STATION LINE.

MEASUREMENT ON SHEET 2

AS FULL SIZE PATTERN OR SHEET 2

PROFILE

SHEER LINE OR TOE RAIL.

EXTEND 6"to 8" BELOW SHEER

STEP 2
MAKE THREE CAMBER BOARDS.

8"x 1" LUMBER

4" OR AS PLAN

4" x 1" SLOT

TRANSOM WIDTH AT WIDEST POINT-USUALLY SHEER

MARK OUT CAMBER AS SHOWN ON Y2L OR T1.

CUT ALL THREE BOARDS SAME SIZE.
TRIM TO WIDTH ON MOULD-STEP 3.

STEP 3

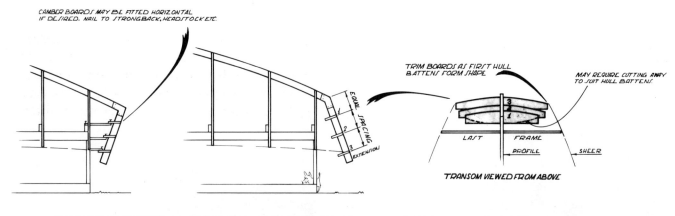

CAMBER BOARDS MAY BE FITTED HORIZONTAL IF DESIRED. NAIL TO STRONGBACK, HEADSTOCK ETC.

EQUAL SPACING

EXTENSION

TRIM BOARDS AS FIRST HULL BATTENS FORM SHAPE

MAY REQUIRE CUTTING AWAY TO SUIT HULL BATTENS.

LAST   FRAME

PROFILE   SHEER

TRANSOM VIEWED FROM ABOVE

STEP 4

ROUGHLY MITRE BATTENS TOGETHER WHERE THEY MEET ON ₵.

NOTE SOME BATTENS STOP SHORT ON PLY STRIPS TO PREVENT OVER CROWDING AT TRANSOM.

SELECT FOUR LONG BATTENS AND ALLOW TO FORM FAIR CURVES OVER FRAMES AS SHOWN. FIT FOUR BATTENS TO TRANSOM AND CUT BOTH HULL AND TRANSOM BATTENS TOGETHER. FORM A FAIR LINE BY EYE - DO NOT ALLOW TRANSOM BATTEN TO PUSH HULL BATTEN UP OUT OF LINE. FILL SPACES BETWEEN SELECTED BATTENS ALLOWING 1½ to 2" SPACING BETWEEN BATTENS AT MID-SHIP FRAMES.

AFTER ALL BATTENING IS COMPLETED REMOVE ANY UNFAIRNESS BY TRIMMING FRAMES UNDER BATTENS FOR BUMPS AND PACKING OUT UNDER BATTENS FOR HOLLOWS.

NOTE 6 to 8" HIGHER ON ₵. THIS HEIGHT WILL BE TRIMMED TO SUIT AFT DECK CAMBER.

SHEER (AND TOE RAIL) BATTEN MUST FORM A FAIR CURVE AND BE LEVEL TO OPPOSITE BATTEN.

ALLOW HULL BATTENS TO RUN PAST TRANSOM AND CUT TO TRANSOM BATTEN.

TRANSOM VIEWED FROM AFT.

ADDING FAIRING STRIPS

After installing the battens on the hull and the transom, the next step is to add strips of plywood between each frame. The plywood strips, as shown in the illustrations, are installed to fair up the battens between the frames. The battens that need to be joined, can be joined on these fairing strips. When installing the fairing strips, two people are required. One person to nail through the batten into and through the fairing strip, and another person inside the hull structure with a "dolly," or heavy weight against which the nail will be driven. This procedure will cause the nail to bend over and clinch up tight. Clinching is a common boat building practice and one that you would use frequently if you were building a wooden boat. The "dolly" will be a piece of steel, something of a size that will fit comfortably in the hand. The ideal shape is a piece of solid round steel say 2 1/2" diameter by 6" long [60 mm x 150 mm]. The dolly is used end on. When the battens are joined between frames on the plywood fairing strip, the battens will remain fair at this point. Any small irregularities can be later dressed off with a light sanding.

Use adequate plywood strips, at least one or two between each frame and no more than 1'-6" [500 mm] apart, so if frames are more than 3'-0" [say 1 metre] apart, use two strips between each frame. Clinch nail to every batten. Best cut the strips into

Two people are needed to clinch nail the plywood strips in place. This will ensure fair battens.

4" [100] widths and use 3/8" [10] or 1/2" [12] thickness plywood.

In areas where the battens are low, they can be very carefully tapped out from inside the hull until they are fair. Again, packing and spiling is used to make sure the re positioned battens stay where you put them.

CHECKING YOUR MOULD

A 1/2" x 3/4" x 6'-0" 12 mm x 20 mm x 2 metres long timber batten laid diagonally across the battens will show up the high and low spots on your mould. If there are any localised bumps or lumps in your mould, such as those where you have joined the

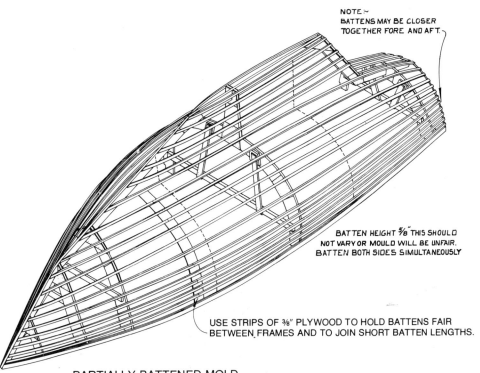

NOTE:~
BATTENS MAY BE CLOSER
TOGETHER FORE AND AFT.

BATTEN HEIGHT ⅝" THIS SHOULD
NOT VARY OR MOULD WILL BE UNFAIR.
BATTEN BOTH SIDES SIMULTANEOUSLY

USE STRIPS OF ⅜" PLYWOOD TO HOLD BATTENS FAIR
BETWEEN FRAMES AND TO JOIN SHORT BATTEN LENGTHS.

PARTIALLY BATTENED MOLD
STRONGBACK AND SEVERAL FRAMES OMITTED FOR CLARITY.

battens, you should now fair these areas using your angle sander fitted with a heavy grit disc. Something in the region of 16 grit should be ideal for the job. If you wish, you may now carefully go over the entire hull and fair off any irregularities using your angle sander. Be careful not to spoil your work by being heavy handed with the sander, as you may create more unfairness than you cure. As in all your work from now on, let your eye be the judge. View the mould from every angle and when you are satisfied that it is as fair as you can possibly make it, then it is time to take the next step in your building programme.

FINISHING THE MOULD

By this stage you should have decided whether you are going to use a PVC core material such as Airex to provide the true sandwich structure; or another cheaper urethane foam and later add stringers to the interior of your hull. The next step is to cover the entire mould structure with builders' plastic. This plastic is quite thin, but heavier than used in garbage bags and the like. Check with your local builder's merchant who will be happy to supply you with the correct material. The plastic comes in rolls and is best installed by taping it into position with plastic tape and only stapling where necessary. As the plastic is relatively fine it tears easily so use tape to

back up the staples. Once you have the mould covered in plastic the next job will be to install the core material.

OPEN FORM VERSES SOLID FORM MOULDS

Before we move on to installing the core material, we should consider one alternative I have not mentioned up to this point. The type of mould I have always preferred and used, is the open form or batten type mould. Some builders of one off fibreglass boats, prefer to take the mould process one step further and cover the mould with a skin and then go on to install the inner laminate first. After the inner laminate is installed then the core is vacuum bagged into position and the outer laminate installed and faired to complete the hull. If you choose this solid form mould, then make sure you are careful when installing the plywood or other hull sheathing material, to provide a fair surface to receive the inner laminate, core and outer laminate. Of all of the custom fibreglass boat builders I have met, about seventy percent prefer the open form, or as I call it, the batten type mould. You can make your own choice after pricing out the additional costs of the mould sheathing materials and considering the extra labour involved.

Beautifully built mold by Rhea Adams. Note plastic to prevent core from sticking to mold. Battens are best when spaced 1½" to 2" apart.

with your fibreglass material supplier who can advise you regarding the latest materials and techniques.

Airex or similar foams, do not need edge gluing. They are best installed with a 1/16" [1.5 mm] gap between the sheets; this allows for expansion and contraction of the Airex before the application of the outer laminate skin. If the Airex is installed with the sheets butted too tightly together, then a sudden change in the weather may cause the material to bow in such a way, as to create hips and hollows on the surface of your hull.

ATTACHING THE CORE

The best method we have found for attaching the Airex to the mould is to sew the core on with nylon yarn or similar. For best results use a medium size bag needle with light string or nylon yarn. Make the stitches about 3" [75] long. Outside the hull the stitches are let into grooves, which you cut as you proceed. The stitches will lie flat with the surface and do not interfere with the installation of the outer laminate.

Inside the mould, the string is led over one or two battens to create approximately a 3" [75] stitch on the inside of the mould. The string is then pushed back through the Airex and so on. The rows of stitching should be 9" to 12" [230 to 310] apart. We have found it best to stitch vertically up the sheet, first along one edge and then progressively working across the sheet with vertical rows of stitching, until the entire sheet is fastened to the mould former. Additional stitching may be necessary where the sheets join, using a cross stitch pattern up the edges of the sheets, which should ensure that both sheets lay uniformly on the mould former.

Install the foam sheeting carefully to insure there no hips or hollows in the hull surface. It will take a considerable amount of work to fair out any large irregularities created at this stage, so utmost care will ensure a fair hull and one that will need the least amount of final finishing to provide a professional looking surface when the hull is completed.

You may use wire toggles, if necessary to help pull the sheets into a fair shape. This is only necessary if the stitching will not do the job in a particular area. A toggle can be a length of copper or other wire with a nail or strong toothpick twitched on to the outside. The toggle wire is pushed through the foam

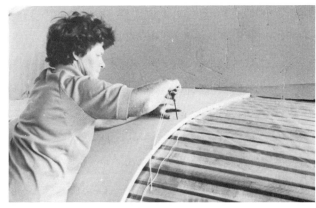
Foam is sewn onto mold.

Foam stem being formed.

Polyurethane foam will form easily onto mold. Here foam is being sewn onto flared bow. This WAVERUNNER design has flat at sheer to make fitting of deck and molding easier.

and twitched on the inside on to a nail inserted into a batten.

NON - CORED AREAS OF THE HULL

There are certain areas of the hull where it is not desirable or necessary to use the Airex or similar PVC core. Such areas include the skeg, keel and areas below the cabin sole line. It would be wasteful to install the more expensive core materials in areas where it will later be removed; it is more practical to use the cheaper rigid urethane foam or waxed Masonite for sections of the hull where the core will not remain. The sides and bottom of the keel can be covered with 1/4" [6] Masonite. The Masonite is waxed and a release agent used to ease the removal of the mould former from the hull. The cheaper urethane foam can be used in areas where the Airex or similar PVC foam would be removed. Make sure

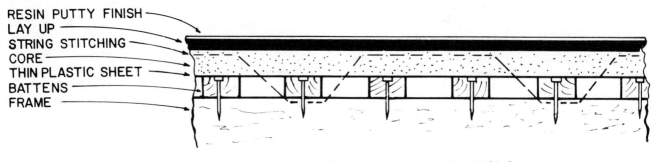

RESIN PUTTY FINISH
LAY UP
STRING STITCHING
CORE
THIN PLASTIC SHEET
BATTENS
FRAME

SECTION OF HULL ON MOLD

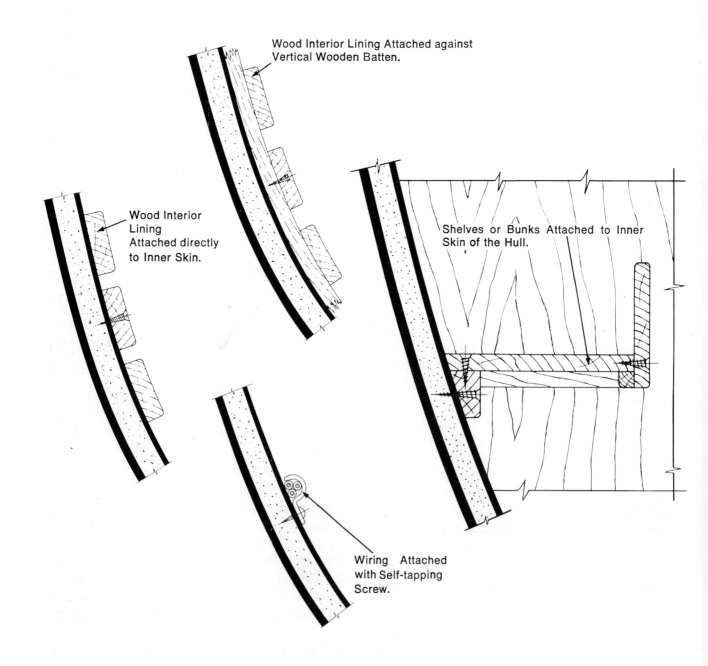

Wood Interior Lining Attached against
Vertical Wooden Batten.

Wood Interior
Lining
Attached directly
to Inner Skin.

Shelves or Bunks Attached to Inner
Skin of the Hull.

Wiring   Attached
with Self-tapping
Screw.

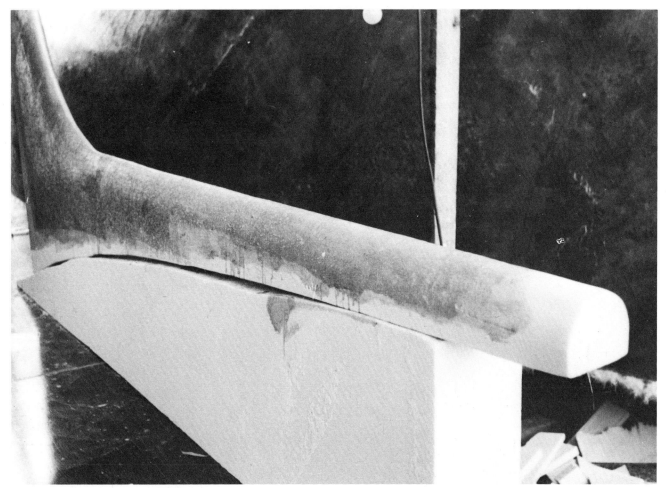

Skegs may be formed from solid urethane foam as this foam is intended for removal after outer laminate is completed.

the thickness of the urethane foam is the same as the Airex, there will be a ridge where the two foams meet. In our own designs we recommend that the area under the cabin sole can be single skin; so this means that the bottom of the hull below the cabin sole; and the keel could be covered with the cheaper foam that will be removed after the hull has been turned upright. As with all forms of construction, there are many ways to achieve the same results. You should follow your plans. If you have a good idea not covered in your plans, then consult your designer before making any major changes to the recommended building methods.

END GRAIN BALSA CORED HULLS

In the past we have been involved in the building of many end grained balsa cored hulls. The end grain balsa simply replaces the PVC core as described in the previous paragraphs. The mould former is built in the same way as the Airex or PVC cored hulls, but the battening has to be closer together as the

Right: *Foam is used to fair stem on Roberts 43. Foam will later be removed from inside and interior and outer glass will join at stem. Extra reinforcing glass will be added from inside hull at stem*

BALSACORE installed and resin coated prior to final fairing and application of outer laminate.

balsa core does not bridge the battens as well as the foam core.

When installing balsa core, I have found the best way is to lay the sheets at a 45 degree angle. Start at the middle of the sheer and work outwards and upwards until the entire area is covered. Use cheaper urethane foam in the area where the core will be later removed. Sew the balsa core on to the mould in a similar manner to that used to secure the foam core. See previous paragraphs. In some areas you may wish to nail the core on to the hull. You can do this by making sure that the nails only go a small way into the batten, leave plenty of nail showing above the core so it can be later easily removed. Once you have installed the core and coated it with resin, and installed some of the first laminate to hold the whole area together, you can remove the nails. Only use nails where the sewing method would not work.

Core can be easily shaped and faired by using a sanding block or a Surform and tricky sections can be held together using toothpicks or small nails. At the bow, it may be best to trim the core flush with the bow in profile. Add a block of foam that can be faired into a rounded shape that will be greater at the deck line and taper to a very small radius at the waterline. Study other boats for ideas. I prefer the foam core to end grain balsa core for hulls. For decks I prefer end grain balsa. One reason to consider the end grain balsa for hulls, are its lower cost and availability in some areas. You will need to check this before making a final decision on which core to use.

PLYWOOD CORED TRANSOMS

You may wish to use plywood as a core material in the transom. If you are building a sailboat with a standing back stay or a powerboat with an outboard or stern drive installation, then the plywood cored transom has merit. As your transom will have some camber or curve, you can pre laminate the transom from several layers of thin plywood and after cutting to the approximate shape install in position. Now you can trim the transom to the exact shape to allow it to tie in with the other core materials on the side of the hull. Make sure you install the transom by fastening from inside the mould so you can release it after turnover, and before you remove the mould from the hull. You may prefer to laminate the plywood transom in place. Install the first layer by screwing from inside the mould and then laminating the other layers of plywood on to the first, by gluing and stapling the outer plywood layers. You can arrange the transom so that the core runs past the transom, or, so the transom overlaps the core on the hull. Always radius, the outer corners of the transom, the stem, bottom edges of the keel and all other corners must be rounded off to receive the first layer of fibreglass.

PRIME COATING THE CORE

After installing the core, the next job after putting radii on sections such as the bow, and other areas, is to apply a prime coat of the resin. After applying the prime coat, you should go over the whole hull checking the fairness and applying resin putty if necessary, to finally fair out any imperfections in your hull surface. A most important thing about building a male moulded fibreglass hull, is to make every step as perfect as possible, before going on to the next stage. Different types of core require varying amounts of prime coating with the resin. Balsa core requires one or two thinned coats and then another coat of regular laminating the resin. Airex needs one coat of the resin that contains extra promoter. Check with your fibreglass supplier, about what special priming, your chosen core requires.

SINGLE SKIN OVER A MALE MOULD

You may elect to build a skin hull over a male mould. The building of the mould follows the same procedure as for a cored hull. You will now need a surface as an alternative to the core material. To build a successful male moulded fibreglass hull, you need a good surface. There are several alternatives.

Perfectly build mold covered with special plastic and ready for laminate to be applied directly onto the mold. Builder. R.J. Rehling.

We have had the most success using the inexpensive urethane foam that can be purchased in sheet form. Usually this rigid foam is available in 6'-0" x 4'-0" sheets [1800 x 1220] by 3/4" [20] or similar sizes. This foam is made in a large bun and cut into sheets by the manufacturer. It is not the type of foam used in seat cushions; this would be totally unsuitable.

As mentioned earlier, the solid form mould offers an alternate method. The procedure is to plank the hull mould with one or two layers of 3/16" [3 or 4 mm] plywood and lay up the hull laminate over this base. I have seen some builders use two layers of 1/4" [6 mm] plywood to skin their solid form mould, in my opinion this is over kill. You will need to wax and apply the release agent to the plywood surface, if you wish to get the mould out of the hull, in one piece. As long as you do not tear the fibreglass laminate, there is no reason that the mould could not be removed in sections. I have seen hull moulds built so accurately that the builder only used stretched builders plastic as a base for laminating the hull. For hulls over 33'-0" [10 Metres] L.O.A. built using any of the single skin techniques, you will need to install fibreglass stringers after the hull is turned over. Our opinion is that the Airex or similar PVC cored hulls offer the most advantages.

FIBREGLASS C-FLEX

You may wish to consider C-Flex as the basic material for your hull structure. Bill Seeman developed C-Flex in the United States; since the early seventies this material has been used extensively in North America and elsewhere. If C-Flex interests you and cannot be obtained locally, then you should contact any Bruce Roberts Design office, regarding obtaining supplies.

THE MATERIAL

C-Flex is a fibreglass sheeting material that is made up of fibreglass rods alternating with bundles of unsaturated roving. The material is held together by two layers of lightweight open weave fibreglass cloth. C-Flex is supplied in rolls of various lengths and the standard width is 12" [305]

The combinations of rigid rods, loosely held together, with pliable areas between, are what makes C-Flex a unique fibreglass construction material. C-Flex is one of the few self supporting fibreglass materials available, that will conform to compound curves, without having to be stretched or deformed in some way.

C-Flex will bend sideways, a property that almost eliminates the problem of having to fit or spile the "planks." In case you do have to spile a plank; see later paragraphs explaining the fitting and spiling techniques in detail. Most boats can be built by starting the first plank parallel to the sheerline, and then butting the next plank right alongside, and so on, all the way up to the keel or centre line of the hull.

Besides the obvious advantage of being able to build your chosen design using the male mould technique, C-Flex affords the designer and builder the opportunity to save weight compared with the conventional single skin fibreglass laminate; no strength is sacrificed.

The reason for the strength associated with this material, is that C-Flex is a unidirectional reinforced fabric and is considerably stronger in the direction of its fibre orientation (lengthwise) than the normal fibreglass mat/roving laminate. Subsequent availability of unidirectional roving material has to some extent dimmed this advantage.

Weight savings can translate into cost savings, a point taken by many builders who have used this material in the past. Although C-Flex costs more per pound or kilo than mat or roving, the completed hull shell will cost slightly less than a hull built using other fibreglass techniques.

THE MOULD

C-flex requires a similar male mould to that used to build an Airex cored hull. The frames are made in a similar manner. As the fore and aft battens are spaced at 4" to 6" (100 to 150) apart, less fore and aft battens are required. Light battens of 1" x 3/8" [25 x 10] are placed vertically and are spaced at 8" to 12 " [200 x 305] apart. If you read the chapter on building a male, batten type mould, and consider the

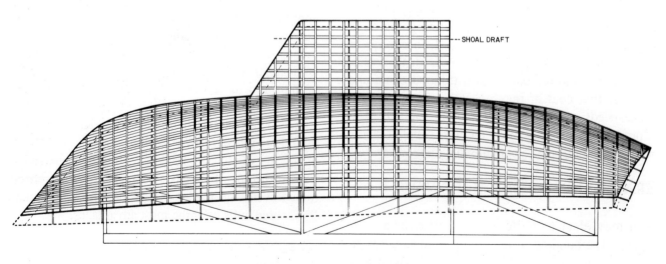

C-FLEX METHOD
FINISH MOLD ABOVE SPACING FORE AND AFT BATTENS 4" APART.
ADD ¾" x ⅜" VERTICAL BATTEN ACROSS THE HULL SPACED 6" APART.
CHECK CAREFULLY FOR TRUE FORM AND FAIRNESS.

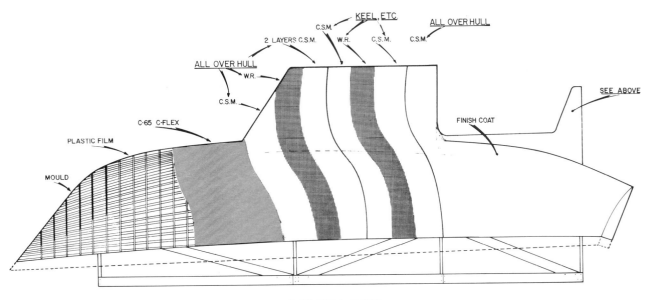

ALL OVER HULL
W.R.
C.S.M.
C-65 C-FLEX
PLASTIC FILM
MOULD
2 LAYERS C.S.M.
KEEL, ETC.
C.S.M.
W.R.
C.S.M.
ALL OVER HULL
C.S.M.
SEE ABOVE
FINISH COAT

C-FLEX LAYUP

Photographs show one of several methods of building mold former — this variation features widely spaced battens and thin plywood strips spaced 8″ and placed vertically. Note foam skeg preshaped for propeller aperture.

Photos: Peter Guiles

Vertical battens being installed on ROBERTS 44 mold former.

fact that you will use less fore and aft battens, but will add some vertical battens, you will have an understanding of how to build a male mould to support the C-Flex. The vertical battens are essential to support the material.

STARTING THE "PLANKING"

On most round bottomed hulls, the easiest place to start is with the first plank running around the sheer.

As stated earlier C-Flex will bend sideways without deforming; you can go on with the planking right up to the keel without having to spile in any stealer planks.

The reason C-Flex will conform to compound curves is that it will bias within itself. Usually it will easily conform to the shape of the hull and you will only need ice picks or staples to hold it in place. If you try to make it bend sideways beyond a certain point you may have to help the material as follows.

Take two small 2" [50] C or G clamps and clamp them tightly to the ends of the single hard rod in the inside of the bend; then pull from both ends. Find a spot in the inside the building of a post right in line with the strand and pull hard. We have used 1/8" [3 mm] nylon line and have occasionally wrapped it through the clamp several times, thus forming a crude block and tackle. The single strand is strong enough, so do not be afraid to pull hard. Since you pull in line with the strand, you probably can achieve the required bend.

Of course there are exceptions to every rule so you may find sometimes there is a limit to which you can bend C-Flex sideways. If your hull has a very straight sheer, a reverse sheer or if your boat has a greater than usual beam, then you may run into a

C-FLEX being unrolled directly onto hull frame.

C-FLEX stem and first layer deck shelf being wet out. Note the absence of vertical battens. C-FLEX was applied diagonally. Rhea Adams builder.

sideways bend that the material cannot handle. There are two possible ways to take care of this situation.

First, if you can foresee that this is going to be a problem, you may start to install the planking in the middle of the hull rather than at the sheerline. Along the waterline may be a good starting point.

Adequate scaffolding is required.

Stringers, when called for in your plan, may be preformed and installed before C-FLEX is applied to mold. See text.

Now you can let the planking run out at the ends when it reaches the sheer and keel lines.

Secondly, if you have already started with the C-Flex parallel to the sheer, and you find that the curve is becoming too tight, you can stop, wet out with the resin the C-flex that is already installed and allow the resin to cure. Next take a plank of unsaturated C-Flex and place it over the frames letting it fall naturally in place. Butt the unsaturated plank alongside the cured planking in the middle of the hull and let it fall across the ends of the cured planking or across the area where you are having the problem. Mark along the edge of the unsaturated plank. Now cut along your scribed line using a hand power saw equipped with an abrasive cutting blade. Be sure to set the blade so it just cuts through the C-Flex and not into the battens or frames. Remove the two off-cut wedge shaped pieces and now you can go on to install the C-Flex with a fresh straight fore and aft line to work from.

On most V bottom boats, particularly power boats we have found the easiest place to start is with the first plank run fore and aft along the chine with half the plank on the bottom and half on the side of the hull. Try to keep the same two small rods each side of the chine batten and this will assure you of a good start to the clean edge you will be looking to obtain in this area. Examine some production fibreglass power boats and you will see what I mean.

If you are not sure as to the best starting point for your particular boat, cut a piece of material and try laying it in different directions using alternate starting points on your hull. You may want to mark each plank location using your trial piece as a guide; this may show any potential areas where you could run into a problem.

CUTTING C-FLEX

Use a hand power saw fitted with an abrasive cutting blade. This type of saw may be used to cut both the unsaturated and the saturated and fully cured C-flex. If you need to make a long diagonal cut on unsaturated material, then put a piece of scrap timber under the C-Flex and cut through the material into the supporting wood.

INSTALLING C-FLEX TO THE MOULD

Roll out the material and cut a piece to the proper length. The C-Flex develops a very slight "set" from

C-FLEX applied to mold as shown above. Note alternate method of laying C-FLEX diagonally on mold. If you use this method, then you will eliminate the need for any vertical battens on your mold.

being rolled; place it over the mould framework with the inside of the roll facing the mould thus taking advantage of the "set".

Either ice picks or staples or large nails may be used to hold the material in place. It best to have a selection of fastening devices available. Use ice picks to hold the material in place and staples or other devices to take care of any troublesome areas.

After you have installed the C-Flex, check over the job carefully. You will find that by putting in a few extra staples and pulling a few hard strands, you can save some work later. Also if you sight along the hard strands of the C-Flex, you can check the fairness of the hull and note and adjust any areas where there any humps or hollows. Once you saturate the C-Flex it will be more difficult to make adjustments. Be very critical at this stage and adjust battens or frames or the C-Flex itself to ensure a fair hull.

SATURATING THE C-FLEX

After we had tried several saturation sequences we settled on the following method. Special slow cure resins are most suitable for the first wetting out of the C-Flex. The idea is to use a heavy coat of resin so it completely saturates the material. In any areas where the resin is has not completely penetrated the C-Flex, then you can take care of this later, from inside the hull.

Some builders try to incorporate the framework for the mould as part of the boat and they can wet out the C-Flex from inside the hull, as well as outside. If the C-Flex is being installed over a mould that will later become a permanent part of the boat, then you will be able to wet out the C-Flex on both sides before the material is placed on the mould former.

My preference is to initially undertake all the saturation from outside the hull and wet out dry areas from inside, after the hull is turned upright and the mould is removed. Which ever technique you use, it important to select and mix the resin that will

First resin coat being applied to C-FLEX

Note C-FLEX sewn at hull-to-transom join.

be applied in the first coat so it will slowly cure, and not cause excessive shrinkage. The reason for this caution; "hot" quick-curing resin will shrink excessively pulling the planking flat between some frames or battens. If you allow shrinkage to occur, then it may not affect the strength, but your hull will require considerably more fairing to obtain a fine finish.

It has been found that the shrinkage problem on the first layer, can be eliminated if you use a casting

If C-FLEX is used on transom, make sure to radius hull-to-transom join after C-FLEX has been wet out and can be sanded.

type resin to saturate the C-Flex. We recommend the type of resin often used to make artificial marble. Check with your resin supplier on the latest developments in slow curing, low shrinkage polyester resins. You should not need a very expensive resin to achieve the desired result. Most of the resins suitable to wet out the C-Flex are more viscous than regular laminating resins; they will saturate properly if you give them extra time.

We have used spray guns, rollers and brushes to apply the resin. All techniques will work, but we recommend a heavy nap paint roller, as the simplest and quickest way to install the saturation resin. We usually catalize two or three gallons [8 to 12 litres] of resin at a time; use a five gallon [20 litres] pail and dip the roller right into the pail. Roll a coat over an area and let it soak for five minutes and then go back and roll more resin over the dry spots; let this soak in and squeegee off the access.

A common mistake made by first time builders is to use too much resin. In the saturation coat for C-Flex you will need to "lay it on" but later, you must be careful not to over wet out the mat and roving; you will end up with an overly resin rich laminate. In the

C-FLEX being installed and progressively wet out as installation proceeds.

Laying up mat and roving over C-FLEX

ROBERTS 53 hull built at BRUCE ROBERTS Australian boat yard. C-FLEX hull.

ROBERTS 53 built by Seaway Yachts of Florida. C-FLEX hull.

saturation coat for the C-Flex, once the material is saturated and wet through completely, you don't need any more resin. All excess resin achieves is to add weight, cause the laminate to be brittle and cause additional shrinkage.

LAYING UP OVER the C-FLEX

After the C-Flex has been saturated and the resin has cured, the hull should be lightly sanded to remove any high spots and excessive resin build up. Use a 7" or 9" [175 or 230] disk sander and 24 or 36 grit paper. Hold the sander with one edge of the disk raised slightly - only enough to keep the sander from bouncing - and keep the sander moving.

We assume that you have studied the chapter on safety and associated equipment and that you are already wearing the necessary protective gear.

The amount and type of laminate you will be installing over the C-Flex will depend on the type and size of boat you are building. You plans should clearly show the amounts and type of reinforcing fibreglass required.

The best practice is to start with a layer of mat next to the C-Flex, laid up wet, in combination with a layer of roving. The installing of a layer of mat in combination with a layer of roving, is accepted commercial practice for hand laid up hulls. The mat develops a superior adhesion to the C-Flex or to any other core type material. The mat also builds up bulk; essential for fairing out the laminate as you go. The roving develops the tensile and impact strength. Do not be concerned by the little valleys between the pre-hardened rods or strands in the C-Flex, the action of rolling the mat and roving with a metal roller will ensure the valleys are filled with mat.

Usually the roving are run at right angle to the C-Flex. The thinking is that the C-Flex layer develops strength in the direction of its fibre orientation but needs additional strength "across the grain". We recommend that half the layers of roving are across the grain of the C-Flex and the other half run fore and aft in the same direction as the C-Flex. Some builders have installed the C-Flex diagonally, in which case all the roving should be run fore and aft. The designer of your boat should impart his intentions to you and the plans should state the

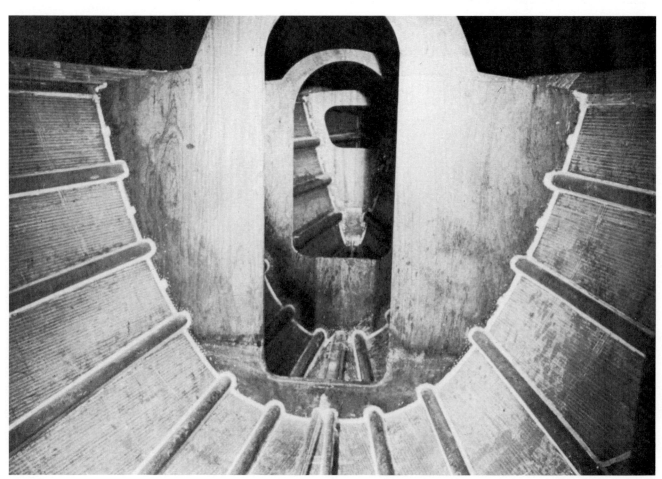

Inside of C-FLEX hull fitted with hollow glass longitudinals which were made up over a form and then bent into place. Photo supplied by the manufacturers of C-FLEX.

preferred style and method of installing the laminate.

As you apply the fibreglass laminate over the C-Flex, be careful to prevent lumps and hollows developing. If you are installing wet, one layer of mat and one layer of roving at the same time then roll harder on the high spots and softer on the low areas, thus evening out your laminate and leaving less fairing up for later.

Most of the information given in the chapter on installing the out laminate as applied to male moulded hulls, will apply when laminating over the C-Flex. We recommend you read and reread the chapters on fibreglass construction, if that is to be your building medium. Much of the advice and many of the tips given for building using one fibreglass method can be gainfully employed on another.

After laying up the recommended layers of mat and roving remembering to squeegee each roving layer while it is still wet, we then cover the hull with a light mat; 3/4 oz or 1 oz is about right. This layer of mat will make a good basis to start your fairing and sanding operation. Lastly now read or reread the chapters on finishing your hull. You can obtain a book, completely devoted to C-Flex construction. Check with your nearest Bruce Roberts design office for additional information.

CHAPTER SEVEN
FIBREGLASS - THE OUTER LAMINATE

APPLYING THE FIRST LAYER

The first layer of your laminate should be a light chopped strand mat, either 1 or 1 1/2 oz per square foot [300 or 450 g/sq m]. These are easy weights to work with and will provide a good key between the core material and the bulk of the laminate that follows. This first layer is very important, the bond between it and the core material must be as perfect as possible. If in doubt, make up some sample pieces using scrap core material as a base. For the bulk of your hull laminate, you should use only unwaxed general purpose laminating resin with a reasonably long cure time. When you reach the final layer of the outer laminate, it must also be mat. Use waxed resins to facilitate the sanding that will be required at this stage. Note that most of the laminate will be installed using all unwaxed resins.

WHICH DIRECTION ?

There are at least five directions you may use to apply the various layers of the glass laminate. We prefer to lay the first layer of mat at a forty five degree angle. You need only butt the joins in the mat. Most fibreglass mats have a slightly braided edge that will blend and make a clean join; if carefully rolled, you will not see where each succeeding mat joins.

The first layer must be carefully wet out and steel rolled to remove any bubbles. You should apply a layer of the resin on to the core, under the mat, and then lay the mat down on to the wet surface, applying additional resin as necessary to thoroughly wet out the first layer. Do not over saturate the mat, but roll out the excess resin as you are rolling out the bubbles. If you work from the top, the top in this case being the centre line of the hull, then the resins will run in the right direction.

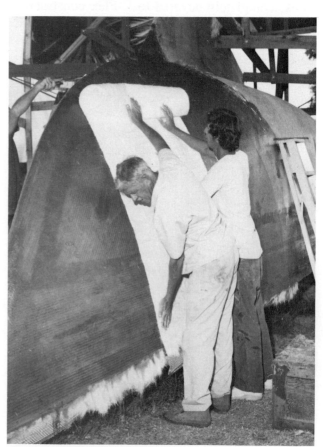

Mat being laid up on Rhea Adams' ROBERTS 36 hull.

Pre-measured and fitted mat makes for easier lay up.

PROGRESSIVE LAY-UP TECHNIQUE

There are two basic ways of laying up your hull. If you are working alone or with only occasional assistance, you may consider the following method, which we call the progressive technique. The method is to commence at the bow and put four strips of the first layer on each side of the hull. You can overlap 3" [75] each way at the stem. The mat can be torn to produce a ragged edge and this is more easily blended into the overlap than if cut with scissors. The next step in this lay up method would be to apply the second layer, which may be woven roving, back to within 6" [150] of your first layer, then apply the third layer of laminate to within 6" [150] of the second, so stepping back each layer until you have installed the correct total laminate in the bow area. Next step is to go back to where you left off the first layer and apply a few more strips on each side; gradually build until your laminate covers the entire hull. The idea of this progressive method is that no part of the laminate has fully cured, before the subsequent layers are installed. This insures a chemical, also a mechanical bond between the various layers of your laminate.

TWO LAYERS AT ONCE

It is common practice for experienced laminators, to apply a layer of the mat and a layer of roving simultaneously. The method is to lay up the mat and use the roving to help soak up the excess resin, which the mat usually holds. The roving and mat are rolled out at the same time. If you become proficient, you will find this method of installing your laminate offers the smoothest finish and the best glass/resin content. This method is also good for evening out the laminate. Press harder on the high points and less hard on the hollows. The object of the exercise, when installing a fibreglass laminate, is to have more glass and less resin. Do not allow your laminate to become resin starved; you will soon recognise a good laminate.

LAMINATING WITH A TEAM

The second method of applying your laminate is to have a team of helpers, so the laminating can be completed without any interruptions, over a few days. You should have enough help to apply at least one full layer per day. Do not apply more than two layers per day as the curing process will generate too

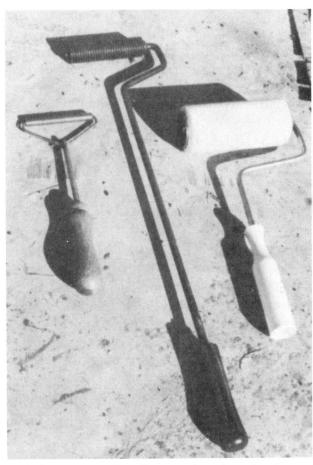

Tools for laying up glass. Large and small steel rollers and mohair roller.

ROBERTS 34 laid up using the progressive method so that no layer of laminate cures before successive layers are installed.

TAPER BACK

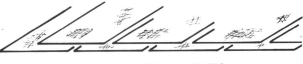

OVERLAP EDGES

much heat and may distort your laminate. Using this method, you will apply one layer all over the hull before starting the second layer. Some of your team may be installing the second layer a few hours behind you, while the others are still completing the first layer. Four people are the maximum who can be gainfully employed on one hull, one mixing the resin and precutting the lengths of fibreglass fabric and three applying the laminate.

Unless you have the help and can lay up your hull within a short period , a maximum of three weeks; it is better to use the progressive method. Within reason, the faster you build up the laminate, the better the bond will be between each succeeding layer. As I mentioned earlier, there is a limit to the speed at which any laminate can be installed. Watch out for excessive heat that is caused by the laminate curing too fast.

NOTES ON LAMINATING - ALL METHODS

Try to obtain mat and other fibreglass materials that are about 30" [760] wide for ease of handling. When installing subsequent layers, always step each layer back a minimum of 3" [75] between the edges of each layer. Never allow the edges of one layer to lay over the edges of the previous layer. Fill in any hollows with the mat, and always tear edges to blend in to the surrounding laminate. Always start and finish with a mat. Never laminate roving to roving without a mat between. Always trim the sheer as

As the laminating proceeds do not hesitate to use small pieces of mat to build up any low areas and to generally fair out the hull. Care taken at this

each layer of laminate cures. It is easy to trim around the sheer and anywhere else where trimming is required, when the laminate has just cured and before it reaches its final hardened state. A sharp trimming knife will do the job nicely. If you let the laminate set really hard before trimming the sheer, you will need to use a jig saw or similar device to cut off the excess laminate. Also when the laminate hangs over the sheer it will usually deform without the support of the mould underneath.

When you have completed the installation of the laminate called for in your plans, do not be tempted to add another layer or two to "make it stronger." If you have any queries about the amount of laminate required, please consult your designer. Do not, under any circumstances, just add a little more because you believe you will improve the strength of your hull. Before you start on the serious finishing work, check over your hull and using mat and/or fibreglass putty fair out the obvious humps and hollows.

The extra laminations needed for the keel and the areas below the waterline can be either installed first or last. You should consider which sequence will provide you with the smoothest complete laminate. Give this matter some thought. Always tear the edges of the extra layers, so they stand a better chance of blending into the completeelaminate. You do not want to end with a hull, where you can see where any extra layers start or finish.

Here we see C.S.M. pre-measured and fitted to hull prior to application of resin. Laminating can be done with one or more people working to a pre-arranged system. Pre-cut lengths of mat and rovings helps to avoid panic as laminating proceeds.

FINISHING TECHNIQUES

If you have been careful, you should have a minimum of tidying up to do before proceeding to the final fairing and finishing of your outer hull. The easiest way to check if your hull has any unfair areas, is to have sunlight or strong artificial light shining from one end as you look along the hull either with or against the light. If you really want to check the fairness, then the best time is at night. Shine your torch along the hull and you will soon see all of the imperfections in the surface of your hull. Use this technique frequently during the final fairing process.

At this stage, you can expect your hull to show some imperfections and these can be removed during the final fairing operation. You have to decide the standard of finish you are prepared to accept. Set your standards as high as possible. Work towards this goal and you will end with a hull you can be proud of. The resale value of your boat effected by the standard of finish.

FINISHING THE HULL

If your hull has been carefully laminated and will not require too much screeding, you could have applied your last layer of mat using a white pigmented resin. We recommended you use waxed resin, for your final layer of the mat, you will find this will make it easier to sand.

The first process of finishing a hull, is to sand the surface with your disc sander running at not more than 4,000 RPM. Use a soft pad equipped with 30 to 40 grit open coat floor sanding type discs. The soft pad will prevent you from digging holes or causing other imperfections as you sand the hull. After you have sanded the outer layer of the mat, you must decide whether you need a professional plasterer to apply your screeding material. If your hull is unfair and has many humps and hollows, you would be best advised to have a local tradesman screed your hull with resin putty "bog."

RESIN PUTTY

The type of resin putty to be used here is made from waxed resin with enough talcum powder added to make it easy to work and not too thin. You will need a steel screed that is about 2'-0" [610] long. The best screeding tools are made out of the type of steel that is used for making hand saws. Your local saw

Screeding using old saw blade. Long even strokes and some practice will give you a first rate job.

doctor or saw manufacturer can supply you with a piece of 22 gauge steel, which should be suitable. An old saw with the teeth ground off would serve the purpose.

The resin putty "bog" will have extra added accelerator, about a half to one percent should be sufficient. Make sure you experiment with your resin putty mix, before you commit it to the entire hull. White pigment added at the rate of three quarters of an ounce to one pound [40 grams to 1 kilo] of resin will give your "bog" a white enough appearance to make it a good backup for the final finish coats that will follow. If your hull is very fair, you can do your own screeding using the materials as outlined in this chapter.

The method is to start at the keel line and work down towards the sheerline, screeding down the hull, until you have covered the entire surface. Now sand off to a smooth finish and repeat the process working along the hull, or diagonally so that the hips and hollows are covered from at least two directions. If your "bog" starts to cure prematurely or if it contains lumps and foreign matter; throw out the unused amount, because it will only cause tracks and grooves, in the area you are trying to screed. You will have very little success if you use "bog" that is not smooth and of the correct consistency. You will need some practice to decide the right amount of the catalyst to use with each mix. It is not wise to use a mix with a setting time of longer than fifteen minutes, as your "bog" will probably suffer from under cure and clog up your sanding discs when you try to sand off the finish. If your mix is too fast, because too much catalyst is used, it will set before you have a chance to screed it out. Never leave your "bog" un sanded overnight, you will have an impossible task to sand it next day. Same day sanding is important; this mix goes HARD.

Start your "bog" operation on the transom. If you do have troubles and the screeded section does not go hard enough for proper sanding, you at least have only a small area to remedy. At worst, you can wet and dry sand the finish, enabling you to sand it with your disc sander. You do not want to waste too many sanding discs on uncured "bog". Another remedy for "bog" that has not cured sufficiently, to be sanded, is to apply a hot mix of waxed resin. This is a batch of the resin to which you have added extra catalyst. This should give you a hard enough surface to sand, and will most likely complete the curing process of the "bog" simultaneously.

Once you have completed the screeding operation you must decide whether you need a final coat of finishing cloth or finishing tissue. It is recommended, if you use cloth, then 10 oz per square yard is about right. The decision will depend on how much screeding your boat has required. If you only have a very thin layer of bog on most areas of the hull, then either surface tissue or your finish coats of paint will be adequate to cover this and prevent any chipping at a later stage. If you have a fair amount of "bog", you will need to install a layer of cloth that will prevent your hull being subjected to surface damage at a later stage.

FINAL LAMINATIONS

Here is a method of putting on the last layers of your laminate, which provides a better than average finish. The prerequisite for using this method is that you must have a carefully laid up laminate to that point. As you have noted, the last of the main layers of fibreglass are usually an all mat laminate. The ideal way to apply the last layer of the mat is to use white pigmented waxed resin and apply the mat and a layer of surface tissue simultaneously. The method uses a slower resin mix than usual. Apply one run of the mat and before this has had time to gel, apply the layer of surface tissue and lightly roll the two layers together.

When using this method do not press too hard on the steel roller; only use firm enough pressure to iron out any bumps you may have in the previous laminate. One tip with all your laminating, press hardest on the humps and lighter on the hollows, this way you will help even out the laminate.

We have found this method of applying the final layer of the mat with the surface tissue in one operation; to be quite useful when forming up sections such as decks, cabin sides and cockpits. The more competent you become in applying the laminate and the finishing materials, the better will be your finished job and the less filling and sanding your laminate will require.

Experienced laminators and this includes builders who have laid up their own hull, can apply a layer of the mat and a layer of woven roving in one operation. The advantages are that the laminate can be rolled out and any previously formed irregularities can be eliminated by using firmer pressure on the high spots and a lighter pressure on the low areas, thus ironing out the laminate and resulting in an even surface. Keep this in mind when installing your main laminate.

Once your hull has been screeded, spot filled and sanded off and any surface tissue or finishing cloth that is required has been applied, you may now go on to removing any small imperfections in the surface. After a considerable amount of experimentation, we have found that the best method is to make up a mix of the following proportions. Four gallons of waxed resin to one gallon of talcum powder [15 litres to 3.78 litres] , half to one percent accelerator and 48 ounces [1360 grams] of white pigment. This will give you a mix of thickened white resin that contains addedaccelerator to assure that the mix will cure quicker than usual. This will help in your sanding operation.

The method of applying this filler resin, is to measure out about two pounds [1 kilo] at a time and add the catalyst to the resin in this small quantity. Carefully brush it onto the surface of the hull, laying on two or three coats, one over the other as each succeeding layer gels sufficiently, to allow the application of the succeeding coat. You do not have to wait for each layer to cure hard, but only until the brush does not disturb the preceding layer.

Using the technique as described above, several coats of this filled resin can be applied one on top of

Sander with soft pad attachment.

the other in quick succession, thus building up a thickness that will fill the small imperfections. The small imperfections will be eliminated when the hull is sanded off. It is usually best to work in a small area, up to a quarter of your hull surface or less depending on the size of your hull. The surface will be ready to sand two to four hours after the last coat has been applied. If these special surfacing resins are left overnight, it becomes very hard and is difficult to sand, because it soon takes the edge off your sanding discs. If you try to sand the surface too soon after the application of the resin, you will find that your discs become clogged and will make the whole operation difficult and very expensive.

By the time you have reached this stage, you will be experienced in handling the materials and you should have no problems in preparing a suitable filled resin and judging the time, when it is ready to be sanded smooth. About now, is the time when many people say enough is enough. It is not enough. If you paint your hull without carefully taking the final finishing steps, you will be disappointed in the appearance of your hull. You will also greatly undermine the resale value of the completed boat.

FINAL FINISHING

Now check over you hull at night. Using a torch only, shine the light end on to your hull and carefully mark the blemishes with a penciled circle. Next day carefully fill these blemishes either by brushing on your thickened resin mix or spot fill with resin putty using suitable paint scraper.

PAINTING YOUR HULL

Now a final sanding of the refilled areas, one last check over your hull and now you are ready for the final finishing. Usually you will be applying one of the polyurethane or epoxy finishes rather than a gelcoat. One last word on finishing. No matter how smooth and fair you think your hull is at this stage, you will find it is not as perfect as you believe. When you apply the final gloss finish, the truth will become apparent. If you consider your finish absolutely perfect, then you will most likely be satisfied with the result. If you accept less than a perfect finish now, you will be disappointed later.

There is a wide selection of Polyurethane and Epoxy finishes that are suitable for protecting the outside of your hull. We favour the finishes made by International Paints as this company has world wide affiliations, you can expect to receive good service, no matter where you are located. The method of application of your finish coatings, will depend on which material you select. If you believe your hull surface is sufficiently perfect to accept a high gloss finish, then you will be spraying your finishing coats. If you are of the opinion that your hull surface will not look it's best with a shiny surface; then you may prefer to roll on you your finish material.

When you roll on your finishes using a short nap mohair roller, you will achieve a slightly orange peel effect. This can be used to advantage by rolling the

Finish coats applied to ROBERTS 43 hull built by Gene Lurwig.

second last coat, lightly sanding the finish and then spraying the final coat. This will take away the high gloss finish that may not be appropriate for your hull. No matter what material you select as a finish coat, make sure you try samples before committing yourself to applying the material to the complete hull surface. Definitely experiment with some trial samples.

One last job before you turn your hull is to trim the sheerline. You should have been doing this right through the laminating process, I hope so, but if not, you will need to do it now. You will need a tungsten tipped circular saw or a jigsaw fitted with a steel cutting blade, to cut the fibreglass sheerline. After carefully marking the sheerline from the sheer batten on your mould, we trust your sheerline batten is absolutely accurate. Now trim off any ragged edges that hang below the sheerline.

PREPARING FOR TURNING HULL UPRIGHT

Now or before you trim the sheerline, install a 3" x 3/4" [75 x 20] timber batten around the sheer. Scarf the batten to a length that it will go right around one side of your hull. The batten is first clamped in place and then secured to the hull using self tapping screws, that are located every twelve inches [305] around the batten. The screw should be long enough to go through the batten, the outer laminate and some way into the core, not so long as to go into the mould. After the mould is removed, install a similar batten inside the sheerline. The reason for installing the outer batten before the hull is turned over is to protect the edges of laminate and add some stiffness to the hull shell after the support of the mould is removed. After the hull is turned; the mould is removed, you will find the hull is flexible, so the outer batten is part of the system that will keep your hull in shape until you can install the inner laminate, bulkheads and other hull stiffeners.

TURNING THE HULL

There are several methods that have been used to successfully turn the hull upright and remove the mould former from the hull shell. In some respects,

Hull has been brought out of shed either on rollers or skids. Two cranes have taken up positions as shown.

Hull is nearly half way over.

Half way mark, cranes will now reverse their attachment points to complete turnover.

Hull upright. Mold is now removed by one or two cranes and can be slung upside down ready for use again.

the method you will choose will depend on the size of your boat. Boats up to, say twenty-five feet [8 metres], both power or sail, can be handled without mechanical assistance. A few bottles of cheer and a number of your friends will take care of the turning over operation. For larger hulls a more serious approach is required.

If you are building in a large shed, it is a simple matter to turn your hull and mould over in one operation. Use two chain blocks and endless slings that are placed around the hull about 25% in from the bow and stern. The chain blocks are then used to raise the hull and mould off the floor and rotate the entire structure in the endless slings. The hull is next lowered into a prepared cradle, next attach the chain blocks to the mould structure. Now lift the mould out of the hull. The hull is now rolled out of the way and the mould lowered or again inverted ready for re-use. Another method of turning hulls of any size,

is to employ a suitably rated crane, fitted with a spreader bar and two endless slings. Assuming the hull is in a shed, then the hull has to be taken outside, either by using pipe rollers placed under the strongback or dragged out on skids.

MOVING HULLS

A word about moving large objects such as boat hulls. You can move large, bulky and heavy items by use of the simplest of devices. A few 2" diam. [50] pipe rollers 9" [230] long can be used to roll your hull, if you set down planks for the rollers to run on and keep taking the rollers from the back and reinstalling at the front as the hull moves along the desired path. If you use 4" x 2" [100 x 50] timber levers say 5'-0" [1.5 M]long, these will multiply a man's strength many times when it comes to lifting weights. This is useful when you want to lift the hull and mould structure to slip pipe rollers under

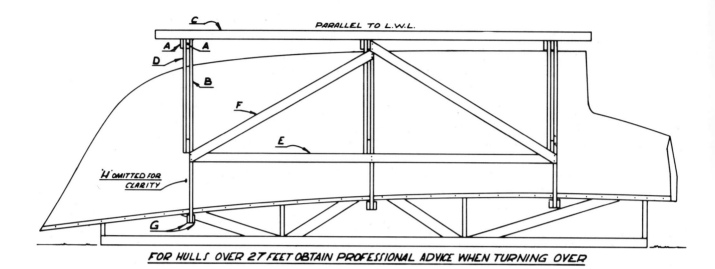

C

PARALLEL TO L.W.L.

A   A
D
B
F
E
'H' OMITTED FOR CLARITY
G

FOR HULLS OVER 27 FEET OBTAIN PROFESSIONAL ADVICE WHEN TURNING OVER

Mold being removed from ROBERTS 44 hull.

the strongback or bedlogs. Take care when handling large and heavy objects.

Another method we have used to turn large hulls, is to build a framework around the hull. A strong cradle built over the hull while it is upside down and braced through under the sheer, will make a good turning over cradle. Use three sets of frames, one forward of the keel, one in the middle of the keel and one aft of the keel. Diagonally brace the cradle.

See illustrations shown here for extra guidance. Use coach bolts throughout the assembly of your turning over cradle. When upright, the cradle should be capable of supporting the hull, until you complete the project. Once your hull is in the upright position, you can have the crane lift the mould from the hull and turn the mould upright ready for sale or for reuse. If you reuse the mould you will be liable to pay the designer of your boat a royalty payment. Check with the designer concerned.

TURNING OVER, BUILDING AND LAUNCHING CRADLE

Build from 6" x 2" 'B' grade or good quality second-hand timber – no nicks, splits or large knots, etc. Use ¼" φ coachbolts for hulls up to 36' and ⅜" φ above. Build with care. Cradle must be a substantial structure because hull must not move out of true after leveling up, must be well supported when fitting ballast or engine. Also, when ready for launching weight has greatly increased from turn-over.

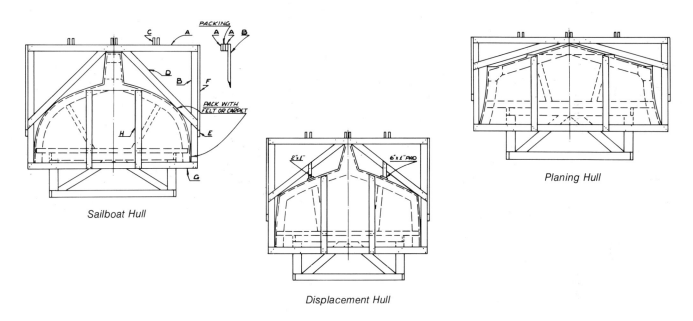

Sailboat Hull

Displacement Hull

Planing Hull

AFTER TURNOVER

REMOVE STRONGBACK, MOULD AND TIMBERS G-H. LEVEL HULL AND CRADLE AS ONE UNIT.
CHECK LEVEL THROUGHOUT CONSTRUCTION.
FIBREGLASS ONLY :~
FIT 4"x 2" SPREADERS ALONG SHEER AT EVERY OTHER STATION OR AS REQUIRED
UNTIL DECKSHELF IS FITTED. RUN A THIN WIRE FROM BOW TO TRANSOM ON ₵ BOAT
AND MAKE SURE STATION MEASUREMENTS ARE EQUAL EACH SIDE - ALLOW FOR MOULD BATTENS
FOAM ETC.- SEE HALF BREADTHS AT SHEER ON SHEET 2.

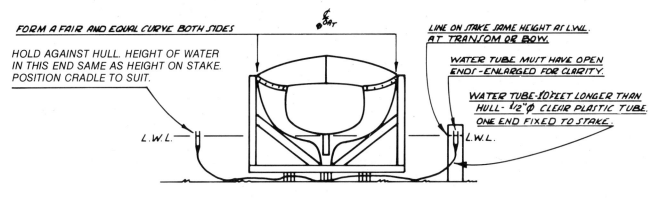

LEVELING THE HULL AND CRADLE

CHAPTER EIGHT
FIBREGLASS "EZI-BUILD" AND PANEL MOULDING.

BUILDING THE EZI-BUILD FEMALE MOULD

If you are considering building a chine hull, such as a power boat, single or double chine sailboat or similar craft, you should consider using the "Ezi-Build" fibreglass technique. There are two main Ezi-Build methods. One where you build an inexpensive Masonite mould and lay up the hull in that mould and another variation where you lay up the hull in panels and assemble the panels inside a very simple mould consisting of just a few frames. First we will deal with the Masonite mould method.

Back in the early sixties, we were designing fishing trawlers that could be built of fibreglass using inexpensive one-off or limited production moulds. With the current rise in the number of people interested in powerboats and the acceptance of chine hulls in general, we decided to reintroduce and improve on our original methods.

When looking at these techniques, we were developing a new range of powerboat designs using a range of computer assisted design programs, which included Auto-Yacht, Auto-Plex and a range of associated software. These new designs all reflected the ability of the computer to produce, in the right hands, absolutely fair, developable hull surfaces, suitable for turning flat sheets of steel or aluminum into attractive rounded hulls. Most of the first designs were directed towards steel or aluminum and many builders prefer to build their boats from these materials. For those of you who prefer fibreglass, we have combined the older Masonite mould techniques with the ability to computer loft hulls with fully developable surfaces and the result is the Ezi-Build technique.

ALWAYS STUDY YOUR PLANS

Armed with a suitable set of plans and full size patterns you first step should be to carefully study your plans. This advice holds good, no matter which building method you are using. Every hour of study can save several hours of construction time. Make sure you have allowed adequate study time before you start to build your boat.

LAYING OUT THE PATTERNS

You will need a large enough work area to lay out the full size patterns. This area should be as wide as the beam of the boat, and a minimum of one foot [305]. The depth should be the depth of the hull, plus a minimum of three feet [1 metre]. This area will enable you to construct the frames over the patterns and to fit the extra height of the extended upper ends of the frames. When you start to work inside the hull, first applying the battens and mould lining and later laying up the fibreglass laminate, you will need the extra height. Study the drawings and decide the best height to give you adequate working room above the hull.

Before making the frames, you may have to enlarge the shape of the patterns by the thickness of the battens and mould lining material. Due to the complex shape of a boat hull, this does not simply entail the reduction or enlargement of a frame by an equal amount. You may request a special set of patterns, from the designer of your boat to cover the reduction or enlargement. If you build your boat without enlarging the frames, you will end with a slightly smaller boat, which, may make only a small difference in the overall performance and accommodation space in the hull.

MAKING THE FRAMES

When marking the frame shapes on to the timber, use a dressmakers wheel, or the nail heads on edge method, or one of the other techniques for transferring the shape of the patterns to the timber framing material. Remember, here you are making female frames. The frame pieces will be joined by using half inch [12]; plywood gussets glued and nailed, screwed or stapled in place. Screws are strongest, staples are quickest and nails the most convenient. Make sure you keep all the gusset materials clear of the inner edges of the timber frames Later you may need to trim or bevel these inner edges with a plane and any nails or gussets will interfere with this process.

Build the hull frames in a way that provides an outer framework to support the whole mould structure. In the smaller designs say under thirty-two feet [10 metres], the bottom of the support structure can be canted 45 degrees. The canting of the mould frames, will enable the whole structure to be tilted, thus enabling the laminating to go on without so much clambering about in the mould. Again in the smaller hull, you could build wooden wheels around the frames so the hull can be tilted sideways. I have seen this method used in hulls up to sixty feet [18 metres]. Usually, for the larger hull moulds, build the frames with a flat level base and set up on bedlogs. Hang the Scaffolding inside the hull structure to support scaffold planks, thus allowing easy access to the interior of the mould.

SPLIT MOULDS

You may wish to consider a split mould. Here you build the mould in one piece, but with the intention of separating the mould at the centre line, so the laminating can take place from a corridor up the centre of the hull. The centre line board, the stem and the transom centre line board are all doubled up and bolted together so they can be separated when the mould is completed and you are ready to commence the laying up process. The transom may be a one piece affair that is designed to be installed after the hull is reassembled.

When you are laying up in a split mould, you install the basic laminate in the normal manner, but you step back the laminate from only one or two layers right on the centre line, gradually installing the extra layers until you have the regular laminate starting at 12" [310] out from the centre line. After the laminating is completed, the mould is reassembled by moving the two halves together and re bolting

Frames being erected for a ROBERTS TRAWLER 48.

along the centre line. Now you install the remainder of the laminate plus the extras usually installed in the areas of the keel etc.

There is virtually no loss of strength when you have completed the hull using the split mould technique. The stepping back of the laminate, and the addition of the extra layers on the centre line, assures the strength factor is equal to a hull laid up in one piece. If your hull shape will not allow the hull to be removed from the mould, then a split mould may be the answer. Of course with the relatively cheap Ezi-build mould you can simply disassemble the mould from around the hull, thus eliminating the need for a split mould, no matter what the hull shape.

For those of you who think that this method may present more work than building a one-off hull over a male mould, let me assure you after having sanded many one-off fibreglass hulls, I feel this method is by far the best and fastest way of building a one off fibreglass powerboat or chine type sailboat hull. If you are building a round bilge hull, then this method is really not suitable and you will need to consider one of the other alternatives.

SETTING UP THE FRAMES

After assembling all the frames, they are set up on a system of bedlogs so that the whole structure is true and level in all directions. If the bedlogs are level the hull structure will also be level. It will be necessary to run a centre line wire or string line up the centre of the bedlogs. The frames will all have a centre line marked on the top headstock and the bottom cross bar. It is a simple matter to set up the frames spaced as shown on your plans. A plumb-bob hung from the headstock centre line of each frame assures that the frame is vertical and on the centre line. A large builders square can be used to make sure the frame is square off the centre line.

SETTING UP THE STEM ETC

Install the stem and centre line board, which is an extension of the stem that runs the full length of the bottom of the hull, simultaneously with the frames. Use adequate props and bracing. A tip on setting up the frames, if the frames forward of frame 5 are set up with their forward face of the station mark and the aft frames are set up with their aft face on the station line, then most of the bevelling and fairing will be avoided. The battens can be nailed to the frames without any, or usually, with a minimum of bevelling or trimming of the frames.

The best sequence for installing the frames is to set up the centre frame first, usually station 5. Make sure this frame is truly vertical, using a plumb-bob hung from the centre line marked on the headstock. Use a large carpenter's square to ensure the frame is at right angles to the centre line. Brace this frame securely so it cannot move and use it as the reference point for setting up the other frames.

When all the frames, stem, centre line board and transom centre line board are in position and securely braced, then you can start to install the battens. Battens are best if made from 5/8" [15] thickness timber. Scarf the battens into full length pieces, the length of the hull plus a few inches for trimming. The batten width may vary. For the bottom you may use wider battens up to 4" [100]. For the sides you may find a width or 2" [50] battens best. You should have a stock of wider boards of the correct thickness and then rip the battens to selected width depending on the requirements of your particular hull shape.

INSTALLING THE BATTENS

First install the chine battens, one close each side of the chine. Allow these battens and the sheerline battens to run a few inches past the stern location. Now you may install the transom section of the mould. Camber boards are half checked at right angles to and on to the transom centre line board. Once the camber boards are in place, batten up the transom with vertical battens. It is usually not necessary or advisable to nail the side and transom battens together, use plywood strips outside the battens placed near the intersection of the side and transom battens, to hold the battens fair.

You should have a fully developed and expanded transom pattern. Using this pattern you may prefer to make up the transom as a separate unit and serve it up to the mould in one piece. If you make the transom as a separate unit, it can be at least partially laid up away from the main mould. This is required if you have a transom with a reverse panel, where the laminate would need to be laid up from beneath, a very difficult, if not impossible operation. If you build the transom in place, then the transom pattern can be used to cut the lining material.

While you are installing the transom battens, you can install the battens on the sides and the bottom of

the mould. Always install battens on alternate sides of the centre line, working progressively on both sides simultaneously. Never install all the battens on one side of any mould at once. You will distort the mould if you do not heed this advice.

After all battens are in place, install fairing gussets or strips of one Half inch [12] thick by four inches [100] wide plywood, clench nailed on the outside of the battens, one or two strips between each frame. The strips run from sheer to the chine and from the chine to the centre line. Clench nail through each batten, two nails per batten. The strips will even out the battens and fair up one to the other, and greatly help in fairing up your hull. You will need two people to install the plywood strips, one inside the mould and one outside with a "dolly" to clench the nails and ensure a tight join between the strips of plywood and the battens. As you will be attaching the mould lining with contact cement rather than nails, you should make sure the battens are all fair before you start to install the lining material.

CHOOSING THE MOULD LINING

When all the battens are installed and you are satisfied with the fairness of the interior surface of the battens, the next job is to install the mould lining. You should use three sixteenth inch [4 or 5 mm] plywood or tempered Masonite or other suitable sheeting material. If you use plywood it will need to be painted. Be careful here, contact your fibreglass supplier about which type of paint is suitable. Some paints will react unfavourably with the styrene and other chemicals in the polyester resins. From this stage onward work closely with your fibreglass materials supplier and take his advice.

If you use tempered Masonite or other hardboard, it will need to have wax added after installation. Johnson's "Traffic wax" is best for this purpose. Anyhow you must use a non-silicone type wax. It is also possible to use a type of plywood that has been pre surfaced with a Melamine finish. This can save on some finishing of the mould surface; however if you use a Melamine coated plywood, a PVC release agent will be required.

INSTALLING THE MOULD LINING

No matter which mould lining material you choose, it will need to be attached to the battens with a contact cement. Wall board cement is a good type to use for this purpose. Use very few nails, only where absolutely necessary, as the nail heads will show up in the finished laminate and are very hard to fill. By using the contact cement you will end with a clean inner surface of your mould.

The method of applying the lining of the mould is as follows. Carefully fit each sheet and lay aside. If you wish you may pre-fit several sheets and number or otherwise mark them for later installation. Coat the battens that will be covered by the first sheet, press the outer surface of the sheet of lining material against the battens to pick up some contact cement. Lay the sheet aside until the contact cement reaches the non-tacky stage, then carefully reinstall the sheet, firmly pressing it into position against the battens.

Do not allow the sheet to touch the battens until you have it in just the right position; once the contact cement has reached the non-tacky stage you will only get one chance to get it right. It is not a difficult job to install the lining, provided you follow the above suggestions and any special directions provided by the manufacturer and printed on the can of contact cement.

FINISHING THE MOULD

Once you have installed the mould lining, you should fill any joins with mould wax. Also radius any areas where you want to have rounded corners. You can use body filler or any other polyester based material that is compatible with the fibreglass laminate you will be installing in the mould. If you have used plywood as a lining material, you should check with your fibreglass supplier about a suitable polyurethane, polyester compatible paint system, for the inner surface of the mould. Two or three sprayed coats will be required. A little sanding between the final coats with some wet and dry sandpaper will help in achieving the desired finish.

If you have a Masonite lined mould, you will now apply Johnson's wax as discussed earlier, if you have a mould with an alternate lining material you will most likely now install PVC release-agent. You should seek some professional advice at this stage. Again your fibreglass materials' supplier can be a great help and may even direct you towards some local person who is experienced in laying up fibreglass hulls. An investment in some professional assistance at this stage may be worthwhile and save you making any big mistakes.

Once all the mold frames have been erected and the structure trued up, then the inside is first lined with battens, usually 1½" x ⅝" pre-spliced to length.

INSTALLING THE LAMINATE IN THE EZI-BUILD MOULD

The most important part of installing the laminate is the gelcoat and first layer. Even if you intend to later paint the hull using a Linear polyurethane or Epoxy based coating. We would recommend you use some form of gelcoat. If you intend to paint your hull, you can use a clear or non- pigmented gelcoat.

For starting the lay up process, choose a day where the temperature is between 65 and 80 degrees F or 18 to 26 degrees Celsius. Brush or spray the gelcoat to the mould surface and it should be approximately 15 to 25 mils, thousandths of an inch thick. You can measure the thickness of the gelcoat by using a special gauge obtainable from your fibreglass supplier.

You will need two or three assistants as you proceed systematically to lay up the hull, to be at the same stage each day with each successive layer. This is a form of temperature control. If the laminate overheats from applying too much material at once, it may distort or pre release from the mould. Your resin supplier can be a great help at this stage, seek his advice and follow it to the letter.

FIRST LAMINATES

The day after you have applied the gelcoat, you should apply the first layer of light mat usually 1/2 ounce per square foot [150 g/m 2], this layer is very important and should be carefully rolled out, thus eliminating any chance of air bubbles. Any bubbles will cause trouble after the hull is removed from the mould and is exposed to the sun for the first time. The bubbles will show through to the

Here we see laminating proceeding on one-half of 48' trawler.

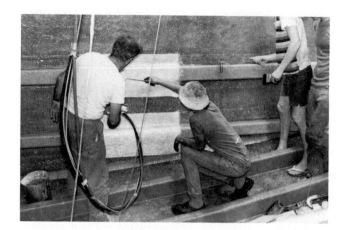

Foam cored stringers being installed in ROBERTS trawler hull. Note use of resin gun as a resin depositor.

outside surface, so take particular care with the installation of the gelcoat and the first layer of the light mat.

Once the gelcoat and first layer of mat are in place, you can breathe a sigh of relief. You have now passed the most critical stage of your laminating process. Providing you follow some form of temperature control, you should go on to complete the laminate without any problems. As mentioned earlier, always finish your laminating at the same part of your hull each day. Three willing workers can lay up any fifty feet [15 metres] hull in a few days. Two layers of fibreglass per day, one mat and one roving, is a reasonable quantity of laminate to install at once, without causing the laminate to overheat.

The number of layers of mat and roving required will be shown in your plans. After the layers that cover the whole hull surfaces are completed, you will most likely be required to install extra layers in the areas of the keel and below the hull waterline. Most laminate schedules call for overlapping and or interleaving the various layers in the areas such as the chine and keel, thus building up extra strength where it is required.

One tip, always trim the sheerline of your hull each day. This will usually be done about two hours after the final layer for the day has been installed. Do not rely on cutting off the excess next morning, or at some later stage, the laminate that is above the sheerline will be uneven and cause problems, especially when installing the subsequent layers of the laminate. Once you have installed the basic laminate and any extra layers called for in your plan

Three views of ROBERTS trawler built using the female molding techniques as described in the text.

laminate schedule, you should add any stringers, sole shelf, deck shelf, bulkhead base ribs and any other reinforcing members called for in your plans.

You should install all the ribs, stringers, bulkheads and web floors before you remove the hull from the mould. After you have completed the installing of the stringers and ribs etc., and if you do not plan to use the mould again, you may prefer to remove only the mould above the chine line, leaving the bottom of the mould to act as a cradle.

EZI-BUILD SANDWICH HULLS

So far we have not mentioned Ezi-Build sandwich hulls. If you are building a sandwich hull, then you will lay up the outer laminate plus any extra layers in the critical areas, before you install the core material. You may be using PVC foam or end grain balsa core. In either case the best method for installing the core is to use Vacuum bagging techniques that we have described elsewhere in this book. If you intend building a sandwich hull, please read the chapters on one off building, where you will pick up a few hints on the handling of the core materials.

PANEL CONSTRUCTION

This method of building a one off fibreglass boat is a variation on the Ezi-build technique. The method is ideally suited to building chine hulls including Power catamarans and any power boat or single or multi-chine sailboat hull. The main advantage of using this technique, is that a full mould is not required. You will retain the advantages that minimum or no finishing is needed to the outer surface of our hull. Very little filling and sanding will be required to achieve a perfect, professional standard of finish.

When using Panel construction techniques, the system of building the female frames and setting them up on a set of bedlogs, is similar to the methods used when building an Ezi-build mould. Only a few battens are required to hold the frames square and vertical. Additional bracing is used on the outside of the frame assembly. Once the frames and the few battens are installed, the next job is to prepare the fibreglass panels.

Please read the earlier description of setting up the Ezi-build mould. The technique of setting up the basic framework to hold the fibreglass panels, is

very similar to the first stages of building the Ezi-build mould. The fewer battens required and the absence of the mould lining material, are the main differences between the Ezi-build and the Panel methods.

The success of the Panel method depends on the builder receiving accurate information, consisting of computer generated full size patterns for the frames and either patterns or computer lofted offsets for the panels. We have successfully used this method when designing Power catamarans and our builders report excellent results using these techniques.

LAMINATING PANELS

Once you have the basic framework in place, you can consider laminating the panels. Before you go on, check over your framework to make sure it is true and level. It is very important that the framework is sufficiently braced to assure that the shape will be maintained during the installation of the heavy panels.

LAMINATING TABLE

Your next job will be to build your laminating table. The surface of the table is very important, any blemishes in the surface of the table will be faithfully reproduced in the outer surface of your laminate, so it is taking the care to get it right now. The top surface of the laminating table can be made of any one of several materials, however 1/4" [6 mm] Masonite backed up with adequate framing, would be my choice. You could use plywood, which will need to be painted with polyester compatible paint, or even a large sheet of plate glass. Any material that can be prepared as a perfect surface and are compatible with polyester resins, will serve nicely. As the panels are usually large in area, the table top material is best if available in one piece. Long lengths of 8'-0" x 4'-0" [2.4 M x 1.22 M] Masonite are usually available. Sometimes longer lengths are available, check this out, as the fewer joins the better. You will, in the case of Masonite need to prepare the surface with a wax, see preparing the Ezi-build mould. A PVC release agent may be needed with other surfaces.

The Panel method requires you to laminate the various panels, such as the two bottom panels, and the two or more that make up the sides of the hull. These panels are laid inside the framework as described above and laminated together at the joins.

The method of making each panel is quite simple, providing you have accurate computer generated patterns or offsets for each panel.

Using masking tape, mark out the shape of each panel on the laminating table, and lay up the required fibreglass to form one panel. If you use sandwich cores, these are installed while the laminate is on the table. Consider which way the panel will need to bend to be installed in the hull, before installing the core. Core usually takes a bend better in one direction than the other. As you will most likely be using scored core, or core that is made up of small blocks on a scrim backing, study which side should be laid on the wet laminate. Usually only outer laminate and the core are installed while the panel in still on the table, however there may be some exceptions to this rule.

STEPPING BACK THE LAMINATE
The edges of the panel do not receive the full laminate. The laminate is stepped back from the edges, so that after installation, the full laminate can be installed where two panels join, thus making up for any potential loss of strength. When the panel has been laminated, it is removed from the table as soon as the resin has gelled. The panel is installed in the framework while it is still "green". When you have all of the panels in place, the total inner laminate is then installed.

Some deck parts, cabin sides, cabin tops and other areas of you boat, can have both sides of the sandwich laminated while the panel is still on the table. This is only recommended in areas where there is a minimum bend required, to place the panel in its final location. Most of the techniques used in laminating Ezi-Build fibreglass hulls, can be used for panel construction. Installing the interior laminate, stiffeners and bulkheads etc., follow similar methods to those used in other fibreglass hulls.

CHAPTER NINE
FIBREGLASS - LAMINATING THE INTERIOR

This chapter covers the interior stiffeners required in most single skin hulls, including those built using either male or female moulding techniques.

SECONDARY BONDING

Before we consider the reinforcing members, we must consider how we are going to attach them to the hull. The most often used method to attach anything to a fibreglass hull is by secondary bonding. The term secondary bonding refers to any laminating where you are adding to, the part cured laminate. For instance, when you are installing a bulkhead, a web floor, a stringer or a rib, in all these cases, you would be making a secondary bond.

If you are forced to stop your basic laminate for over 48 hours, when you recommence the laminating process, this could be considered a secondary bond, although I doubt if most boatbuilders would class it as such. Usually, secondary bonds are not as strong as the primary bonding that takes place when you install all the laminate without more than 24 hours' interruption between the individual laminates.

In practical terms, it is impossible to build a fibreglass boat without incurring some situations where secondary bonding is a necessity. Providing you understand the process and take due care, there is no reason to expect problems during construction, or when the boat is in service. You must try to accomplish your secondary bonding as soon as possible after the primary bonding has been installed. There are several ways you can prepare your already in place laminate to receive another part.

You can sand the primary part so that no shiny surface remains where the new part is to be bonded in place. This method of preparing for secondary bonding is required and gives best results, if the basic laminate is over two weeks old. Another way to prepare for a secondary bond, is to soften the surface of the basic laminate, by laying a rag soaked in styrene over the area. As styrene released into the atmosphere is not environmentally friendly, you must use this method with some care. A similar result will be achieved if you soften the original

laminate surface using a wipe of acetone. There is room for copious amounts of discussion on these methods, effects and long term results of secondary bonding.

Secondary bonding is a necessary part of building a

Sole lines marked out in ROBERTS 36 hull built by Rhea Adams of Florida.

First layer of deck shelf being installed. Note homemade clamps.

fibreglass boat and in some cases a "Belt and Braces" approach is justified. For instance, if you are installing a bulkhead, you should laminate it in place, and if the bulkhead is a vitally important part of the boat; not all bulkheads are there for strength; you may decide to through bolt the laminate to the bulkhead, also taking great care with the bond between the laminate and the bulkhead. Always prime coat plywood before you bond it into place.

STRINGERS AND RIBS

Single skin fibreglass hulls will almost certainly require stringers, ribs and web floors. Sandwich hulls may require stringers and ribs and will require web floors. Your plans will show you what types of stiffening your hull requires and where it is to be located. Stringers and ribs have similar construction. It is normal to install the stringers first and then use an intercostal type of rib. An intercostal is simply a short length of rib between each stringer, running from the sheer or deck shelf down to the sole stringer or sole shelf. The transverse webs take over from there in supplying the athwartship stiffening.

There is no reason why you should not lay out the system of ribs and stringers with foam and then apply the laminate to the stringers and ribs simultaneously. The problem may be that the foam cores of the stringers and ribs are easily damaged and you would need to be very careful until you can install some laminate over the cores. A foot in the wrong place and you can do much damage. Using this method will help with some problems associated with secondary bonding.

STRINGERS AND RIBS

Stringers and ribs are generally foam cored. Rigid urethane foam of about 2 1/2 pounds density, can be purchased in sheets of a thickness equal to the depth of your stringers and ribs. Cut this material into strips on a band saw or other fine bladed saw. Use your not so favourite handsaw if you wish. Angle the saw to make stringer cores that are wider at the base than the top, alternate the cutting angle and there will not be any wastage. Stringers and ribs can be various shapes to play special roles in the hull. For instance, a stringer that will form a deck shelf will be flat on the top to accept the deck panel, but

Stringer and ribs system in ROBERTS 43 hull.

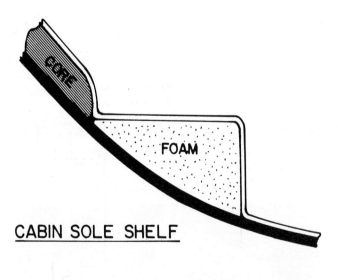

CABIN SOLE SHELF

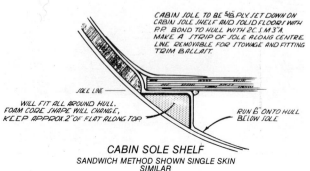

Laminating the interior of a ROBERTS 34 BALSACORE hull.

angled underneath. A sole stringer will be flat on the top and shaped to fit the contours of the hull. The engine bed stringers may be vertical in the inside and flared outwards on the outer sides.

All the shapes can be arranged when you cut the foam into strips, so make sure you have the right materials on hand. The various lengths of foam stringer material are butt joined and laid in the hull and are easily held in position using a hot mix of resin putty. A few spoon size lumps of putty set about six inches [150] apart will hold any foam

stringer in place until you can apply the stringer laminate.

Stringers and ribs are generally covered with a mix of mat and roving. Some stringers have extra layers of roving on the top, to create an I beam effect. Your plans should give you the laminate requirement for all the stringers and ribs in the hull. When installing the stringer and rib laminate, you will extend the laminate out a varying amount on to the hull surface. This is often referred to as "bonding". This bonding extends out from 4" [100] to about 6" [150] each

NOTE: IF YOU DECIDE TO BUILD USING SINGLE SKIN CONSTRUCTION YOU WILL USE ¾" FOAM OVER MOULD AND APPLY ALL GLASS ON OUTSIDE— AFTER YOU HAVE TURNED HULL REMOVE FOAM USING PAINT SCRAPER—IT COMES OUT EASILY. LEAVE STRIPS OF FOAM 3 TO 4" WIDE AND FOLLOW DETAILS AS SHOWN BELOW, AND ON SHEET 4 OF YOUR PLAN. STRINGERS WILL BE 18" APART APPROX. AND RIBS WHERE THERE IS A BULKHEAD PLUS EXTRA RIBS WHERE THERE IS A LONG SPAN BETWEEN BULKHEADS—CONSULT SHEET 4. THE TWO LOWER LONGITUDINALS CAN BE SPACED TO PROVIDE BASE FOR ENGINE BEARERS—ADD EXTRA GLASS IN ENGINE BED AREA.

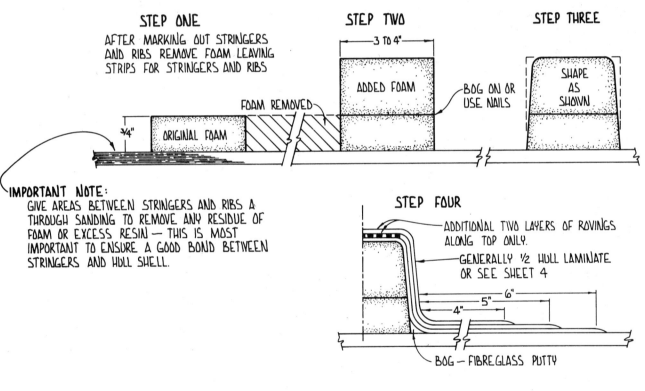

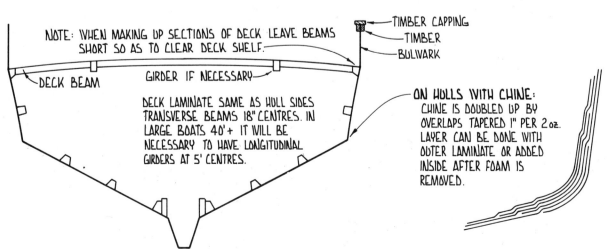

Tanks may be built into the hull. Note some baffles already installed.

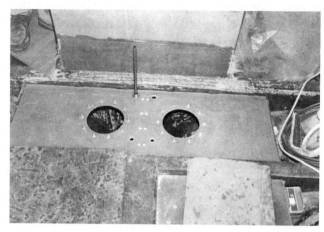

Tank top being fitted. Note large inspection holes which are essential for cleaning, etc.

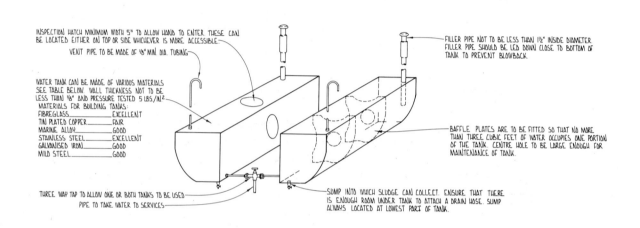

INSPECTION HATCH MINIMUM WIDTH 5" TO ALLOW HAND TO ENTER. THESE CAN BE LOCATED EITHER ON TOP OR SIDE WHICHEVER IS MORE ACCESSIBLE.

VENT PIPE TO BE MADE OF 1/8" MIN. DIA. TUBING.

WATER TANK CAN BE MADE OF VARIOUS MATERIALS SEE TABLE BELOW. WALL THICKNESS NOT TO BE LESS THAN 1/8" AND PRESSURE TESTED 5 LBS./IN².

MATERIALS FOR BUILDING TANKS:

FIBREGLASS	EXCELLENT
TIN PLATED COPPER	FAIR
MARINE ALLOY	GOOD
STAINLESS STEEL	EXCELLENT
GALVANISED IRON	GOOD
MILD STEEL	GOOD

FILLER PIPE NOT TO BE LESS THAN 1 1/2" INSIDE DIAMETER. FILLER PIPE SHOULD BE LED DOWN CLOSE TO BOTTOM OF TANK TO PREVENT BLOWBACK.

BAFFLE PLATES ARE TO BE FITTED SO THAT NO MORE THAN THREE CUBIC FEET OF WATER OCCUPIES ONE PORTION OF THE TANK. CENTRE HOLE TO BE LARGE ENOUGH FOR MAINTENANCE OF TANK.

THREE WAY TAP TO ALLOW ONE OR BOTH TANKS TO BE USED.

PIPE TO TAKE WATER TO SERVICES.

SUMP INTO WHICH SLUDGE CAN COLLECT. ENSURE THAT THERE IS ENOUGH ROOM UNDER TANK TO ATTACH A DRAIN HOSE. SUMP ALWAYS LOCATED AT LOWEST PART OF TANK.

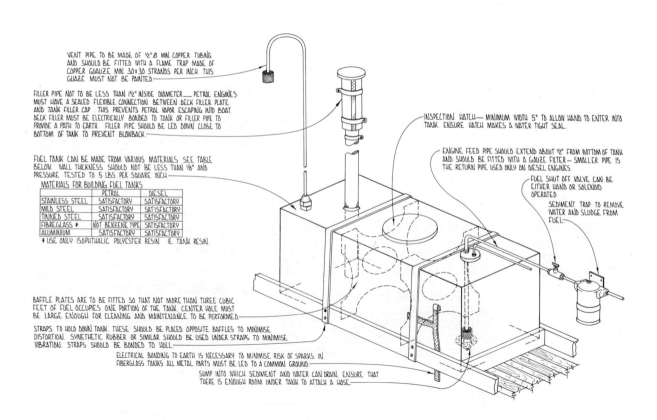

VENT PIPE TO BE MADE OF 1/2" Ø MIN COPPER TUBING AND SHOULD BE FITTED WITH A FLAME TRAP MADE OF COPPER GUAUZE MIN. 30x30 STRANDS PER INCH. THIS GUAUZE MUST NOT BE PAINTED.

FILLER PIPE NOT TO BE LESS THAN 1 1/2" INSIDE DIAMETER — PETROL ENGINES MUST HAVE A SEALED FLEXIBLE CONNECTION BETWEEN DECK FILLER PLATE AND TANK FILLER CAP. THIS PREVENTS PETROL VAPOR ESCAPING INTO BOAT. DECK FILLER MUST BE ELECTRICALLY BONDED TO TANK OR FILLER PIPE TO PROVIDE A PATH TO EARTH. FILLER PIPE SHOULD BE LED DOWN CLOSE TO BOTTOM OF TANK TO PREVENT BLOWBACK.

FUEL TANK CAN BE MADE FROM VARIOUS MATERIALS SEE TABLE BELOW. WALL THICKNESS SHOULD NOT BE LESS THAN 1/8" AND PRESSURE TESTED TO 5 LBS. PER SQUARE INCH.

MATERIALS FOR BUILDING FUEL TANKS

	PETROL	DIESEL
STAINLESS STEEL	SATISFACTORY	SATISFACTORY
MILD STEEL	SATISFACTORY	SATISFACTORY
TINNED STEEL	SATISFACTORY	SATISFACTORY
FIBREGLASS *	NOT BENZENE TYPE	SATISFACTORY
ALUMINIUM	SATISFACTORY	SATISFACTORY

* USE ONLY ISOPHTHALIC POLYESTER RESIN. IE. TANK RESIN.

INSPECTION HATCH — MINIMUM WIDTH 5" TO ALLOW HAND TO ENTER INTO TANK. ENSURE HATCH MAKES A WATER TIGHT SEAL.

ENGINE FEED PIPE SHOULD EXTEND ABOUT 1/2" FROM BOTTOM OF TANK AND SHOULD BE FITTED WITH A GAUZE FILTER — SMALLER PIPE IS THE RETURN PIPE USED ONLY ON DIESEL ENGINES.

FUEL SHUT OFF VALVE CAN BE EITHER HAND OR SOLENOID OPERATED.

SEDIMENT TRAP TO REMOVE WATER AND SLUDGE FROM FUEL.

BAFFLE PLATES ARE TO BE FITTED SO THAT NOT MORE THAN THREE CUBIC FEET OF FUEL OCCUPIES ONE PORTION OF THE TANK. CENTER HOLE MUST BE LARGE ENOUGH FOR CLEANING AND MAINTENANCE TO BE PERFORMED.

STRAPS TO HOLD DOWN TANK. THESE SHOULD BE PLACED OPPOSITE BAFFLES TO MINIMISE DISTORTION. SYNETHETIC RUBBER OR SIMILAR SHOULD BE USED UNDER STRAPS TO MINIMISE VIBRATION. STRAPS SHOULD BE BONDED TO HULL.

ELECTRICAL BONDING TO EARTH IS NECESSARY TO MINIMISE RISK OF SPARKS. IN FIBERGLASS TANKS ALL METAL PARTS MUST BE LED TO A COMMON GROUND.

SUMP INTO WHICH SEDIMENT AND WATER CAN DRAIN. ENSURE THAT THERE IS ENOUGH ROOM UNDER TANK TO ATTACH A HOSE.

side of the stringer or rib. Webs in a power boat are usually arranged in an "Egg crate" configuration so they not only stiffen the bottom of the hull, but also support the cabin sole. You may arrange the tanks in these areas.

INTERNAL TANKS

I personally am not in favour of internal, integral fibreglass tanks. Some builders swear by them. My experience is that if you do get a leak, it is almost impossible to find or repair. I prefer tanks built outside the hull and installed as separate units.

WEBS

Webs are best formed of fibreglass laminate, which has been laid up flat on a laminating table. An alternate method is to install Masonite webs and then install the laminate on either side, installing the bonding on to the hull while. The webs are generally set on ribs or stringers, so as to not to create a "Hard spot" where the web meets the hull. The tops of the webs should be fitted with a 1" x 2" [25 x 50] timber or foam rib. Cover this rib with the web laminate and will add strength to the arrangement and provide a landing for the plywood sole. Before proceeding, study the section of your plans covering the installation of the ribs, stringers, web floors and bulkheads. Often the bulkhead positions will govern all the spacing of the transverse webs, so making out the bulkhead locations is an important step in you building programme. We generally

recommend spacing the webs and ribs if required, equally between the bulkheads, but there may be exceptions to this rule.

ENGINE BEDS

As the bottom stringers are generally installed first, we recommend the engine stringers and beds are installed at this time. The location of the engine stringers, especially if there is a twin engine installation, will govern the spacing of the other bottom stringers. Engine bed stringers can be all foam and glass construction or they may have timber or steel inserts. Your plans should specify the recommended method for building the engine beds for your particular boat. Size of the engines, both physical and by horsepower ratings will be important factors in deciding just how you build the beds. There are special high density cores available for constructing items such as engine beds etc., check with your supplier for details. Overkill in this area is recommended.

Usually engine beds have a laminate that consists of alternate layers of mat and roving with extra layers on the top of the beds. A required system of athwartship webs is installed to support the engine beds. These webs will be cut away below the engine to allow room for the sump. If you are using a foam and glass, or a foam glass with timber or steel inserts, it is best to build the basic core structure and then laminate the complete structure as one unit. This avoids as much secondary bonding as possible. The area under and around the engine will need to

Simple gauge for making patterns for solid floors.

After patterns for solid floors are obtained, next step is to make up masonite formers as shown. Note 2" x 4" timber top which will later support cabin sole.

61

Note filler P.V.C. pipe to tank and rectangular P.V.C. construction pipe used to vent engine compartment both to port and starboard.

You may wish to install your engine before starting work on the decks and superstructure. Note well prepared engine beds and area completely gelcoated prior to engine installation.

Pre-laminated solid floors incorporating mast step. Next glass into keel.

Here we see foam stringers and engine beds being installed and laid up. Laminate of C.S.M. and W.R. is being applied over foam stringers.

be particularly well covered with interior gelcoat. You should consider a fire retardant resin in this area.

BULWARKS

On sandwich hulls with a fibreglass bulwark, or where the deck shelf is set below the sheer, we recommend that the bulwark area be solid glass. You can remove any core in this area and you may have used cheaper urethane foam for the area above the deck shelf. You will later add strength to the bulwark by carrying the deck laminate and bonding up to the top of the sheer. You may also add bulwark posts to complete the strength of the bulwark.

BULKHEADS

Once all the stringers and ribs are in place, install

Solid floor engine bed combination.

the bulkheads next. The bulkheads may be installed before the webs, as the bottom of some bulkheads may serve as a web. Bulkheads are generally made of one or more layers of plywood. As most boats are wider than the available plywood sheets, and as scarfing is a difficult operation and half checking is not as strong, we recommend making bulkheads out of more than one layer of plywood. For 1/2" [12] bulkheads you can laminate two layers of 1/4" [6] and for 3/4" [20] you can laminate two layers of 3/8" [10] and so forth. Stagger the joins of the sheets and glue and temporally staple together. Before you bond the bulkhead to the hull, be sure to give the plywood bulkhead a prime coat of the resin. This prime coat of the resin should extend all around the edge of the bulkhead and about 6" [150] on to the bulkhead surface. Let this resin cure before proceeding. This will ensure that there is not too much moisture content in the plywood, which would inhibit a good bond between the bonding and the plywood. One reason not to coat the whole surface of the bulkhead at this stage, is that you may wish to glue timber grounds for joinery on to the bulkhead when you are installing the interior and some glue will not take over the polyester resin. Generally speaking, epoxy resins can be used over polyester but polyester cannot be used over epoxy.

Fiberglass engine drip pan in ROBERTS 36 hull. Engine beds will later be laminated into this area.

In most cases bulkheads will be installed on a rib. An angle joint of fibreglass bonding should be extended for about 4" to 6" [100 to 150] on to the hull and the bulkhead. Holes of about 2" [50] diameter may be cut around the perimeter of the bulkhead at say 6" [150] centres, then the holes are chamfered from both sides. The bulkhead bonding can then be joined from each side, through these holes, thus greatly increasing the strength of the bulkhead to hull join.

Another method is to rebate all around the perimeter of the bulkhead, a four inch [100] wide by a depth of the estimated thickness of the bonding rebate, so that the bonding finishes flush with the surface of the bulkhead. Mask off the bulkhead inside the 4" [100] line to protect the surface of the bulkhead from resin drips etc. Trim the bonding while the laminate is still green. Now you may install a trim strip of timber to cover the bonding. Some builders may wish to back up the bonding with a system of bolts through the bonding and the bulkhead.

Anyhow, some form of covering will be desirable to cover the bonding etc. Only the main structural bulkheads need to be installed at this stage. These will be arranged so that the tops are allowed to rise far enough above the sheerline of the hull, to allow for the later shaping to accept the deck and the superstructure. Don't forget to allow for the deck and cabin top cambers. On larger pleasure boats and on most commercial vessels, it will be required to have some form of bulkhead stiffening. The stiffeners can be timber with a laminate of fibreglass covering. The plywood bulkhead, may have one or

Bulkhead to hull shows stringers, rib under bulkhead, connecting holes in bulkhead.

more laminates of fibreglass on each side. Your plans should cover these points. In small to medium size boats, the bulkhead stiffening may take the form of the framing for the furniture and joinery, which will be joined on to the bulkhead. It is possible to make up the bulkheads as a sandwich structure. For instance, it would be possible to make either Airex or Balsa core sandwich bulkheads, but our experience shows it is better to make the bulkheads from plywood unless there is some compelling reason to use fibreglass sandwich for this purpose.

LAYING OUT THE SIDE DECKS ETC

Once the bulkheads have been installed, you may now mark out the deck camber, the angle of the cabin sides and the cabin top camber on your bulkheads. Your full size patterns may include camber patterns for the decks, cabin tops and the pilot house. It is usual for the decks to have the least camber, the cabin tops a little more, and the pilot house to have the most camber.

When marking out the cambers, start with the deck camber and mark this right across the hull, now measure in the side deck width and mark, now draw in the cabin sides at the correct inboard angle and lastly measure up the correct height for the cabin top and mark in the cabin top camber. Now you should

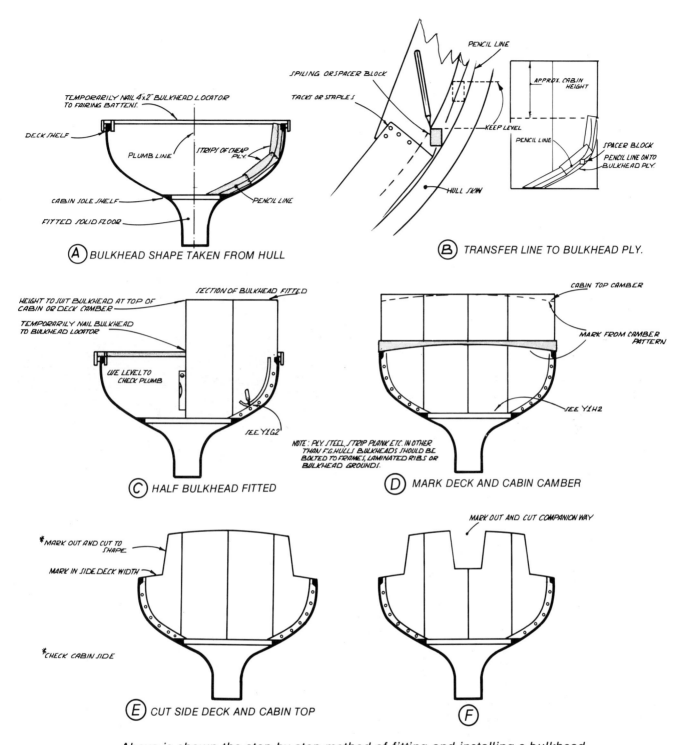

A BULKHEAD SHAPE TAKEN FROM HULL

TEMPORARILY NAIL 4"x2" BULKHEAD LOCATOR
TO FAIRING BATTENS.
DECK SHELF
PLUMB LINE
STRIPS OF CHEAP PLY.
CABIN SOLE SHELF
FITTED SOLID FLOOR
PENCIL LINE

B TRANSFER LINE TO BULKHEAD PLY.

PENCIL LINE
SPILING OR SPACER BLOCK
TACKS OR STAPLES
KEEP LEVEL
HULL SKIN
APPROX. CABIN HEIGHT
PENCIL LINE
SPACER BLOCK
PENCIL LINE ONTO BULKHEAD PLY.

C HALF BULKHEAD FITTED

SECTION OF BULKHEAD FITTED
HEIGHT TO SUIT BULKHEAD AT TOP OF
CABIN OR DECK CAMBER
TEMPORARILY NAIL BULKHEAD
TO BULKHEAD LOCATOR
USE LEVEL TO CHECK PLUMB
SEE Y1G2

D MARK DECK AND CABIN CAMBER

CABIN TOP CAMBER
MARK FROM CAMBER PATTERN
SEE Y1H2
NOTE: PLY, STEEL, STRIP PLANK ETC. IN OTHER
THAN F.G. HULLS BULKHEADS SHOULD BE
BOLTED TO FRAMES, LAMINATED RIBS OR
BULKHEAD GROUNDS.

E CUT SIDE DECK AND CABIN TOP

*MARK OUT AND CUT TO SHAPE
MARK IN SIDE DECK WIDTH
*CHECK CABIN SIDE

F
MARK OUT AND CUT COMPANION WAY

Above is shown the step by step method of fitting and installing a bulkhead

have an end on view of that section of the cabin structure. Mark out all of the bulkheads in a similar manner. Double check everything before you cut the bulkheads to shape and make sure you check you have the correct headroom. Stand in your hull and check the headroom between the sole and the cabin top. Do not increase the headroom without consulting the designer of your boat, you may adversely affect the stability if you increase the height of the cabin, without taking other factors into consideration.

As it is wise to install all of the bulky items into your hull before the deck and cabin are installed, your next steps are to rough out the interior furniture, install the tanks and the engine.

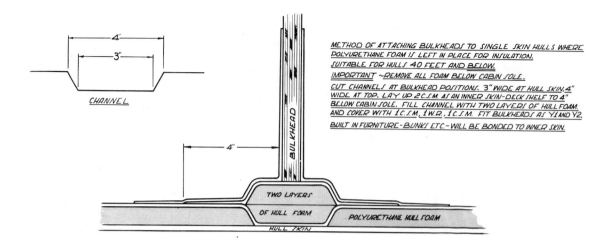

CHANNEL

METHOD OF ATTACHING BULKHEADS TO SINGLE SKIN HULLS WHERE
POLYURETHANE FOAM IS LEFT IN PLACE FOR INSULATION.
SUITABLE FOR HULLS 40 FEET AND BELOW.
IMPORTANT ~ REMOVE ALL FOAM BELOW CABIN SOLE.
CUT CHANNELS AT BULKHEAD POSITIONS. 3" WIDE AT HULL SKIN. 4"
WIDE AT TOP. LAY UP 2 C.S.M. AS AN INNER SKIN-DECK SHELF TO 4"
BELOW CABIN SOLE. FILL CHANNEL WITH TWO LAYERS OF HULL FOAM.
AND COVER WITH 1 C.S.M., 1 W.R., 1 C.S.M. FIT BULKHEADS AS Y1 AND Y2.
BUILT IN FURNITURE-BUNKS ETC - WILL BE BONDED TO INNER SKIN.

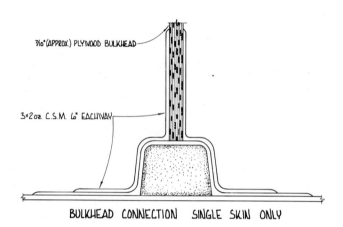

BULKHEAD CONNECTION   SINGLE SKIN ONLY

Rib, stringer and bulkhead bonding.

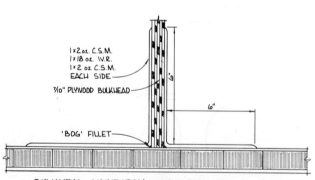

BULKHEAD CONNECTION — AIREX FOAM & BALSA SANDWICH

A small rib may be added between core and bulkhead
to ensure no hardspot will form.

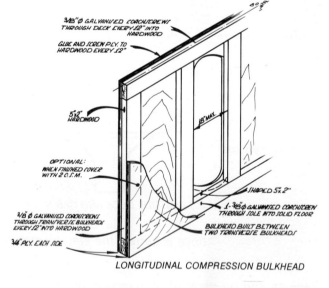

LONGITUDINAL COMPRESSION BULKHEAD

Pre-laminated half of centerboard case for ROBERTS 53.

Leave bulkhead square above hull. Must be high enough to give desitred headroom. You will latert cut to shape.

Mask off around bulkhead when you are installing bonding between bulkhead and the hull. Note the bonding holes in bulkhead.

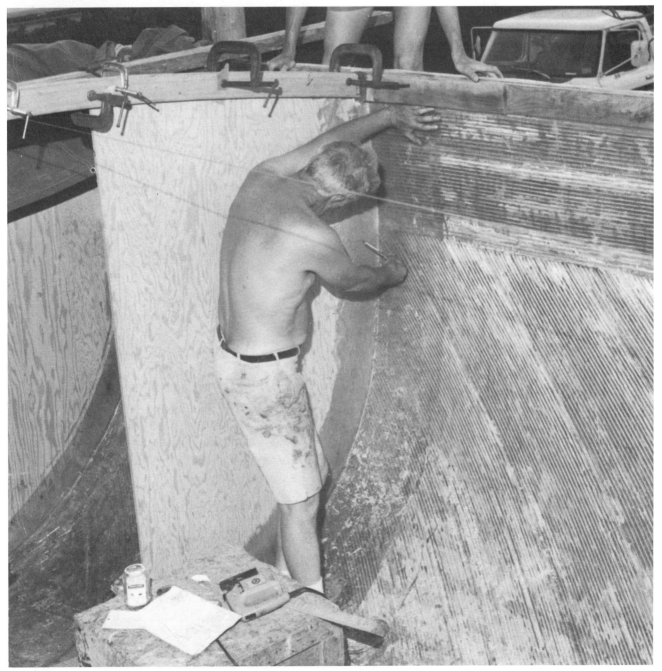

Installing a bulkhead in ROBERTS 36 built by Rhea Adams.

CHAPTER TEN
FIBREGLASS - TANKS, APERTURE AND RUDDER

TANKS - ALL TYPES

Make well-constructed tanks for your boat. Mild steel tanks are suitable for diesel fuel. I oppose the use of petrol or gasoline as a fuel for engines, or for any other use in a boat, I suggest you seek advice from the engine supplier, should you decide to ignore my advice in this matter.

You can make water tanks of fibreglass. They should be constructed using a special resin that requires a low catalyst content. Never use Aluminium for constructing holding tanks, there are chemicals in the human waste that will corrode the aluminium. Don't forget to correctly vent all tanks. The line for drawing off the liquid should enter through the top of the tank and not quite reach the bottom and be fitted with a filter that you can clean. The drain cock should be easily accessible and at the bottom of the tank. Access holes large enough to allow cleaning of the tanks' interior, are strongly recommended. The tops of access holes should bolt in place and the tops should be fitted with a sealing grommet.

Throughly test all tanks for leaks before installing in the boat. Test tanks with up to 3 pounds of air pressure. You may prefer to buy ready made tanks, these are generally available made of heavy duty plastic, aluminum, fibreglass or stainless steel.

Do not over tank your boat, I have seen some builders turn their boat into a virtual tanker. Today it is unnecessary to carry great quantities of water as the water makers are now more affordable. Estimate your fuel and other requirements sensibly. Flexible tanks made of various forms of plastic or rubber, are available and have some use as additional tankage for one off long distance trips, where the normal tankage would not be sufficient.

I would not recommend installing flexible tanks as a permanent arrangement. Some builders use them where the irregular shape of the area calls for special treatment, such as installing one of these flexible tanks. My advice is to consider all other options before considering using a flexible tank in other than a temporary situation.

Stainless steel straps are used to hold these tanks in position.

Integral water tanks built below salon sole - bulkhead in upper left is galley separation from sette - bulkhead in upper right separates NAV STA from settee. Tanks are made from 0.5" Mahog. ply coated min 3 times with WEST EPOXY. Notice pressure test gauge

APERTURES, HEELS AND SKEGS

On long keel boats you may be called to cut an aperture in the aft end of the keel to accept the stern bearing and propeller. Today most long keel boats are arranged with a longer heel attached to the aft end of the keel, so apertures are less often cut into the keel itself. In the case where there is not room for the propeller aft of the keel and ahead of the rudder, an aperture will be required.

Cutout made for aperture and shaft put into approximate position.

Foam being faired to correct shape by Gene Lurwig on his ROBERTS MAURITIUS 43 hull.

As it may be desirable to place the engine in your hull before the installation of the deck and superstructure, now is a good time to consider forming the aperture or arranging the heel on your hull.

The size and location of the propeller govern the angle of the engine and engine beds and the size and location of the aperture. Next you need to figure out the shaft line. This can be arranged with a profile cutout of the engine. The profile cutout can be made of strips of plywood or a sheet of Masonite or similar material. The profile should show the shaft line in relation to the engine and gear box. It is possible to obtain engines with gear boxes set at an angle to allow the engine to remain level or near the level in the hull.

First layers of glass installed, cutless bearing in place ready for final glass and finish coating.

The pre prepared profile can be arranged so that it is in the proper position relative to the engine beds. Once the beds are satisfactorily installed, then the profile can be used to arrange a string line from the line of the drive shaft through to the position of the aperture. Calculate the angle and the centre line of the shaft where it will exit the keel or skeg and drill a hole at this point. The string line is then lead from the position of the gear box drive shaft, through the hole in the aft end of the keel or skeg, to a point aft of the hull. Now you can check where the centre line of the aperture should be located.

There are three basic types of apertures, one type is

Fabricated mild steel heel ready for fitting prior to molding hull.

where the aperture is cut out of the aft end of the keel, the second type is where there is a skeg and the aperture is cut out of the skeg and the third and more desirable arrangement, is where the bottom of the keel is extended as a heel piece which is used to take the lower rudder bearing. The first two are usually found on sailboats, the third is found on both sail boats and displacement hulled power boats. For the first type of aperture, it must be cut out so that it will provide room for the propeller and the bearing in profile, and if possible, enough clearance so you can remove the propeller without having to remove the rudder. You may find this difficult or impossible with a skeg type aperture, as skegs are usually not of sufficient depth to allow too large an aperture to be cut, without weakening the skeg itself. The aperture must be of sufficient width to allow at least 2" [50 MM] propeller tip clearance both top and bottom. Once the aperture is cut out, then it must be reconstructed from foam and shaped to allow the installation of the bearing and fluted above and below the line of the shaft line, to allow a clean flow of water around the propeller. On one off power boats and on some sailboats, the aperture may be arranged as a heel. See photographs.

APERTURES IN SKEGS

In the many designs I have completed over the past few years, I have not designed skews with apertures. Much of the benefit of the separate skeg is lost, when a large area needs to be removed to fit the propeller and bearing. Either the shaft should exit the hull ahead of the skeg or some alternate arrangement should be considered. Another thing to avoid is a rudder with a cut out for the propeller. In days past, the aft end of the keel was raked to such an extreme, that half of the aperture was cut from the rudder. This resulted in steering problems. In recent years I have favoured the heel arrangement where the bottom of the keel is extended to the location of the bottom of the rudder shaft, thus creating a space for the propeller and bearing. The shaft now exits the keel at a location to give the propeller tips adequate clearance.

STERN TUBES

You may wish to manufacture your own fibreglass stern tube, study the illustrations shown here and this will give you a good idea of how you can achieve this.

Fabricated heel and timber deadwood fitted to mold before glassing.

Fabricated heel on WAVERUNNER 40. Steelwork was built into hull during molding stage and will be faired off with foam and glass.

SAILBOAT RUDDERS

The first step in building the rudder is to make a template of the shape, using the measurements and other information shown in your plans, plus some check measurements taken directly off your boat. The pattern should allow for the top and bottom bearings and is best made from 1/4" [6 mm] Masonite or plywood. The rudder stock may be made of 316 grade stainless steel and may be solid round or heavy walled tube.

Your plans should give you recommended sizes for either solid or tube stock. When welding the tangs to the stock, be very careful not to distort the stock by applying too much heat, in any one area, at any one time. Make sure the welding is undertaken in a progressive manner, to minimize the chance of distortion. The rudder core may be made of plywood or timber or a combination of both. The inner core should be the same thickness as the tang. Next, you can cut out for the tangs and then laminate in place, the remainder of the core over the tangs to build up the rudder to the desired thickness. Next, dress off the rudder to its desired airfoil shape. Many builders use foam to core their rudders, however, I do not believe foam has sufficient strength for this job.

Lastly you will install a heavy laminate of fibreglass to the entire rudder. It is important to achieve a good seal where the fibreglass meets the steel shaft. Epoxy resin would give the best bond between the fibreglass and the stainless steel, so this may be an alternative for this area.

Boatbuilder using time honored technique for boring the shaft hole.

The builder made this fibreglass propellor tube from Bruce Roberts plans

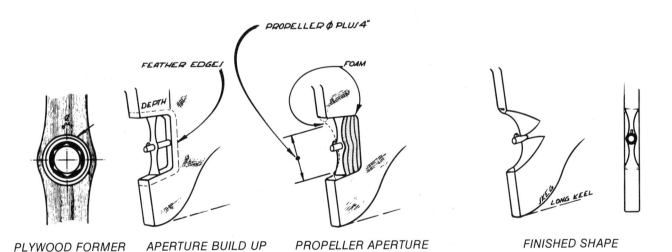

PLYWOOD FORMER   APERTURE BUILD UP   PROPELLER APERTURE   FINISHED SHAPE

Drawings show progressive forming of aperture on fiberglass hull. See text and photographs on previous page for further details.

PROPELLER TUBE ～ TUBE WILL HAVE A FLEXIBLE STUFFING BOX FW'D. AND A CUTLESS BEARING AFT.
TWO WATER SCOOPS ARE FITTED FW'D. OF CUTLESS BEARING

TIMBER FORM ½"Ø SMALLER THAN STUFFING BOX Ø AT STUFFING BOX END AND FULL Ø
OF CUTLESS BEARING AFT. LENGTH TO SUIT MOTOR INSTALLATION PLUS 3" FOR
TRIMMING. WAX FORM WELL AND APPLY 2 C.S.M. – CUT STRIPS 6" WIDE
AND SPIRAL FULL LENGTH IN OPPOSITE DIRECTIONS.

WHEN CURED CUT OFF AND FIT TIMBER PLUGS EACH END SAME Ø AS FORM.
THIS MAKES FOR EASY REMOVAL WHEN FINISHED.

LAY UP WEIGHT SHOWN ON PLAN.
BUILD UP OR REMOVE LAY-UP AT STUFFING BOX END TO GIVE A PUSH FIT
TO RUBBER HOSE.
<u>IMPORTANT</u> :～ GEL COAT INTERNALLY.

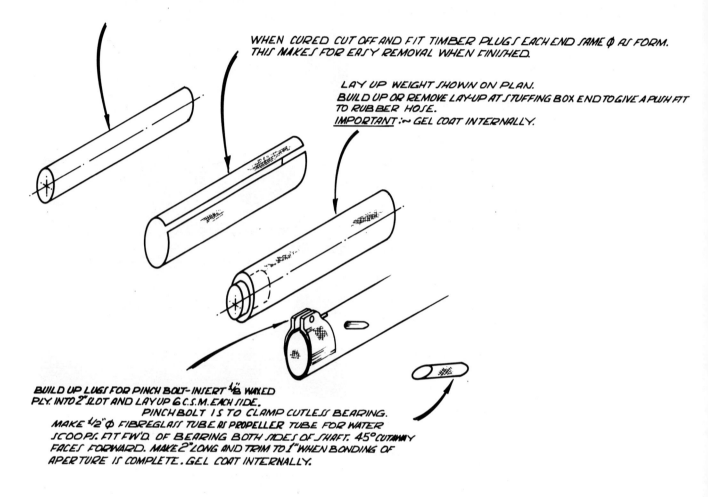

BUILD UP LUGS FOR PINCH BOLT – INSERT ⅛" WAXED
PLY. INTO 2" SLOT AND LAY UP 6 C.S.M. EACH SIDE.
　　　　PINCH BOLT IS TO CLAMP CUTLESS BEARING.
MAKE ½" Ø FIBREGLASS TUBE AS PROPELLER TUBE FOR WATER
SCOOPS. FIT FW'D. OF BEARING BOTH SIDES OF SHAFT. 45° CUTAWAY
FACES FORWARD. MAKE 2" LONG AND TRIM TO 1" WHEN BONDING OF
APERTURE IS COMPLETE. GEL COAT INTERNALLY.

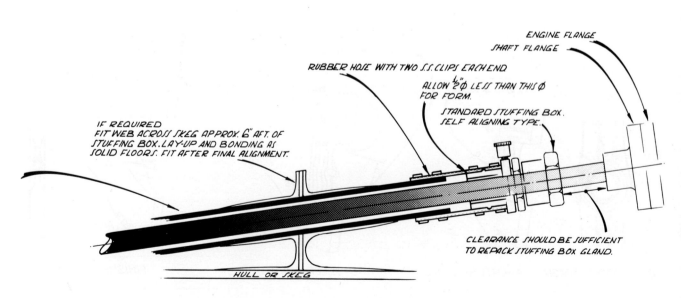

ENGINE FLANGE
SHAFT FLANGE

RUBBER HOSE WITH TWO S.S. CLIPS EACH END.

ALLOW ½" Ø LESS THAN THIS Ø
FOR FORM.

STANDARD STUFFING BOX.
SELF ALIGNING TYPE.

IF REQUIRED
FIT WEB ACROSS SKEG APPROX. 6" AFT. OF
STUFFING BOX. LAY-UP AND BONDING AS
SOLID FLOORS. FIT AFTER FINAL ALIGNMENT.

CLEARANCE SHOULD BE SUFFICIENT
TO REPACK STUFFING BOX GLAND.

HULL OR SKEG

PROPELLER TUBE AND STUFFING BOX

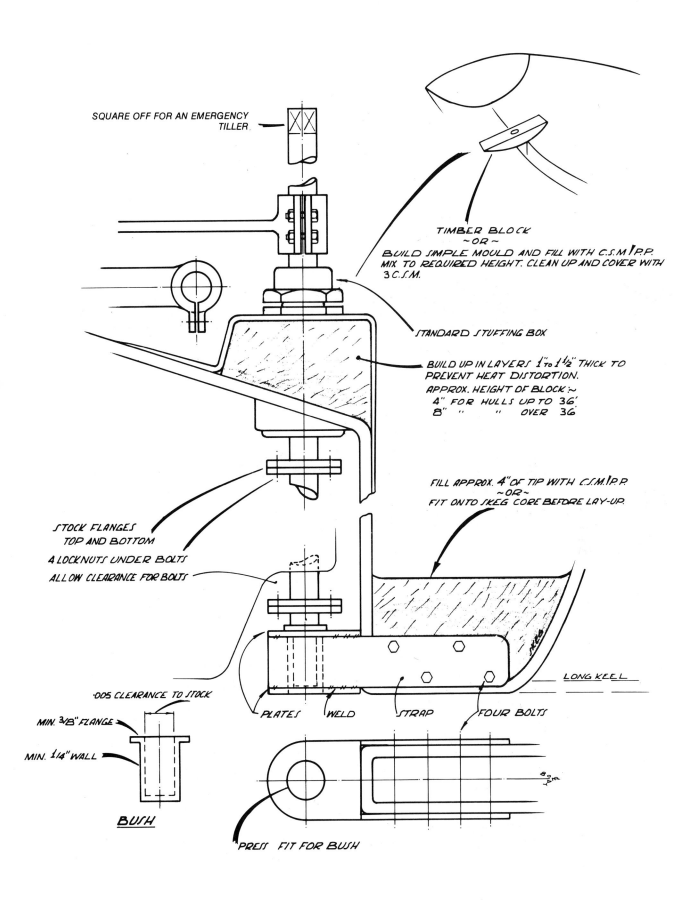

SQUARE OFF FOR AN EMERGENCY TILLER.

TIMBER BLOCK
~ OR ~
BUILD SIMPLE MOULD AND FILL WITH C.S.M/P.P.
MIX TO REQUIRED HEIGHT. CLEAN UP AND COVER WITH
3 C.S.M.

STANDARD STUFFING BOX

BUILD UP IN LAYERS $1''$ TO $1\frac{1}{2}''$ THICK TO
PREVENT HEAT DISTORTION.
APPROX. HEIGHT OF BLOCK :~
4" FOR HULLS UP TO 36'
8" " " OVER 36'

FILL APPROX. 4" OF TIP WITH C.S.M/P.P.
~ OR ~
FIT ONTO SKEG CORE BEFORE LAY-UP.

STOCK FLANGES
TOP AND BOTTOM
4 LOCKNUTS UNDER BOLTS
ALLOW CLEARANCE FOR BOLTS

LONG KEEL

·005 CLEARANCE TO STOCK

MIN. $^3/8$" FLANGE

MIN. $1/4$" WALL

BUSH

PLATES   WELD   STRAP   FOUR BOLTS

PRESS FIT FOR BUSH

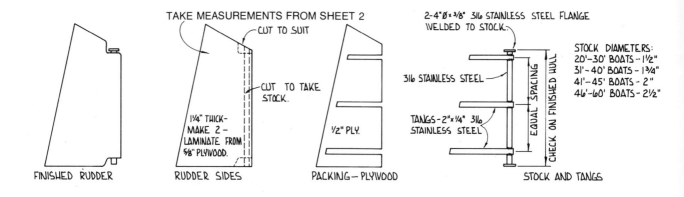

TAKE MEASUREMENTS FROM SHEET 2
CUT TO SUIT

CUT TO TAKE STOCK.

1¼" THICK—MAKE 2—LAMINATE FROM ⅝" PLYWOOD.

½" PLY.

FINISHED RUDDER

RUDDER SIDES

PACKING—PLYWOOD

2-4"∅ x ⅜" 316 STAINLESS STEEL FLANGE WELDED TO STOCK.

316 STAINLESS STEEL

TANGS-2" x ¼" 316 STAINLESS STEEL

EQUAL SPACING

CHECK ON FINISHED HULL

STOCK AND TANGS

STOCK DIAMETERS:
20'-30' BOATS - 1½"
31'-40' BOATS - 1¾"
41'-45' BOATS - 2"
46'-60' BOATS - 2½"

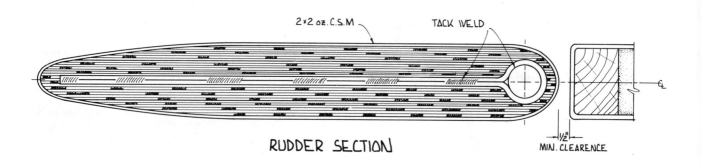

2 x 2 oz. C.S.M

TACK WELD

½" MIN. CLEARENCE

RUDDER SECTION

Fitting rudder shaft before fabricating rudder. ROBERTS 53 builder. Michel Gagnon.

Top end of rudder shaft will need adequate support and provision must be made for steering arm or quadrant plus key to take emergency tiller.

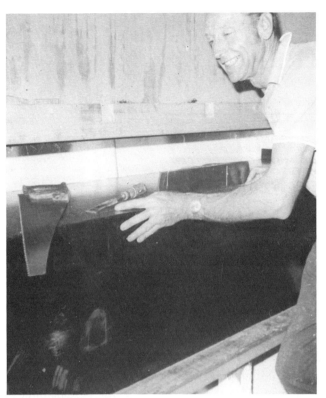

Many designs will accept welded mild steel diesel fuel and water tanks. Always test for leaks before installation.

Systems of webs in ROBERTS 50. Here we see them being adapted for use as fuel and water tanks.

Custom built ROBERTS 53 hull. Note rudder and fairing and stern bearing. This boat built by Seaway Yachts of Florida.

CHAPTER ELEVEN
DECKS AND SUPERSTRUCTURE

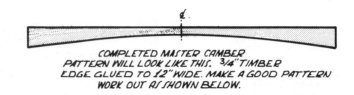

COMPLETED MASTER CAMBER
PATTERN WILL LOOK LIKE THIS. 3/4" TIMBER
EDGE GLUED TO 12" WIDE. MAKE A GOOD PATTERN
WORK OUT AS SHOWN BELOW.

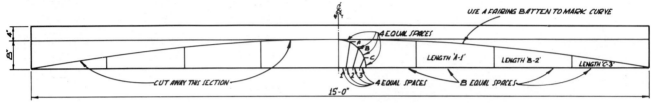

MARKING OUT A CAMBER BOARD

MARKING OUT THE BULKHEADS

By now you should have your deck and cabin top camber pattern to hand. If you have not already done so, consult your plan and transfer the measurements for the deck widths, cabin lay-in, cabin heights etc., on to the bulkheads. Mark out each bulkhead ready to receive the decks and cabin structure.

You should cut several temporary camber boards that will be used to form up the basic deck shape from sheer to sheer. As it is unlikely there will be enough bulkheads to support the deck structure, while you are moulding it in place, or bonding on a pre-laminated section of the deck, the camber boards should be installed. Temporarily nail the camber boards to the deck shelf and the boards will then either support the Masonite form work that makes up the in-place mould, or the parts of the prelaminated deck as mentioned above. You should consider one of the two methods to build your decks. The first method I will detail, is an in-place Masonite mould. The second option involves a purpose built master deck mould section, on which the deck is laid up in sections. I will now detail the two methods. One option I have not mentioned, is the installation of a plywood deck on a fibreglass boat, I prefer an all fibreglass boat. Why mix your materials?

MASONITE IN-PLACE DECK MOULD

This method involves building a timber and Masonite mould on the hull. After the decks and

cabin are laminated in place, the masonite mould is removed in pieces from underneath. This method is well proven and thousands of decks have been built this way. Using this method, you will finish with a smooth interior, something like a fibreglass liner in a fully moulded boat. If you wish, it will be a simple matter to attach any suitable fabric lining material to this smooth interior. You must sand the exterior of the decks, cabin and cabin top to achieve an acceptable finish. Think of this option as a male moulded deck and superstructure.

Now to the method in detail. The camber boards, or

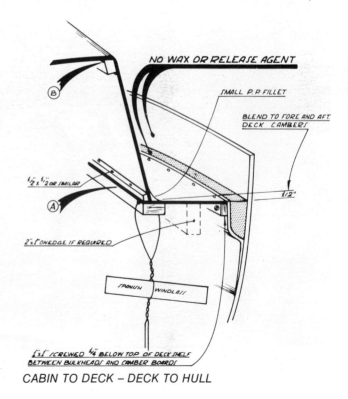

CABIN TO DECK – DECK TO HULL

temporary deck beams, are cut and installed at say 24" [610] centres, by nailing to the deck shelf. Next install sufficient longitudinal battens or deck stringers, to support the Masonite lining. Generally stringers should be about 9" [230] apart and these are checked into the temporary camber boards. You can expect to use 1/4" [6 mm] Masonite, or a similar material. While we refer to Masonite in the text, you may be using a similar material such as melamine coated plywood or whatever, but to avoid confusion, we will refer to the lining as Masonite. The whole structure of camber boards and stringers should be set 1/4" [6 mm] or at a thickness equal to your lining material, below the upper surface of the deck shelf. This is so the fibreglass laminate will go on smoothly from the Masonite lining material across the top of the deck shelf, be bonded on to the top of the deck shelf and go on either up the bulwark or on to the exterior of the hull to form a "Coffee can" hull to deck join.

A minimum number of nails should be used when fastening the Masonite to the framing for the in-place deck mould. Nails should only be used at the edges where there will be bonding from the inside to cover the nail head impressions. Any nail heads will show on the finished laminate from inside. Fasten the Masonite to the framing using contact glue, such as wall board cement.

The upper smooth face of the Masonite will provide a smooth surface on to which you will laminate the deck. Study the sketches shown here and your plan should give you guidance for the deck join, the bulwark, if any, and other features of your deck and cabin structure. You will note there are certain areas that the Masonite will not cover. Firstly it will only extend out to the inboard edge of the deck shelf. As mentioned earlier, your laminate will go from the Masonite on to the top of the deck shelf.

After all of the Masonite sheeting is completely installed, remove any unevenness by placing supports under the formwork. Radius all edges and corners a minimum of 3/8" [10]. You will need to fine sand and coat with two or three coats of polyurethane, any areas where you have installed the material to form the radius. You may find, to obtain the rounded corners on the superstructure, you will need to introduce some urethane foam or timber at the corners. This material can be shaped to suit. Again this surface will need sanding and coating to provide a suitable surface to receive the fibreglass laminate, without the laminate sticking to the surface. Remember this is a mould and the sheeting, the material used to form inside and outside radii, so the laminate will not adhere to the surface.

PREPARING FOR THE DECK LAMINATE

If you are satisfied with the completeness of your form work for the deck and superstructure, you should then cover all the Masonite surfaces with four coats of non-silicone wax polish. Make sure

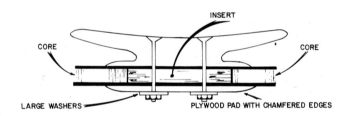

TYPICAL LARGE DECK FITTING

Above is shown the typical use for plywood inserts in balsa core decks and cabin tops.

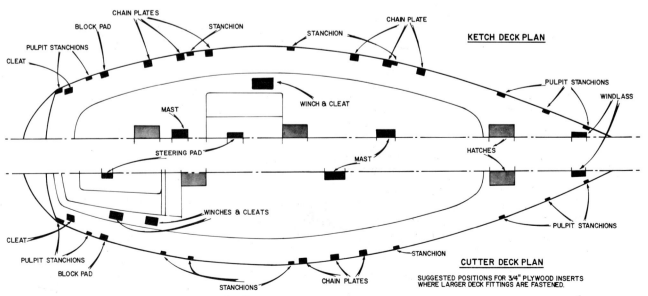

this is a non-silicone type otherwise you will have an undesirable interaction between the wax and the laminate. Allow at least one hour drying time between each coat of wax. Pay particular attention to the corners and joins. The areas to be waxed are those where you will be later removing the formwork, such as the Masonite, and any special shaping you have arranged for the corners. When the final coat of wax has been applied and polished, you may then coat the entire area to be laminated with a PVA release agent. Consult your resin supplier about the supply and use of this material.

Do not wax or cover with release agent those areas where you want the fibreglass laminate to adhere to the surface. Areas such as the top of the deck shelf, tops of bulkheads, the toe rail, the hull sides where the laminate will be attached to the hull, either outside or inside the bulwark, or any other area where you want the fibreglass of the deck to be bonded to an area of the hull or elsewhere as noted.

PLYWOOD PADS

Now is the time to consider where you are going to place any plywood inserts to allow for later through bolting of the various fittings. These fittings may include such items as chain plates, stanchion bases, windlass, bow fittings, cleats, sail track, mast step or where the mast will go through the deck in the case of a deck stepped mast and winches. All these areas

require plywood pads equal to the thickness of the core material you will be using on the deck and superstructure. The plywood pads may be only slightly larger in area, than the base of the fitting concerned. The idea is that the plywood will not crush when the fitting is through bolted and the bolts taken up tight. Although the balsa core has excellent compressive strength qualities, it is not equal to the type of strains imposed by through bolting the fittings. You may make up all of the plywood inserts, mark their location and identify each piece and now put these aside ready for installation at the same time as the core material.

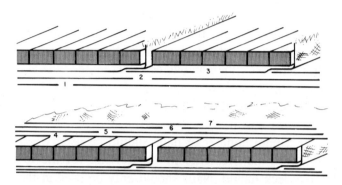

Sketches show the sequence for installing mat and balsa core when sandwich molded in place. Method is used to build decks and cabin tops.

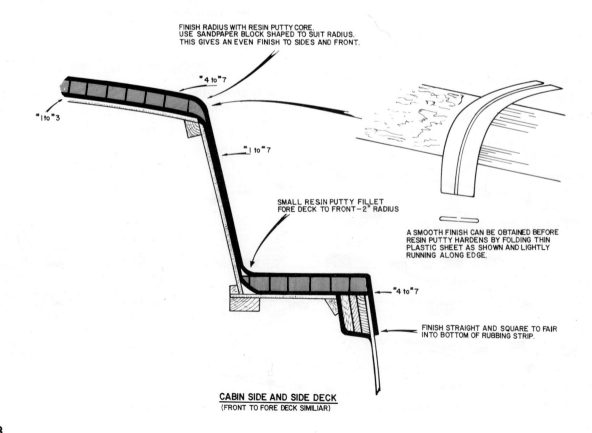

FINISH RADIUS WITH RESIN PUTTY CORE.
USE SANDPAPER BLOCK SHAPED TO SUIT RADIUS.
THIS GIVES AN EVEN FINISH TO SIDES AND FRONT.

"4 to "7

"1 to "3

"1 to "7

SMALL RESIN PUTTY FILLET
FORE DECK TO FRONT–2" RADIUS

A SMOOTH FINISH CAN BE OBTAINED BEFORE RESIN PUTTY HARDENS BY FOLDING THIN PLASTIC SHEET AS SHOWN AND LIGHTLY RUNNING ALONG EDGE.

"4 to "7

FINISH STRAIGHT AND SQUARE TO FAIR INTO BOTTOM OF RUBBING STRIP.

CABIN SIDE AND SIDE DECK
(FRONT TO FORE DECK SIMILIAR)

APPLYING THE DECK LAMINATE

The first job in laminating the deck, will be to install the inner laminate. The inner laminate will consist of a varying number of layers of mat and roving. The number of layers will depend on the type and size of your boat, however this should be clearly shown in your plans. The inner laminate should finish with one or more layers of mat. Before you reach the stage of installing the last of the mat, check over the installed laminate and carefully sand off any irregular spikes, sharp corners, or bumps.

INSTALLING THE DECK CORE

When you are satisfied with the evenness of the laminate installed so far, simultaneously install the last one or two layers of the mat and the balsa core material. The balsa core material will usually be 1/2" or 3/4" [12 or 20] or maybe even more than one layer to make up a thicker core. The sheets are usually about 36" x 18" [1 metre x .5 metre] and in most areas you can install complete sheets. In other areas, such as around cabins, you will need to cut the core to fit. It is a good idea to prepare one area at a time, say one third of the deck and cabin area can be pre-fitted with the balsa sheets. The sheets should be numbered and laid out in an area next to the deck, in a manner similar in which they will be applied to the deck and cabin structure. It is necessary to work quickly during this part of the proceedings, so everything should be well prepared.

When installing the last layers of the Mat before the core is to be fitted, use more resins than normal, wet out the mat and the face and edges of the balsa sheet. Next lay the balsa sheet on the wet mat, apply enough pressure to feel that the balsa is well set into the mat. The resin should squeeze up between the joins in the blocks and where the sheets join. It may be necessary to use a system of weights to hold the balsa in position, this should only be necessary in difficult areas, such as places where there is excessive camber, or where you are trying to install the balsa where it will not lay smoothly in position. It is a good idea to use plastic sheeting under any weights, so that the weights do not get glued to the balsa surface. You may wish to use "Vacuum bagging" to install the deck core.

Once the balsa core is installed and the resin has cured so that the balsa stays in place, then seal the top of the balsa with two coats of waxed resin. The reason for the waxed resin, is so you can lightly grind over the balsa, removing the rough edges and other irregularities in the surface of the balsa sheets. If necessary, you may also use resin putty screed to smooth out the surface of the balsa, however do not overdo this as you may impede the bond between the balsa and the outer layers of the laminate. The more attention you pay to achieving a smooth surface to the core before proceeding, the easier it will be to end with a smooth outer and final surface finish to your deck and cabin. Many designs call for solid glass cabin sides, solid glass cockpit sides and coamings. On other occasions you will be required to apply the core to the vertical surfaces. Your plans should clearly answer all of these questions.

Once the balsa core is in place and dressed off to your satisfaction, it is time to install the outer deck and cabin laminate. Use the same techniques here as suggested for laminating a male moulded hull, roll firmer on the high spots and softer on the low areas. There is no point in installing more laminate than your plans specify. You will cause more harm than good, if you install extra layers, thus causing excessive weight. This is your last opportunity to even out your laminate and make life easy when you come to the final finishing of your decks and superstructure. Once you have installed the outer laminates to the decks, cabin sides, cabin top and cockpit area, then it is time to consider finishing the surface using similar techniques to those explained in the chapter on building male moulded hulls.

DECK TO HULL JOINS

When considering the deck to hull join and using the forms of construction as described here, it is intended that there be a chemical, frictional and mechanical join. A "Belt and braces" approach, but one that has proven 100 per cent successful in all boats built using this type of hull to deck connection.

Coamings and fairings may be formed using foam to obtain basic shapes.

The chemical bond is where the fibreglass on the deck joins the fibreglass of the hull structure. Read again the earlier text on "Secondary bonding", before you go on further. If too long has elapsed between the lamination of the hull and the installation of the deck, you may not achieve a true

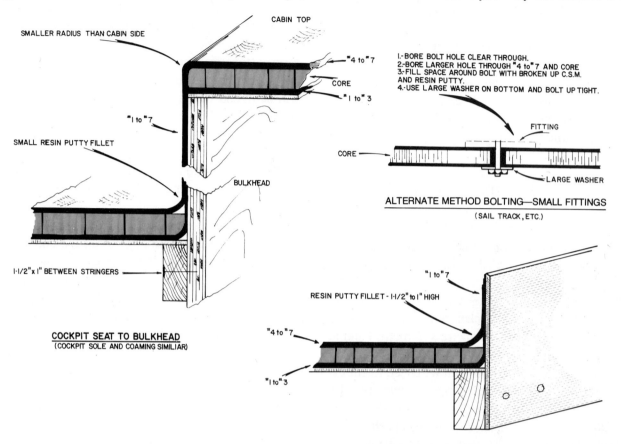

CABIN TOP

SMALLER RADIUS THAN CABIN SIDE

"4 to "7

CORE

"1 to "3

"1 to "7

SMALL RESIN PUTTY FILLET

BULKHEAD

1-1/2" x 1" BETWEEN STRINGERS

COCKPIT SEAT TO BULKHEAD
(COCKPIT SOLE AND COAMING SIMILIAR)

1.-BORE BOLT HOLE CLEAR THROUGH.
2.-BORE LARGER HOLE THROUGH "4 to "7 AND CORE
3.-FILL SPACE AROUND BOLT WITH BROKEN UP C.S.M. AND RESIN PUTTY.
4.-USE LARGE WASHER ON BOTTOM AND BOLT UP TIGHT.

FITTING

CORE

LARGE WASHER

ALTERNATE METHOD BOLTING—SMALL FITTINGS
(SAIL TRACK, ETC.)

"1 to "7

RESIN PUTTY FILLET - 1-1/2" to 1" HIGH

"4 to "7

"1 to "3

HATCH AND HATCHWAY COAMING

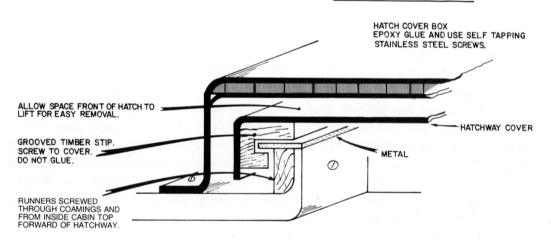

HATCH COVER BOX
EPOXY GLUE AND USE SELF TAPPING STAINLESS STEEL SCREWS.

ALLOW SPACE FRONT OF HATCH TO LIFT FOR EASY REMOVAL.

HATCHWAY COVER

GROOVED TIMBER STIP. SCREW TO COVER. DO NOT GLUE.

METAL

RUNNERS SCREWED THROUGH COAMINGS AND FROM INSIDE CABIN TOP FORWARD OF HATCHWAY.

FINISHED SLIDE HATCHWAY

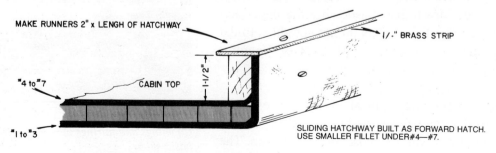

MAKE RUNNERS 2" x LENGH OF HATCHWAY

1/-" BRASS STRIP

1-1/2"

"4 to "7

CABIN TOP

"1 to "3

SLIDING HATCHWAY BUILT AS FORWARD HATCH. USE SMALLER FILLET UNDER #4—#7.

FINISHED SLIDING HATCHWAY COAMINGS

Deck being installed on ROBERTS 53. Note the almost deck high walk around scaffold which makes the job much easier.

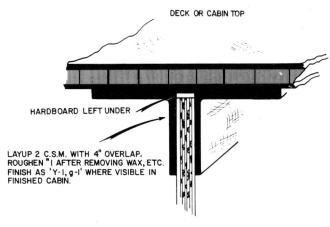

DECK OR CABIN TOP

HARDBOARD LEFT UNDER

LAYUP 2 C.S.M. WITH 4" OVERLAP.
ROUGHEN "I AFTER REMOVING WAX, ETC.
FINISH AS 'Y-I, g-I' WHERE VISIBLE IN
FINISHED CABIN.

BULKHEADS TO DECKS AND CABIN
(FURNITURE SIMILAR)

LAID TEAK DECKS

If you wish to install a teak deck on top of the fibreglass deck, this is possible. Keep the thickness of the teak down to say 3/8" [10] and install the teak planks using epoxy resin. The grooves or spaces between the planks should be filled with thickened epoxy. You can obtain graphite or carbon from your fibreglass supplier, to give the black colour associated with the traditional tar or pitch caulking between the planks.

NON-SKID DECK FINISHÈS

You may wish to finish your decks with a non-skid finish. This can be achieved, using either a prepared deck paint which incorporates pumice or other non-skid material, or by applying fine clean sand in the last two coats of the outer surface gelcoat. Another method is to apply one of the cork based, non-skid materials which are sold in sheet form and are cut, fitted and glued to your decks. Do not have too many spaces where the sheets meet, lengths of say 3'-0" or one metre along the decks, are about right. If the material has too many spaces' it looks too fussy.

Bulkhead to hull and deck join. Note masked off bulkhead 4" in from hull and deck.

chemical bond. However a frictional bond will be achieved and this, combined with whatever percentage of a chemical bond is present, will make for a strong join. We have taken test panels of the type of joins described here and in destruction tests, the laminate has failed elsewhere before it failed at the join.

Add to this a mechanical join, which is achieved when the toe rail is bolted through the hull and deck laminates where they meet at the sheer. Another mechanical join will be made when the rubbing strip is bolted through the deck laminate, which has been brought over the edge of the hull for three or four inches [75 to 100 mm] to form a "Coffee can" join. Another join is made when bolting the rubbing strip through the deck shelf and any inner bonding that joins the underside of the deck to hull. So now we have the possibility of bolting both vertically and horizontally.

No matter what method you use to create a non-skid surface, make sure you arrange the non-skid material in such a way as to provide small sections, strips or panels of smoothly finished deck around the edges of the sheer, around the inner surface of the decks where they meet the bottom edges of the cabin sides. Of course there is no non- skid material on any vertical surfaces. There should be a small smooth strip around all hatch coamings and areas where fittings are to be installed. Check out other boats, you can obtain many ideas from the boats you see in the local marinas.

While you are finishing off your decks and superstructure, you can consider building your hatches. If you are going to fit commercially made hatches, do not cut the hatchways in your deck until you have the items on hand and can make accurate templates or take proper measurements off the hatches themselves.

REMOVING THE MOULDING MATERIALS

Once the decks and superstructure are completed, it is time to remove the inner timber and Masonite formwork. First, carefully remove all the timber camber boards and supports and the longitudinal stringers. You will find some longitudinal stringers locked into the structure by the bulkheads, so very carefully saw through the stringer on either side of the bulkhead, thus leaving the small piece intact above the bulkhead. Some glue can be added if necessary to firmly fix this remaining piece in position. This small irregularity will be covered with the fibreglass bonding and or a timber trim strip. You will find some Masonite is locked in place between a bulkhead and the underside of the deck and in other areas, where you could not remove the Masonite entirely, without damaging the surface. Use a very sharp knife or a saw set to a very fine depth, to cut along the edge where the Masonite is locked in. The thin edge of the Masonite will be later covered with a trim strip or bonding.

BONDING THE BULKHEADS

After you have removed all the form work, you may find that your plan calls for the bonding of the bulkheads to the under side of the deck, cabin sides and top. Mask off the bulkhead and the underside of the deck, parallel to the areas where the bonding is

Deck and cabin molding fitted to hull. Aft deck and cockpit is made up of small separate glass panels and bonded into place.

Simple cabin and deck mold for ROBERTS 24 and similar sized sail and power boats. Note balsa being used to stiffen top of cabin.

Sliding hatchway and hatch cover box being built on ROBERTS 53 by Michel Gagnon of Quebec City, Canada.

Finished cockpit area on ROBERTS 25 built by Ian Waymark of Vancouver.

MOLDING A CABIN — *Female Molding*

Simple frame mold lined with ply. Use melimine faced ⅛″ ply or hardboard and fix to battens with hardboard contact cement – nail at corners only.

Apply Gelcoat after applying wax and/or release agent to inner surface. Gelcoat may be omitted and applied as for custom building if you feel further finishing will be needed.

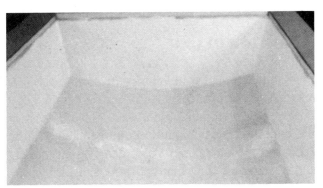

Use plasticine to form radii in the corners and to fill joins in ply; joins may also be bridged with thin clear durex or Bear tape.

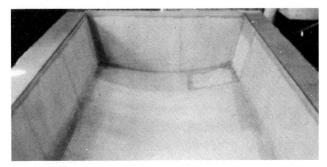

Laminate being applied to mold.

Inner laminate being applied – note section upper right hand of picture where laminate not full thickness – this is hatch section and will be cut out later.

Outer laminate, foam core and strips of timber have been applied. Now proceed with inner laminate. Core can be omitted and replaced with foam beans glassed over.

__LEFT:__ Cabin removed from mold, windows marked and cut out and cabin bonded to hull.
The methods shown here are ideal for Henry Morgan, Spray, R30, Waverunner and any simple shaped cabin structure. See printed building instructions for tips on female molding technique.

to take place, otherwise the bonding will have an untidy edge. Normally the bonding will extend three or four inches [75 to 100] on to the bulkhead and to the deck or cabin side or top. Make sure you thoroughly sand the areas where a residue of wax or release agent would inhibit the bonding of the deck to the bulkhead etc.

Once the inner bonding has been completed, you have basically completed the building of your decks and superstructure. You can now consider what type of lining material you will use to finish the interior of your boat. There are many attractive and serviceable types of lining materials for fibreglass boats. Short pile carpet that is glued to the interior, or you may choose one of the foam backed vinyl materials, or you may go the traditional route and install timber lining. If you are using timber, keep it light in weight, thickness and colour. Too much timber trim in a boat makes it excessively dark below. In the areas where the bonding between the hull and the bulkheads and between the under side of the deck head has taken place, you may install a timber trim strip to cover the join. While you have been planning to build your boat and in the early stages of construction, you should spend sometime studying other boats. Pay particular attention to the various fitting out and finishing techniques.

FEMALE AND PANEL MOULDED DECKS AND SUPERSTRUCTURES

In recent years we have favoured these methods for building the decks and superstructures. These methods avoid much of the sanding, which is required to obtain a satisfactory finish on male moulded decks and cabin structures. If you are building a boat under thirty-three feet [10 metres], you may wish to consider building a female deck mould that includes the deck and superstructure in one piece. This mould would be female in form and would give you a smooth outer surface. The inner surface could be covered with a lining material, as described for the male moulded methods. Another alternate method is to build female moulds for the cabin, cockpit and similar parts. These shapes are reasonably basic, and you can line the mould with Masonite.

EZI-BUILD DECKS AND SUPERSTRUCTURES

The main reason for using the following techniques, is to save on the amount of sanding that is required

to achieve a perfectly finished deck and superstructure. Ezi-build decks and superstructures are constructed using a combination of female moulded parts and fibreglass panels. Your first decision will be whether to use single skin, backed up with fibreglass foam cored deck beams and girders, or the generally preferred balsa cored sandwich. Sandwich decks have several advantages, they are insulated by the core material, they need a minimum of beams and girders, and they generally are a more efficient structure. Single skin decks are suitable for workboats of over forty five feet [13 metres], where a heavyweight system of beams and girders is required to take the extreme loads of fishing gear and deck equipment.

SANDWICH DECKS

For sandwich decks, the choice of core material is either PVC foam, such as Airex and end grain balsa. For decks, I prefer end grain balsa. The thickness of the core and the laminate requirements should be specified in your plans. Your plans should clearly show if any, or how many, beams and girders are required. A well-engineered sandwich cored deck for boats under forty feet [12 metres] will not require extra beams. Boats over forty feet require some beams, while boats over fifty feet [15 metres] may well require some girders besides the beams. Girders run fore and aft and are usually deeper in section than the beams. One pair of girders is usually sufficient for boats up to sixty feet [18 metres].

Your first job will be to cut a master camber board; sometimes your full size patterns will include this item; you will need to lay out the camber from measurements. You should make up a full width plywood or timber camber pattern. By using a wide plank, which can be edge laminated to a suitable width, you can make both male and female patterns with the one saw cut.

MASTER DECK MOULD

Next job is to build the master deck mould. This mould will serve to mould for all the deck and cabin top panels and even curved cabin fronts can be laminated on this mould. Make the mould wide enough to fit the widest section of the deck on your boat. This may be the aft deck, poop deck or perhaps the cabin top. On sailboats and on some power boats without a flybridge, the camber is often greater for the cabin tops than the deck, however for a power boat with a flying bridge, the camber is best if the

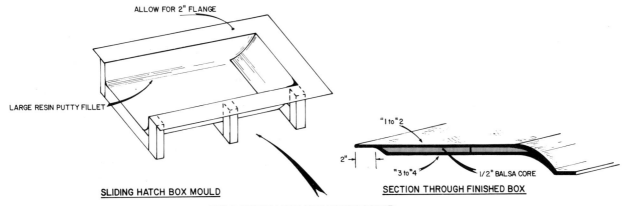

ALLOW FOR 2" FLANGE

LARGE RESIN PUTTY FILLET

"1 to "2

2"

"3 to "4   1/2" BALSA CORE

SLIDING HATCH BOX MOULD

SECTION THROUGH FINISHED BOX

BUILD SIMPLE MOLD FOR HATCH COVER.
TAKE DIMENSIONS FROM COMPLETED SLIDING HATCH.
GIVE TRIAL FIT TO CHECK WORKING.
AFT END OVERLAPS HATCHWAY 2".
ENSURE MINIMUM 2" CLEARANCE AT SIDES.

standard deck camber is used for all purposes. The reason for this is, you do not want a heavily cambered deck in the flybridge area.

The length of the master deck mould should be a few inches longer than the longest panel required, this may be the cabin top, or a poop deck. As panels can be joined, sixteen feet [4.9 metres] long is sufficient for most boats up to about sixty-five feet or [20 metres]. Build the deck mould without sheer; when first moulded, the deck panels will be flexible enough to take up the sheer of the hull.

Build the deck mould using similar techniques to those used to build the hull mould. Set up the structure on bedlogs. Build the deck mould with the camber in reverse. Use the female camber boards as the frames and install battens to receive the mould lining. Waxed Masonite will serve well as the mould lining. Attach the mould lining with contact cement and nail only around the edges if necessary. Any nails will show up in your finished part so try to avoid excessive nailing. Prepare the mould by waxing, give the mould two coats of wax, eight hours apart.

Place temporary beams across the hull in the areas where the deck is to be installed. These beams should be inside the deck shelf so the pre-laminated deck part can sit flush on the shelf. Make a pattern of the section of the deck you are going to laminate on the mould. Use strips of plywood stapled together to get the approximate shape and then use a spiling block to obtain the exact shape marked on to the pattern. A half section will do; hopefully your boat will be the same on both sides. Carefully trim the patterns and using masking tape, lay out the shape on the deck mould. Mark out both sides where appropriate.

It is optional whether to use gelcoat, however, we recommend its use even if you select a clear version. It is possible to arrange a so-called non-skid pattern in the mould surface; however, we do not recommend this. Moulded-in-place non-skid patterns are rarely successful, you will later be bonding the deck in place and would probably spoil the effect of the moulded-in pattern. Use a similar laminating technique to that used for the hull, no more than two layers per day, otherwise the deck piece may distort and pre-release from the mould. It is important to remove the deck part from the mould when it is completed. This means that it will be "green" and can take up the sheer, if any, of the hull. Therefore, make sure the centre of the panel is well supported, camber boards set right across the hull at every three feet [one metre] apart should be sufficient. Check after you install the first piece, do not allow the part to sag.

Any deck beams, girders or special stiffening specified in your plans, should be laminated on to the panel, while it is still in the mould. Allow for the deck shelf when installing beams, and they should be shortened by the width of the shelf. If you wish to use interior gelcoat, then gelcoat may be applied to the deck panel while it is still on the mould. Keep the gelcoat away from the edges of the panel where it will later be bonded to the deck shelf. If your deck is the cored sandwich variety, make sure the core is stepped back from the edge to allow the inner and outer layers of laminate to join, by way of a tapered edge of the core, as shown in the drawings. Side decks are made up from patterns taken off the hull, using the methods previously described.

BONDING THE DECK

Bond all deck panels in place both inside and

HARDBOARD MOLD DECK METHOD — SUITABLE
FOR USE ON BOATS 12′ TO 100′

STEPS IN MOLDING DECKS AND CABIN TOPS

1. IGNORE SHEER — DECK CAN BE LAID UP WITH STRAIGHT SHEER AND WILL TAKE UP PROPER SHAPE WHEN LAID ON HULL.
2. WAX HARDBOARD SURFACE OF MOULD 3 TO 4 TIMES USING 'CHIEF' BRAND FLOOR WAX — DO NOT USE SILICONE TYPE WAXES.
3. DO NOT USE RELEASE AGENT.
4. MASK OUT SHAPE OF DECK SECTION ON MOULD — PATTERN SHOULD BE TAKEN DIRECTLY FROM HULL — ALLOW FOR SECTIONS OF DECK TO JOIN ON BULKHEAD.
5. OPTIONAL — APPLY GELCOAT TO MOULD — IF DECKS ARE TO BE SANDED OR NEED OTHER ADDITIONAL BONDING LATER THERE IS NO POINT IN GELCOATING AT THIS STAGE.
6. APPLY 1 LAYER C.S.M. AND SUBSEQUENT LAYERS.
7. APPLY CORE IF BEING USED — NO BEAMS REQUIRED.
8. FINAL LAYER OF GLASS
9. TRANSVERSE DECK BEAMS 18″ CENTRES — USE FOAM CORE.
10. REMOVE FROM MOULD AND FIT TO HULL — TRIM AS REQUIRED.

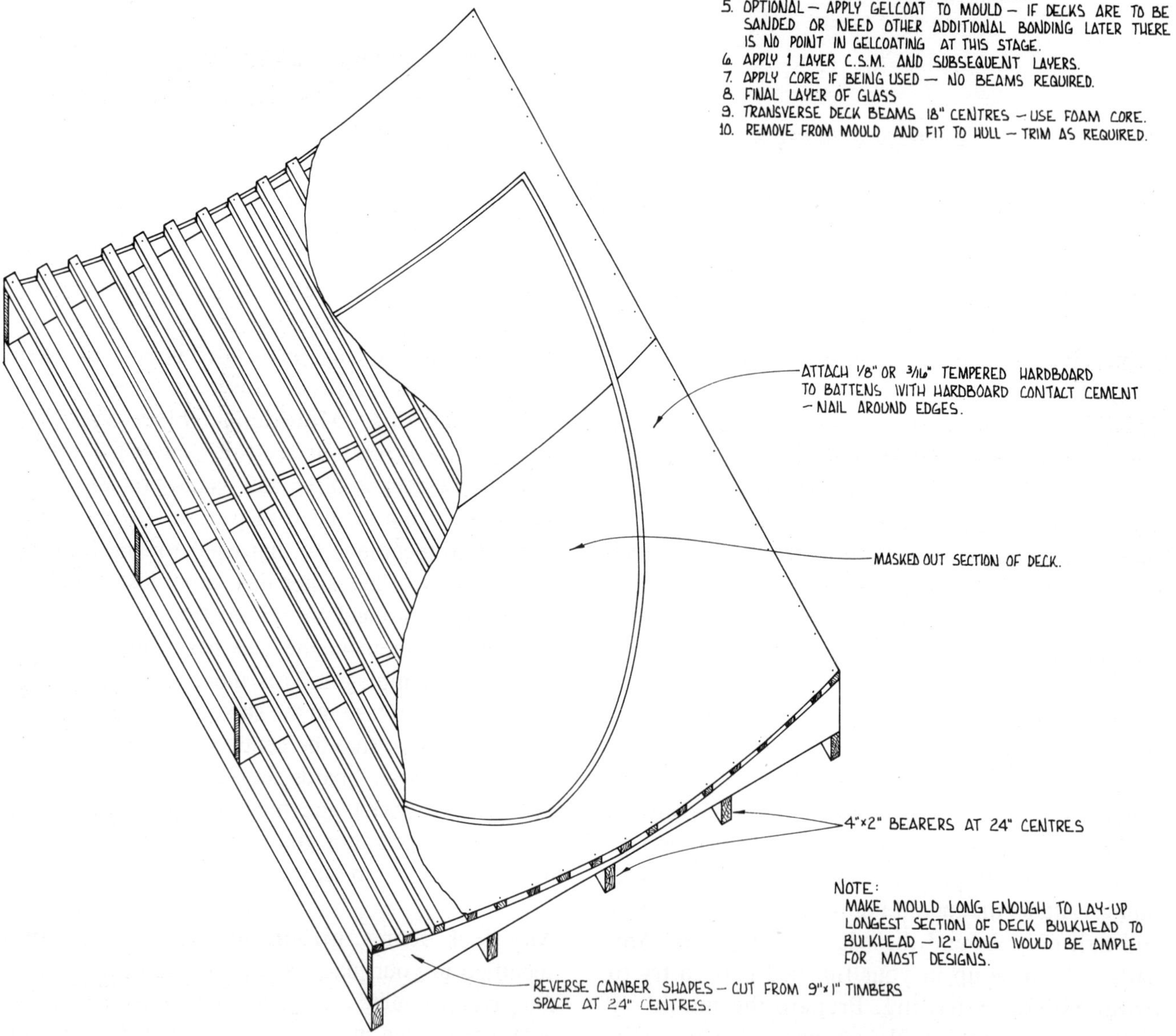

ATTACH ⅛″ OR ³/₁₆″ TEMPERED HARDBOARD TO BATTENS WITH HARDBOARD CONTACT CEMENT — NAIL AROUND EDGES.

MASKED OUT SECTION OF DECK.

4″×2″ BEARERS AT 24″ CENTRES

NOTE:
MAKE MOULD LONG ENOUGH TO LAY-UP LONGEST SECTION OF DECK BULKHEAD TO BULKHEAD — 12′ LONG WOULD BE AMPLE FOR MOST DESIGNS.

REVERSE CAMBER SHAPES — CUT FROM 9″×1″ TIMBERS SPACE AT 24″ CENTRES.

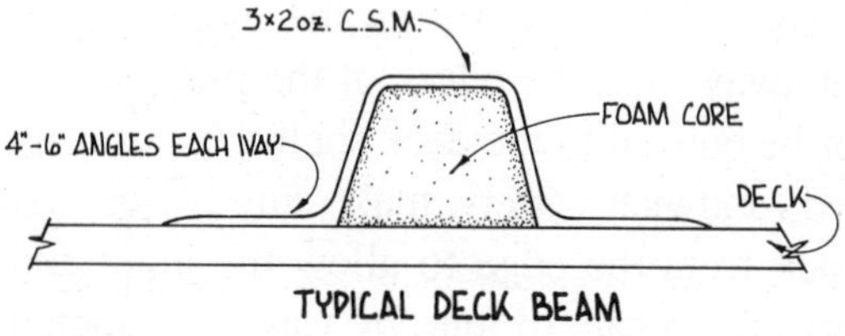

3×2oz. C.S.M.

4″-6″ ANGLES EACH WAY

FOAM CORE

DECK

TYPICAL DECK BEAM

ADD OUTER GLASS AFTER INSTALLING DECK SECTION ON BOAT.

BALSA CORE

INNER GLASS

GEL COAT

HARDBOARD

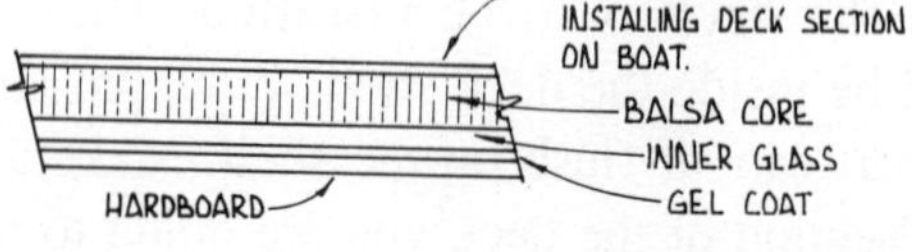

BALSA CORE DECK

outside. Your plans should show the bonding amounts and layout. You may omit some laminate near the edge of the panel, so you can make up the laminate when installing the bonding, by interleaving the laminate and extra bonding. This will help in avoiding ugly bulges, where the bonding is installed. Remember to sand off any residue of wax, before attempting to bond any fibreglass piece in position. Where wax is used, the laminating process always picks up some residue, clean off all wax and release agent before bonding or painting.

ROBERTS 25 hull mold being removed from plywood disposable plug.

CABIN SIDES

Lay up the cabin sides on a single flat Masonite table or similar mould surface. A flat mould can produce many and varied panels for use in the superstructure and elsewhere.

BULWARK STIFFENERS

If you have arranged a single skin bulwark, then you should consider some bulwark stiffeners. These stiffeners can be very attractive and give your boat a "Little Ship" appearance. You may build the stiffeners like ribs; you can make them with or without a core. If you laminate as a single skin, then they can have a flange on the inner edge, similar to the stiffeners you see on the bulwarks of steel boats. The top of the bulwark stiffeners should be at least as wide as the cap rail.

HULL DECK JOINS

If you are using the "Coffee can" join where the deck laminate is continued over the hull sheer down a few inches on to the hull, then you will need to mask off the hull below the line where the overlap bonding will end. Sand the area of the hull above this line so you will have a good key for the overlapping bonding. As the bonding proceeds, make sure you trim each layer cleanly along the top of the tape on the hull side. This will create a fair line with a clean edge that can be covered by your rubbing strip or moulding.

When you are moulding the various sections of deck, it is wise to join these on the top of a bulkhead. The top of the bulkheads can be thickened with suitable timber flanges.

Once you get used to the "Ezi-build" methods you will find many ways to use the methods we have briefly outlined here. Using panel construction combined with inexpensive moulds, will allow you to build just about anything. There is nothing new in the methods we have described, just the re introduction and rearrangement of a few techniques we have been using for many years.

These methods are best used for one off boats or where a few boats are to be produced. If you are intending to build more than five fibreglass boats of any one type, then you may want to consider building timber plugs and "Taking off" fibreglass moulds capable of producing up to two hundred hulls.

PRODUCTION MOULDS

As mentioned above, if you are planning to build many hulls, you may want to consider a full production mould. The usual method is to build a plug and from this highly finished hull, make a mould capable of withstanding long and frequent use. You can build the plug of timber, in a similar manner to building a one off timber and batten mould. Cover the exterior with three or more layers of plywood and then sanded and painted. The plug must be perfect on the outside, but underneath the construction can be rough and ready, as the plug only has to last until the mould is laid up and removed.

The mould is laid up over the plug. First a parting agent, such as wax or PVC release agent or a combination is applied to the plug. Next a coat of tooling gelcoat is installedand then the laminate is gradually built up to a thickness that will make the mould strong enough to last as long as required. The outside is fitted with foam and glass ribs to stiffen the structure. Finally plywood and timber, or sometimes steel, are bonded to the mould to allow it to be tilted or set on a cradle when in use. Remove the mould from the plug and if everything goes according to plan, the mould with some final interior preparation is ready for use.

Deck moulds are built in a similar manner. First a plug is constructed from plywood, chip board or whatever will do the job, then a mould is taken off in a similar manner to the laminating of the hull mould. Give some thought to the hull to deck join that can consist of a flange or coffee can join or similar arrangement. Often the join is designed to be made under the top of the toe rail. A coffee can join is where the deck overlaps the hull in the manner of the older types of coffee can lids.

As you are aware, fibreglass is only one of several methods you can use to build a boat, however it is one of the most versatile and one of the easiest, for a person without previous experience to master. I have seen many, indeed hundreds, of beautifully built one off fibreglass boats. Unfortunately I have seen a few, fortunately a very few, horrible examples. Please work towards making every stage one that you can be proud of, this way, you can be assured that the

ROBERTS DINGHY. *A good project to practice female molding technique.*

Split female mold for ROBERTS 36 hull built by master boatbuilder Barry Long of Brisbane, Australia.

result will have a top resale value and will bring you, the builder, considerable enjoyment and profit.

VACUUM BAGGING

This technique can be useful in several stages of your fibreglass boat building programme. Used for instance, to install the core on you male moulded hull; install the core on a female or Ezi-build hull and install the core on your decks. You can use the vacuum bagging methods with Airex PVC foam or balsa cores. Vacuum bagging harnesses the weight of the earth's atmosphere to apply pressure where you are seeking to clamp or hold things together. A perfect example, is when you are installing core over an existing laminate and you want to assure a good bond between the core and the laminate. Once the special bonding paste you apply between the core and the laminate is cured, then the core is held in place and you can remove the vacuum bagging arrangement.

As air applies equal pressure from all sides, you have the potential of a perfect clamping system. The effect of vacuum bagging is to put up to 2,000 pounds weight, on every square foot of core you are installing using this method. Try doing that with lead weights or another means. Your mould would certainly sag and distort. Using vacuum bagging employs nature as your assistant and you are effectively applying up to 2,000 pounds per square foot without applying any weight to the mould structure. Too much pressure is not desirable see below for more detail.

The method is simple. Once the outer skin has been laid up and an area of core material set in place, after being well prime coated with a special resin putty mix, a sealing tape is laid around the perimeter. Next a sheet of bubble-pack is placed over the core, this acts as a breather. Finally a film covers the whole area and a suction hose is introduced though a

PIAB L190D Vacuum Pump

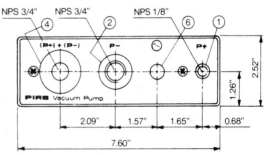

Air Consumption: 9.3 scfm at 87 psi
Optimum Feed Pressure: 58 psi to 87 psi
Max. Supply Pressure: 100 psi
Max. Vacuum: 18 in. Hg. at 58 psi
                  21.9 in. Hg. at 87 psi
Working Temperature: -4°F to 176°F

Weight: 1.98 lbs.
Material: anodized aluminum, brass, nitrile rubber
Sound Level: unloaded: 76 dB(A)
                loaded up to 18 in. Hg.: 72 dB(A)
Article No: 32.01.006

suitable hole cut in the bag. Use a regulator to control the suction, which is less than you would imagine. The method you will be using is sometimes called "Dry bagging" as opposed to wet bagging that was developed to draw off excess resin and is a messy and expensive business and is not needed or considered here.

In dry bagging the outside skin should be cured before vacuum bagging the core. The cured resin prevents dislocating or damaging the existing laminate when positioning the core materials and minimizes any chance of print through that could show on the outer surface of the hull or deck part. If you use too much pressure in the vacuum bagging operation, you may end with too thin a bond line between the laminate and the core material. Generally 5-10 pounds per square inch is adequate, providing 720 to 1,440 pounds per square foot of clamping pressure. Piston, diaphragm, or rotary

pumps all work well. The size of the pump will depend on the size of the largest area you intend to treat, the larger the area, the larger the pump. Shop or industrial vacuum cleaners are unsuitable because you would be drawing flammable gases into the area of the electric motor. Most fibreglass suppliers can supply suitable vacuum bagging equipment including pumps and gauges.

Above: Female moulded Roberts 25 - over 250 sold to date

Below: Roberts 53 built with extensive use of vacuum bagging techniques

CHAPTER TWELVE
STEEL - BUILDING HULLS

The first thing you will need to consider is the availability of a suitable design. Do not be tempted to try to convert a plan that was designed for another material, this is a recipe for almost certain disaster. Only select a plan that has been specifically designed for steel. If you see a design or a particular boat that you favour, but it is only available in another material, then approach the designer or if the designer is unavailable, approach another competent designer and ask if plans can be prepared to build your chosen design in steel. The designer will need to consider several factors before advising you if is possible to design and prepare plans for a steel version.

These chapters on steel boat construction, are about building a steel boat and not a substitute for a good knowledge of welding. We do touch on various aspects of the art of welding; we have only included these, to fine tune your knowledge of welding as it applies to steel boat building. Steel as a boat building material for small boats; boats under 100 feet [30 metres] has been in use for many years. There are throughout the world, many thousands of fine examples of boats using this material. In recent years, especially throughout the eighties and nineties, steel has become more widely used and appreciated as a boat building material.

SMALL STEEL BOATS

Steel can be used to successfully build boats as small as the fifteen feet [4.5 metres] dinghies I have seen in Holland. We have designed and built sail and power boats as small as twenty-two feet [6.7 metres] and I believe smaller steel boats are not only possible but practical as well. There are examples of successfully built steel boats, in service in every country. The steel boat building industry is now well established throughout the world. You may have already realised that steel, is the bargain boat building material. After undertaking many detailed cost comparisons, we are convinced that steel is the most economical material for building boats between 22 and 100 feet [6.7 to 30 metres]. Any intending builder, would do well to study the benefits of steel construction, before making a final decision, about which material they select for their

Roberts Tom Thumb 24. One of our smaller designs for steel construction.

Small steel boat. Dinghy photographed in Holland.

next boat.

THE BUILDING SITE

Most boat building techniques require some form of shelter, however, with steel construction it is possible to build in the open. Sometimes this feature makes the difference between being able, and not able, to build a boat at all. Economics, local building restrictions, or the unavailability of suitable covered space, may make steel the automatic and only alternative. For reasons of comfort and security, we do recommend, building under cover where possible, however if space is not available, then build your steel boat outside.

You may like to set up an overhead gantry system, which can be two pairs of A frames running on a pair of simple rails. Use this arrangement to suspend one or more chain blocks, to lift plates and other heavy sections of your boat, into the desired position.

TECHNICAL ADVANCES

The old objections to steel, that the boats were unduly heavy and required considerable maintenance, have long been overcome. On the question of weight, modern building techniques have virtually eliminated this potential problem. In the case of cruising sailboats and displacement powerboats, weight was not a problem. Planing power boats can now be built in steel. We have many successful examples built to our own designs, currently in service around the world. Modern, long lasting coating materials, remove any suggestion that steel requires more maintenance than other materials.

STEEL, THE MATERIAL

We recommend you use pre-shot blasted and prime coated steel. If you are building outside, you will lose some benefits of using this material; it may still be worthwhile using prime coated steel, as it makes for a cleaner working environment. When welding pre-prime coated steel, you will need to wear a protective mask to avoid inhaling the fumes released when the prime coating is burnt off in the area of the weld.

When you are ordering your plating, try to obtain "Plate mill" not "Strip mill" plate. Plate mill stock is plate that has never been rolled. Strip mill stock is plate that is manufactured and then rolled into big coils. Later this steel is unrolled and sold as flat plate. The Strip mill plate has a memory so it will not be as neutral before you start to bend it, as the Plate mill stock that we recommend.

We recommend low carbon mild steel as the basic material for building your boat. There are many different grades of steel available. The two you should consider are LOW CARBON steel that has a carbon content of under 0.15 percent and MILD steel that has a carbon content of between 0.15 and 0.30 Percent. The highest carbon content acceptable to most classing authorities is 0.23 percent, so make sure the carbon content of your steel is well below the 0.23 percent figure. Both the fore-mentioned materials are available in various shapes, strips and plate and offer good welding characteristics. As the code numbers vary from country to country, you should seek advice locally when choosing the exact material to suit your boat building project.

Avoid materials such as Cor-ten, also high tensile steel and other specialised products that were developed for different uses and has either no benefit for or only limited boat building uses. As there is considerable difference of opinion on the benefits and advantages of various grades of steel, you should seek local advice, but make sure the person giving the advice is a recognised authority on the matter. Stainless steel has no place in a boat below the waterline. Oxygen starvation will surely promote crevice cracking and other corrosive activities that can cause problems. Stainless steel is a suitable material for deck fittings, stanchions and the like. If you weld it to your steel decks, make sure you bring the deck paint at least up two inches [50] on to the stainless item. Special rods are available to weld stainless steel to mild steel. Under no circumstances consider the building of a stainless steel hull, deck and superstructure.

SAFETY EQUIPMENT

One of the least expensive and best safety promoting items, is a clean work area. Keep your area clean and avoid leaving anything laying about that you can trip on, slip on or slash yourself on. Safety equipment will form a very important part of the equipment you will need, before you start construction on your steel boat. All the operations employed when working with steel, produce hazards of varying degrees. You can easily protect yourself against injury, by having the correct safety equipment. Under no circumstances sell yourself short in this area. You will need to protect the various parts of your body, so give this list of equipment your earnest and serious consideration.

Starting with your Head, always wear a proper industrial safety helmet. You never know when something may fall or be dropped, that could injure this most vulnerable part of your body. Safety goggles are a must and should have side guards to protect you against the flying metal particles, always present when you are grinding or chipping. You will also need a face shield, and the various lenses used while welding. Don't forget your ears and hearing, good earmuffs are essential. A respirator is required. Invest in good coveralls or overalls. A leather apron and gloves with cuffs are definite requirements. One of our customers once built a steel Roberts 38 in a Florida nudist colony. I wonder how he dealt with the weld splatter ?? Wear steel toed shoes or boots, please, no sneakers around your steel boat building project. Protective hand cream and an adequate first aid kit are a must. Make sure you have plenty of eye wash on hand. A fire extinguisher, and industrial vacuum cleaner are also well in the realm of safety equipment.

THE TOOLS

You will need a variety of tools to build your steel boat. Fortunately the cost of tools for working in steel, is not beyond the resources of most people who are planning to build a steel boat. You probably can acquire second hand, many of these items ; conversely, you can sell off the tools you do not want to keep, when your boat building project is completed. You will not need all these tools; some are alternatives to the others listed. This list is offered to give you some idea of the range of tools and aids you should consider acquiring.

Bolt cutter, crimper, hacksaw, jig saw, straight edge, tin snips, oxy acetylene torch and associated bottles and gauges, plasma arc cutter, nibbler, power hack saw, metal workers vice, saw horses, a variety of metal workers hammers, cold chisels, metal files, a high quality angle grinder, a good quality portable electric drill and steel cutting bits, bench grinder, an assortment of clamps, and of course your primary welder that can be one of several varieties.

For a welder, you may choose an electric arc welder, commonly known as a stick welder, or you may have access to a MIG shielded gas welding set up. The MIG welding has done for welding what plasma arc, has done for cutting. It may be worth your while investing in the MIG equipment, even if you are building only one boat. Again investigate used equipment or consider selling your MIG outfit when your boat is complete. You can weld outside with a common stick welder but you are advised to have adequate draught protection if you are using MIG equipment.

HULL SHAPES

Perhaps the biggest objection in the past was, that building with steel limits the shape of the hull. First, in the case of power boats this was never true and as for sailboats, these you can now be build using the "Radius Chine" technique. This method involves computer assisted designing and lofting methods, which have produced many beautifully rounded sailboat hull designs, which when built, are indistinguishable from their fibreglass cousins.

MULTI-CHINE

Multi-chine sailboat hulls have their own beauty and admirers, and to prove this point, there are many fibreglass boats on the market with multi-Chine hull forms. The multi-chine hull, is reasonably close in shape to the round bilge or radius chine hull form. Performance wise there is nothing in it.

RADIUS CHINE

The radius chine hull has many benefits, including all of those attributed to a full round bilge hull, including additional strength and lighter weight. Perhaps the best reason for choosing a rounded hull form, such as radius chine, is the perceived improved resale value. The secret of radius chine, is the way the radius, is faired through the bow. Previous attempts at this type of hull form, involved fading out the radius before it reached the bow, and this usually resulted in an unfair area up forward. By designing the radius chine hull completely in the computer, and by using specially designed yacht design software, it is now possible to have a totally fair round bilge steel or aluminum radius chine hull.

Do not confuse radius chine with a hull built with a pipe chine. The radius chine hull has a 30" to 36" [750 mm to 900 mm] or larger radius where the chine would be. This makes them more akin to a round bilge hull, than a chine one. In some ways the word chine in the naming of this method is a misnomer.

STEELWORKING EXPERIENCE

Regarding your ability to build a steel boat, we have to say that most builders who tackle this medium, are enthusiastic about the merits of their chosen material. For those of you who do not already posses welding experience, it is possible to learn the necessary techniques and practice the skills, in special schools where night classes are available. We have fine examples of steel boats, built by people who had no previous welding or steelworkers experience, before taking on the building of their own boats.

We would recommend that unless you are already an experienced welder, which you hire a person with the necessary skills, to run the final and important welds on your hull. You can prepare the project to that stage, but the final welding is so important, as to require the proper skills to assure the safety and long life of your hull. Please note our comments at the beginning of this chapter, the information in this book, is about building a steel boat, not teaching you how to weld.

UPRIGHT OR UPSIDE DOWN

Often, the shape of the boat and the chosen steel building method, will determine whether you build the hull upright or upside down. Another factor will be the space and facilities available for turning the hull. There are many simple systems for turning the hull, so this will not play a big part in making your decision.

Advocates of the upside down method, say they prefer to build this way because most of the welding in done in the down hand position. Some welding must be done from inside. For instance, the stringers must be at least part welded to the skin from inside the hull, while it is still in the upside down position. It is easier to fit the plating in position on the upturned hull. Also all the final welding, a very important part of the building programme, will all be done in the down-hand position. Building the hull upright offers easy accessibility during the entire welding operation. You can overcome the

disadvantages of laying on the plating using adequate scaffolding. There is the little trick of drilling a hole in the plating and pulling this area of the plating into position by means of chains, wedges and threaded bolts; there is not much to choose between the two systems. As I stated earlier, the characteristics of your particular boat will govern your choice. For instance, I always recommend that Radius chine hulls are built upside down.

MAKING THE FRAMES

You will be making your frames out of flat bar, angle or T bar. Your plans will usually specify which material to use. We usually recommend flat bar for frames; there are arguments in favour of flat bar or angle or T. Usually flat bar is easier to obtain and available in a wider variety of sizes. In the finished boat, flat bar offers less chance of rust as opposed to the angle frames that are very difficult to keep fully protected. It is worth remembering that most steel boats will rust from the inside out and the interior must be kept as fully covered with protective coatings, as the outside. Flat bar frames are easier to keep fully protected. You can usually convert plans calling for one alternative, to the other, so in some ways the choice is yours.

If your plans include full size patterns for the frames, also the stem, deck camber pattern and other major elements of your boat, then you are off to a good start. Your patterns may be of the paper variety. Do not let this bother you, the small changes

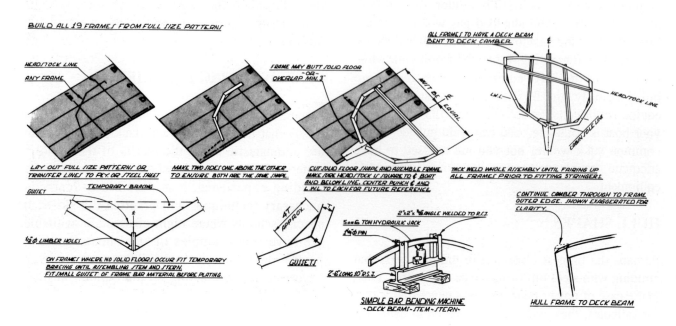

in the size of the paper, will be over the whole of the area, so your boat may be a fraction of an inch bigger or smaller. These changes will be uniform over the whole of the patterns and will not affect the final performance of the vessel. If you have a deep pocket and a perfectionist temperament, then you may request your designer to supply the patterns on Mylar film.

Choose a dry day and lay out your patterns carefully. It is advisable to transfer the patterns on to a more durable material such as plywood or steel plate. Later the plywood can be used for the bulkheads and the steel plate could be some hull plating material. It is probably easier to transfer patterns on to plywood, as a dressmaker wheel makes the job a snap. Once you have assembled the patterns, and satisfied yourself that you are working from an accurate and permanent record of the frames, stem and deck beam shapes, your next job will be to start building the frames. Cut the flat bar or other frame making material into the lengths required. On some frames, especially near the bow, there will be some curvature in the frame sections.

BENDING FRAME BARS

If a frame piece is to be bent, it will need to be over length to start with, otherwise it will be too short once you have made the bend. Most frames are not entirely straight lines. There is a simple device you can make to bend the framing material. Use the same device to bend the deck beams. The device consists of some heavy angle formed up so that the various pieces of framing bar can be clamped in position and a hydraulic jack is then used to achieve the required amount of bending. The actual bending should be done a small amount at a time. First divide off the length flat bar into increments of about 3" [75], and then arrange the bar on the bending

device. Now you can move the section to each of the three inch points, and apply some pressure to achieve a small amount of the desired bend. Using this "small amount at a time" method, you will achieve a totally fair curve. Make sure you frequently check the piece against the pattern.

The solid floors, also known as web floors, are the bottom part of the frame that can be cut from plate. Form the web floors to a height, as indicated in your plans. In our own plans, this height is generally to the sole line. In sailboats, the web floors also are the frames around which the plating for the keel sides is installed, to form the envelope keel. The web floors are generally the same thickness as the framing material, and can be butt welded to the frame bar. Some builders overlap the webs with a short length of the bar, this may add additional strength with the extra welding area available ;we do not like overlaps where rust can start between the layers of unprotected steel.

If you are building frames for a radius chine design, we recommend that you have the radius section of the frames bent by a professional, while you are having the radius plating rolled to the correct radius. Most local engineering or metal shops can undertake this work for you, at a reasonable price. Once you have cut the various sections of the frames to size and pre-bent as necessary, then each frame should be tack welded together on top of the pattern. At this stage any bracing by way of headstocks, baseline

Stem being checked against full size patterns.

Simple device for bending deck beams, stem and frames as required.

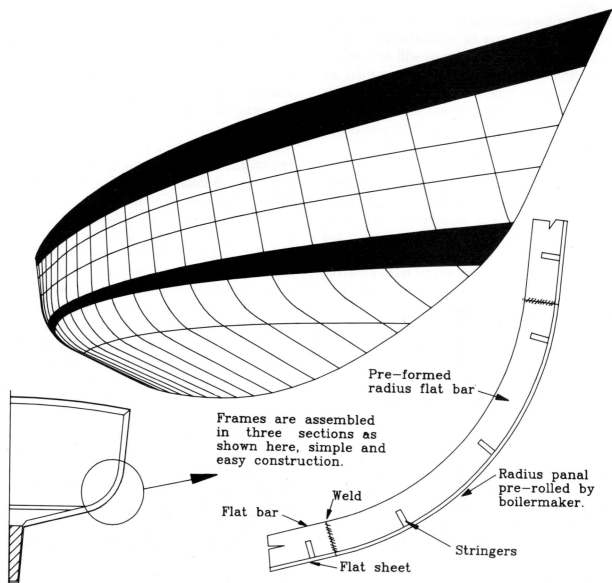

Pre—formed
radius flat bar

Frames are assembled
in three sections as
shown here, simple and
easy construction.

Radius panal
pre—rolled by
boilermaker.

Weld

Flat bar

Stringers

Flat sheet

At last it is possible to build a round bilge steel boat without the great time and effort, not to mention experience, required using traditional methods. Radius Chine building techniques are developed through Computer fairing which provides you the builder with Full Size Patterns of all the frames, full size stem and full size expanded transom pattern. The secret of Radius Chine depends on FAIRING THE RADIUS THROUGH TO THE BOW. Most other attempts at this type of hull form have tried to fade out the chine before it reaches the bow. This usually results in a flat spot or unfair area up forward. Previous methods have been (are) more difficult to build than Multi Chine. Our Radius Chine is very easy to build, the secret lies in the exact way in which we develop these hulls using our In-House Computer programs. The Full Size Patterns are all plotted on Milar film.

bar, deck beams or extra stiffening material, can be added and tack welded to the frame.

When making the frames, you can install the slots for the chine bars, if any chine bars are required. Your frames, may not have the intermediate stringer positions shown. You could work these out by evenly dividing the outside of the frame, by the number of stringers specified in your plans. Make sure the stringer slots are square off the outside of the frame, at the point where the stringer is to be

located. If you prefer, you may temporally erect the frames, and using a fairing batten, mark out the various stringer locations on each frame. The frames are then taken down and the slots cut, before re-erecting the frames and installing the stringers. You will sometimes find that when cutting the stringer slots into the frames, this causes some distortion to the frame. Make sure you recheck the frame against the patterns and remedy any distortion before erecting the frame.

Radius Chine 1. Frames are stood up starting at station 5 or midstation of hull

Radius Chine 2. Once all the stringers are located then plate radius section first.

Radius Chine 3. Radius panels around the centre of the hull are split lengthwise and fitted in place.

Radius Chine 4. After both radius chines plated then proceed to install bottom & side plate working

Radius Chine 5. Hull ready for turnover.

Radius Chine 6. Hull has been turned upright ready for bulkheads & deckbeams etc.

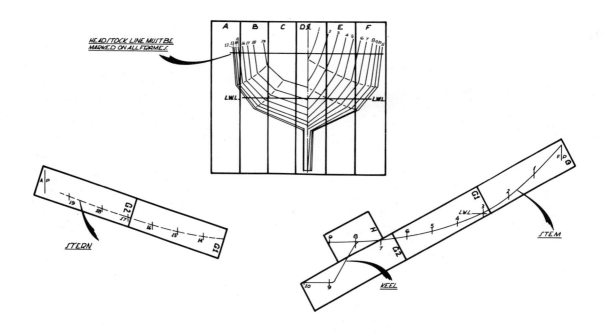

HEADSTOCK LINE MUST BE
MARKED ON ALL FRAMES.

STERN

STEM

KEEL

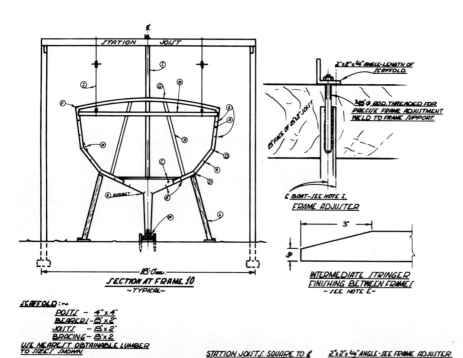

STATION   JOIST

Section At Frame 10
~TYPICAL~

18'-0 max.

SCAFFOLD:~
POSTS - 4"x4"
BEARERS-6"x2"
JOISTS - 8"x2"
BRACING- 8"x2"
USE NEAREST OBTAINABLE LUMBER
TO SIZES SHOWN.

2"x8"x44" ANGLE-LENGTH OF
SCAFFOLD.

3/8" ø ROD-THREADED FOR
PRECISE FRAME ADJUSTMENT
WELD TO FRAME SUPPORT.

FACE OF END JOIST

ℓ BOAT-SEE NOTE I.
FRAME ADJUSTER

3"

INTERMEDIATE STRINGER
FINISHING BETWEEN FRAMES
~SEE NOTE E~

NOTES TO LETTERED FRAME 10

A - FRAME - 2½"X3/8" FLAT BAR. OBTAIN FROM FULL SIZE PATTERNS NOT FROM TABLE
OF OFF SETS ON SHEET 2.

B - HEADSTOCK - 2"X2"X ¼" ANGLE FITTED TO FRAME ON W.L.3A - SEE FULL SIZE
PATTERNS. FIT WITH CARE AND SET UP FRAME WITH HEADSTOCK LEVEL ACROSS
HULL AND LEVEL TO HEADSTOCKS ON OTHER FRAMES. THIS ENSURES THAT FRAMES
ARE IN CORRECT RELATION TO EACH OTHER.

C - SOLID FLOOR - ¼" PLATE WITH 2"X ¼" BAR WELDED ALONG TOP TO TAKE CABIN
SOLE. CABIN SOLE IS 17" BELOW L.W.L. ALLOW FOR 5/8" PLYWOOD CABIN SOLE.
SOLID FLOORS OCCUR AT FRAMES 6 TO 13. FRAMES 14 AND 15 WILL HAVE PART
SOLID FLOORS FITTED AFTER HULL IS PLATED.

D - CHINE STRINGERS - 1¼"X5/16" FLAT BAR-OR-3/4" ROUND BAR. USE SMALL TACK
WELDS TO HOLD INTO FRAME NOTCHES AFTER OBTAINING FAIR CURVES FORE AND AFT.
MITRE OFF AT STEM AND TRANSOM - SEE NOTE 6 FOR FITTING TRANSOM.

E - INTERMEDIATE STRINGERS - 1¼"X5/16" FLAT BAR EVENLY SPACED BETWEEN CHINES
FROM FRAME 8 TO 13. ALLOW TO COME TOGETHER FORE AND AFT. END WHEN SPACE
BETWEEN STRINGERS IS APPROXIMATLEY 12". FINISH BETWEEN FRAMES RELIEVING
ENDS AS SHOWN IN SKETCH. SOME INTERMEDIATE STRINGERS WILL RUN FULL
LENGTH OF HULL - END THESE ON STEM OR TRANSOM. SEE NOTE 6 FOR FITTING
TRANSOM.

F - DECK STRINGER - 1¼"X5/16" FLAT BAR. FIT AS CHINE STRINGERS. FORM FAIR
CURVES. MAKE SURE BOTH ARE LEVEL ACROSS HULL AT EACH FRAME.

G - DECK AND CABIN TOP BEAM - 2½"X5/16" FLAT BAR - OR - 2"X2"X ¼" ANGLE.
TAKE CARE TO OBTAIN A FAIR SHAPE OVER ALL BEAMS - USE A FAIRING BATTEN.

H - BRACING - 1¼"X1¼"X ¼" ANGLE. TACK WELD TO LARGER FRAMES.

I - FRAME SUPPORT - 1¼"X1¼"X ¼" TACK WELD TO FRAME ON CENTER LINE OF BOAT.
MAY BE ATTACHED TO GIVE A FLAT FACE TO CENTER LINE. THIS GIVES A PLACE
TO HOLD A SPRIT LEVEL TO CHECK VERTICAL ALINGNMENT AND IS ALSO USEFUL FOR
LINING UP ALL FRAMES TO A STRING LINE.

J - TWICHED TIE WIRE - SUPPORTS AND HELPS HOLD FRAME LEVEL AFTER ALINGNMENT.

K - FRAME GUSSETS - FROM 2½"X3/8" FLAT BAR. MAY BE FITTED TO ALL FRAMES.
FRAMES 8 TO 13 MUST HAVE. FIT BEFORE OR AFTER ERECTING FRAMES AND
FITTING STRINGERS.

L - SUPPORT AS BUILDING PROGRESSES.

M - BOTTOM OF KEEL - ½" PLATE. TAKE 1/8" MASONITE TEMPLATE FROM BOTTOM OF
ERECTED FRAMES AND KEEL.

N - STEM, STERN, AND KEEL - 3½"X ½" FLAT BAR.
STEM AND LEADING EDGE OF KEEL MAY BE 1" DIAMETER BAR IF DESIRED.

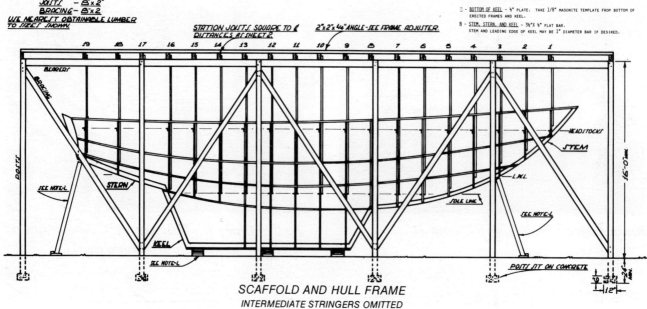

STATION JOISTS SQUARE TO ℓ
DISTANCES AS SHEET 2.

2"x2"x44" ANGLE-SEE FRAME ADJUSTER.

BEARERS

BRACING

POSTS

SEE NOTE-L

STERN

KEEL

SEE NOTE-L

HEADSTOCKS

STEM

L.W.L.

SOLE LINE

SEE NOTE-L

16'-0 max.

POSTS SIT ON CONCRETE

12"

SCAFFOLD AND HULL FRAME
INTERMEDIATE STRINGERS OMITTED

THE STEM

If you have not done so already, now is the time to bend the stem into its correct shape. You may use the bending device described earlier. If you prefer, or if your plans specify, you may cut the stem from flat plate of a suitable thickness. Next install the stem and the backbone. The backbone will usually bend on edge, simply by laying it into the slots, heavy flat bar that is specified for the backbone may need some pre-bending. When installing the stem, make sure it is firmly fixed on the centre line.

KEEL

Some power boats and almost all sailboats have keels that can be identified as separate appendages. The template for the bottom of the keel will be occasionally included with your full size patterns, however, usually you have to make your own pattern. One method of obtaining the shape of the bottom keel plate, is to have all the frames erected, and then run a batten around the bottom of the webs through to the leading edge pipe and aft to the stern bar. This will create the shape of the bottom of the keel and you can slip a piece of Masonite or plywood either under or above the keel, depending on whether you boat is upside down or right way up. Run a pencil line around the batten and now you have the outline of the shape for the bottom of the keel. Trim to get a perfect fit and then cut the bottom of the keel to shape. Don't forget to make allowance for the side keel plating, as it is usual for the bottom to overlap the sides. If you are building right way up, the keel plate is blocked into position and the stem, keel leading edge pipe and backbone are tack welded to the frames. During this stage, keep everything well braced by using lengths of angle, and either clamping, or tack welding the bracing into position.

If you are building the boat upside down, then you need not install the plate for the bottom of the keel, until the rest of the hull is completed. The extra weight will not be properly supported until the structure is almost fully plated. If you leave the bottom of the keel un-plated, this will allow the light to enter the inside of the hull, until you install the bottom of the keel.

STRINGERS AND CHINE BARS

The first longitudinal stringers you should install,

Solid round chine bar and flat bar stringers notched into frames.

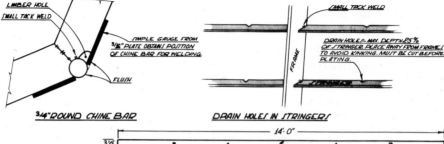

LUMBER HOLE
SMALL TACK WELD

SIMPLE GAUGE FROM 3/16" PLATE OBTAINS POSITION OF CHINE BAR FOR WELDING.

FLUSH

3/4" ROUND CHINE BAR

SMALL TACK WELD

FRAME

DRAIN HOLE:– MAX. DEPTH 25% OF STRINGER. PLACE AWAY FROM FRAMES TO AVOID KINKING. MUST BE CUT BEFORE PLATING.

DRAIN HOLES IN STRINGERS

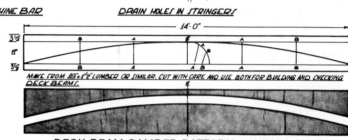

14'-0"

MAKE FROM 1⅛" x 1½" LUMBER OR SIMILAR. CUT WITH CARE AND USE BOTH FOR BUILDING AND CHECKING DECK BEAMS.

DECK BEAM CAMBER PATTERN: 11" IN 14 FEET

Note: *Cambers will vary from boat to boat and often deck and cabintop camber will be different.*

will be the sheer stringers. Next, in the case of a chine hull, install the chine stringers. There is room for some discussion about whether you should fit solid round or flat bar chine bars, or chine stringers as they are also called, or for that matter no chine stringers at all. Your plans should spell out these details. For the record we have used all three chine bar treatments, which is solid round, flat bar or in smaller boats no chine bar at all.

In a radius chine hull install the two stringers, one each side of the radius. Only tack weld the stringers into the slots. Later you may want to release some welds, to allow the stringers to take the fair line that the plating will naturally take at a later stage. In some parts of the world, builders let the stringers stand proud of the frames by say 1/8" [3], this is to make sure that the plating and the frames do not touch, the theory being that only the stringers need to be welded to the plating. Weld the stringers in

Keel and stem in place, frames erected and chine bars installed on ROBERTS SPRAY.

turn to the frames. Anyhow, on no account over weld the frames to the plating, or your boat will look like a starved cow.

Now is a good time to give your hull a very careful check, to make sure all the frames are square off the centre line, again check that the stem is true to the centre line, check throughout the stems entire length. No bends or twists in the stem, please. Adequate bracing and your attention to detail will pay dividends later. Under no circumstances should you final weld the intermediate stringers into the slots at this time. Tack them into position. Sometimes builders simply install the intermediate stringers into the slots, the tension caused by pulling them in at the bow and stern will hold them firmly in position with no welding at all.

It is worth repeating, which when the plating is installed, it may be necessary to release the stringers slightly in some areas, so that the stringers rest snugly against the plating. The plating usually forms a fairer shape than the stringers. By being able to release the stringers you will achieve a much fairer hull and avoid pulling the plating into an unfair shape that will result in bulges and hollows in your hull. At a later stage you will weld the stringers into the slots and against the plating.

When all the stringers and chines if any, are in position, the next job is to again conduct a through check of the fairness of the hull. A batten that could be either steel or timber, sized approximately 1" x 1/2" [25 x 12] and 6'-0" [1.75 m] long, can be laid diagonally across the various areas of the hull, and your eyes will probably give the best indication of the fairness of the hull up to this point. Check over the whole structure and make sure there are no unfair spots.

DRAINAGE

This is a good time to think about drainage in the inside your hull. When the hull is in its correct position, there will be low points on the stringers. This is the area where moisture would collect inside the hull, and could cause a potential rust problem. If you are intending to install foam insulation material, especially the "Blow in place" variety, then you will not have a problem because the foam will come to at least level to the stringers, thus providing a flush surface and leave nowhere for the moisture to collect. The moisture will simply run to the bilge where it belongs. As your boat will need insulation,

Overhead gantry set on simple rails will make handling of plate much easier.

then this is the obvious answer to the potential problem of moisture collecting at the low points of the stringers. Later you will need to arrange limber holes in the bilge so the water can all run to one or more collection points where it can be pumped overboard using you bilge pumping system.

In the case where you are planning to install "Insulation bats" or another insulation material, where the area that is not fully sealed between the stringers, then you should decide the potential low point of each stringer and carefully grind a nicely half rounded drain notch so when the stringer is resting against the plating, there will be a drain hole to allow the collected moisture to drain through to the bilge. Give this matter some thought now. Avoid kinking your stringers and install temporary back up stringer material if necessary to hold the stringer fair until the plating is installed.

PLATING THE HULL

Remember to try to obtain Plate mill stock, which has never been coiled and has no memory to contend with. Whether you start plating on the keel sides, or on the hull sides or hull bottom, will largely depend on the method of construction you have chosen. Please read the sections covering the plating of Radius chine hulls and regular Chine hulls.

CUTTING THE PLATE

There are several ways of cutting your plate. In the early days of steel boat construction, we had to use Oxy acetylene torch cutting to cut the plates to shape. This type of cutting leaves a very rough edge and heat involved, willdistort the plate. Next advance was the availability of cutting disks that

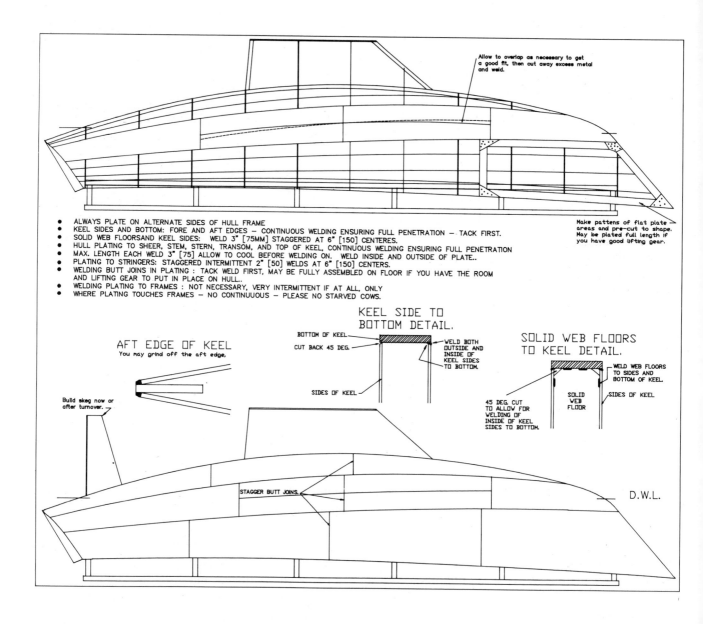

Allow to overlap as necessary to get a good fit, then cut away excess metal and weld.

Make pattens of flat plate areas and pre-cut to shape. May be plated full length if you have good lifting gear.

- ALWAYS PLATE ON ALTERNATE SIDES OF HULL FRAME
- KEEL SIDES AND BOTTOM: FORE AND AFT EDGES — CONTINUOUS WELDING ENSURING FULL PENETRATION — TACK FIRST.
- SOLID WEB FLOORSAND KEEL SIDES: WELD 3" [75MM] STAGGERED AT 6" [150] CENTERES.
- HULL PLATING TO SHEER, STEM, STERN, TRANSOM, AND TOP OF KEEL, CONTINUOUS WELDING ENSURING FULL PENETRATION
- MAX. LENGTH EACH WELD 3" [75] ALLOW TO COOL BEFORE WELDING ON.   WELD INSIDE AND OUTSIDE OF PLATE..
- PLATING TO STRINGERS: STAGGERED INTERMITTENT 2" [50] WELDS AT 6" [150] CENTERS.
- WELDING BUTT JOINS IN PLATING : TACK WELD FIRST, MAY BE FULLY ASSEMBLED ON FLOOR IF YOU HAVE THE ROOM AND LIFTING GEAR TO PUT IN PLACE ON HULL..
- WELDING PLATING TO FRAMES : NOT NECESSARY, VERY INTERMITTENT IF AT ALL, ONLY
- WHERE PLATING TOUCHES FRAMES — NO CONTINUUOUS — PLEASE NO STARVED COWS.

AFT EDGE OF KEEL
You may grind off the aft edge,

Build skeg now or after turnover.

KEEL SIDE TO BOTTOM DETAIL.
BOTTOM OF KEEL
CUT BACK 45 DEG.
WELD BOTH OUTSIDE AND INSIDE OF KEEL SIDES TO BOTTOM.
SIDES OF KEEL

SOLID WEB FLOORS TO KEEL DETAIL.
WELD WEB FLOORS TO SIDES AND BOTTOM OF KEEL.
SOLID WEB FLOOR
SIDES OF KEEL
45 DEG. CUT TO ALLOW FOR WELDING OF INSIDE OF KEEL SIDES TO BOTTOM.

STAGGER BUTT JOINS.

D.W.L.

could be attached to your angle grinder. Many of these cutting disks were required to cut any quantity of plate and as the disks were relatively expensive, this was a costly operation. Another alternative is the nibbler, this tool could be best described as an industrial strength, electric tin opener and the nibbler works well on the lighter plate say up to 3/16" [4 mm]. Now we have plasma arc cutting. What a great boon this tool is to the steel boatbuilder. The plasma arc cutter will cut your plate without heat distortion. Use this device to cut the plate in any location, and literally slices through the metal. The cutting is clean and neat and very fast. Plasma cutting can be used on plate up to 5/16" [7.5 mm] and the width of the cut is only 1/8" [3 mm]. The plasma cutter is capable of cutting almost all types of metals. The operating costs in terms of electricity and the tip replacements are higher than gas cutting,

but the additional cost is worth paying, to get accurate distortion free cuts, which require almost no cleaning up before you are on to welding the parts together.

PLATING RADIUS CHINE HULLS

In the case of radius chine hulls, we recommend that you plate the radius section first. Use preformed rolled plates, rolled to the radius specified in your plans. The recommended length is about ten feet [3 metres]. Form the radius plate to match the largest width required. Measure the greatest arc of the radius section. You will generally find the widest radius panel at the stern. The radius panels will taper as they go from stern to bow. Perhaps this is a good reason to start fitting and installing the radius panels, at the stern of your boat. Keep the edges neat, trim

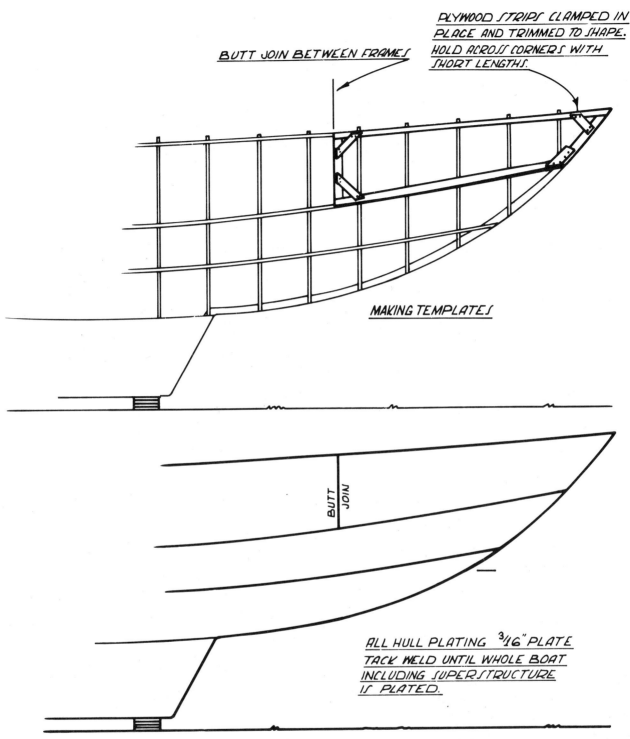

BUTT JOIN BETWEEN FRAMES

PLYWOOD STRIPS CLAMPED IN PLACE AND TRIMMED TO SHAPE. HOLD ACROSS CORNERS WITH SHORT LENGTHS.

MAKING TEMPLATES

BUTT JOIN

ALL HULL PLATING ³⁄₁₆" PLATE TACK WELD UNTIL WHOLE BOAT INCLUDING SUPERSTRUCTURE IS PLATED.

to a fair line so it will be easier to match up with the flat bottom and side plating, at a later stage. You can use a batten to make a fair line along the point where the radius and flat plating meet. You should have marked this intersection on all your frames, also the stem. The ends of the radius will be easier to plate, than the centre sections. Start at either the stern or the bow, where the radius plate will lay in position without any, or with a minimum of compound curve to worry about.

The centre of the hull will almost always involve some compound curvature. The more beam the hull has in relation to its length, the more compound curve there will be in the centre sections of the hull. This does not mean that you cannot build beamy radius chine hulls, only that in the centre of your hull, the radius panels will need some special attention. In the centre of the hull, split the radius plates lengthwise into two or three sections. Serve the plates up to the hull and where the plates overlap at the ends, mark and remove the excess material. Now refit the plates and weld into position. When you are satisfied with the installation of the radius chine section of the plating, you may now go on to plate the bottom and side areas of your hull.

You should find it an easy matter to fit the bottom and side plating, simply lift on the plating, overlap the radius area, clamp in position and mark from underneath. Next trim the plate to shape for a perfect fit. Don't forget to always plate both sides simultaneously. When a plate is fitted on one side, install the corresponding plate on the other side of the hull. Tack weld only at this stage, do not attempt to run any of the finish welding, until you have the whole of the hull plating tacked in place.

Most builders find it best to install the transom after the plating is completed. Sometimes, you may not install the transom until after the hull has been turned upright. This allows easy access to the interior of the hull until the last moment. After you have checked the fairness of the tack-welded hull plating, you can go on to run the finish welds.

PLATING CHINE HULLS

When plating chine hulls you may decide for yourself, if it is more convenient to start at the keel and work up or down as the case may be, to the sheer. It will be most practical to work from the ground up, this will enable the structure to be stiffened by the plating, before it is required to accept the weight of the plating above. As mentioned earlier, no matter whether you are building upright or upside down, it is generally easier to plate up the stern after the rest of the plating has been completed.

You may find that your plans do not call for a stringer or chine bar at the actual chine. Some designers believe that the angle of the plating at the chine, is sufficient to provide the necessary strength. This will make fitting the plates somewhat more difficult than if you have a chine bar as a guide. You can use a batten, usually stringer flat bar material, clamped in place to provide a line at which to fit the plate. With chine hulls and for the flat panels of radius chine hulls, you should assemble the plating on the ground by making up temporary patterns. Use strips of Masonite or plywood, and fit these to the hull framing.

After you have made the templates for any one section, clamp them temporally in place and trim with a plane or saw. Now re-clamp in place and check for accuracy. Mark any special reference points on to the template. Always cross brace the template by installing cross pieces to prevent movement during the raising and lowering of the

template. One test for the template, will it lay flat on the floor? If it will lie flat on the floor, then you know that the plate cut from the template will lay around the curve of your boat without any problems.

If you template the largest panel first, you may be able to re-use it for a slightly smaller section; simply by trim off the excess material and make the new fit. When you are satisfied with your template, lay it flat on the plate to be cut, and clamp it into place so it cannot move. Next scribe around the template, marking frame or other important locations on to the plate for future reference. Don't forget to allow for the correct welding gap between the plates. Next job is to cut the plate along the scribed lines. Make sure you remove any slag with your chipping hammer or grinding wheel. Smooth the edges also bevelling any butt joints on the thicker plating. For 1/8" [3] or less, it is preferable to slightly space the plates to allow for butt welding. If you are using a plasma cutter, there will not be much slag to remove, as these cutters leave a very tidy edge.

JOINING THE PLATE

You may wish to join the various sections of sheet together that will go to form up one chine panel and weld these together on the ground. You can then install the panel complete from stem to stern in one operation. To give you an example, we have one person who built one of our Roberts 53 sailboats, who installed all full length plates on his hull. As each plate weighed approximately one ton [1000 k] this was no mean effort. Before you install the steel panel into position on your hull, you may find it advantageous to clean and prime the inside of the plate. Obviously if you are using pre-prime coated plate as we recommend, you will not need to do this. In any case it will easier to prime at this stage, while the plate is still on the ground. There is one method of plating we do not recommend, that is to serve up a sheet of plate to the hull, and then torch cut the plate using the chine bars as guide. Please do not try this method, as it can only result in a very poor fitting plate and the heat of the torch cutting will probably distort the chine bars as well as the plate itself.

TRANSOMS

Your plan should show you the best method for forming the transom, for your particular design. Sometimes you will be supplied with an expanded plate pattern for the transom. You should transfer

Stern and rudder tubes installed prior to plating up of ROBERTS 36 hull.

Reinforced skeg on Roberts 53 built by A. Skjodt in Canada

Skeg and rudder pre-built and later welded to hull. Builder D. Johnson of Canada

this pattern on to Masonite or thin plywood and then check the pattern against the actual boat. Adjust the pattern as required.

ALTERNATE TRANSOM INSTALLATION METHOD

If you do not have a pattern, then you may wish to follow the following sequence. You should have a centre line transom-bar set upright at the correct angle for your transom to be installed. Check the lines and other sheets of your plans for details. Next make a rough oversize pattern of the transom by serving up a large sheet of Masonite or plywood to the boat, make sure it is formed into the correct camber or round, otherwise it may end up being too small. Make sure you allow for the deck camber at the top of the transom. Now cut a piece of plate, the same size as the pattern, and roll, or have it rolled to the correct camber or round. Now serve this plate up to the hull and hang it off the stern bar. Adequately brace the plate and support it while you mark it to a proper fit. After trimming to the exact shape, you may install the transom and weld it in to its final position. If you are confident you can make the pattern accurate enough, you may progress from pattern to final trimming of the transom plate, and then install the transom in one operation.

WELDING SEQUENCES

It is usual to "lightly" weld the frames to the steel plating. As mentioned earlier, in some countries including, Holland, the birthplace of steel boat building, the plating is not welded to, but deliberately kept away from the frames. We have seen many hulls ruined by over welding the plating

Almost completed rudder for ROBERTS 34 built by Helge Andersson.

Completed rudder and shaft for ROBERTS 34. Note plug in top of rudder for filling rudder with oil.

Plating being installed on ROBERTS 36.

Interior of hull showing how plating is tack welded to frames, chine bars and stringers until all hull plating is in place. Later chines only will be welded continuously while stringers are welded intermittently and frames may be left spot welded or receive only short runs of intermittent welds. See text.

to the frames. If you do weld the shell plating to the frames, use staggered intermittent 1 1/2" [30] at 6" [150] to 9" [225] centres. If you are building to survey or to a rule that states otherwise, you may be forced to weld all the frames to the plating, using the sequence as specified in the rule. For pleasure boats built to normally acceptable standards, we recommend you either follow the directions in your plans or consider our suggestions as outlined above. Weld the frames as follows. If you have gussets on your frames, these are continuous welded. Ends of frame bar to solid web floors, require continuous welds. On the frames for radius chine hulls, a continuous weld is required where the straight bar meets the radius bar.

If you use steel bulkheads, the joins between the sheets that go to make up the full width bulkhead are tack welded first and then continuous welded. Where required, stiffeners need intermittent welding to the bulkhead plate. The bulkheads themselves are usually welded to frames with a chain intermittent weld. Keel sides, bottom, fore and aft edges, tack weld first, then all continuous welding, assure complete penetration. Web floors to keel and to hull plating where applicable, weld 3" [75] staggered at 6" [150] centres. Hull plating to sheer, stem, transsom, and top of keel, all continuous welding assuring full penetration. Hull plating to stringers, weld at staggered intermittent 2" [50] welds at 6" [150] centres. Hull plating butts, tack weld first. You may fully assemble these plates on floor, if you have the room and the lifting gear to place a large plate on the hull. Continuously weld oil and watertight bulkheads.

STERN AND RUDDER TUBE

Before you commence the plating, you will need to decide if you are going to install the stern tube and the rudder tube at this stage. It is reasonably easy to install the rudder tube in its correct location before the plating is in place. The stern tube for the propeller shaft is more difficult to place correctly at this stage. If your hull is upside down, you need some very accurate calculations and measurements to get the correct angle and position for the stern tube. It may be better to leave the installation of this tube until you have completed the plating and turned the hull. In hulls built upright, you can figure out where the engine beds are and where you should locate the stern tube. This can be done before the plating is installed.

SKEGS

If the plans for your hull call for a separate skeg and rudder arrangement, you will need to assure yourself that the skeg will stay with the boat under all conditions. The skeg is probably one of the most vulnerable areas of your hull, so consider the installation in some detail.

Most hulls have a substantial centre line bar and a centre plate for the skeg. The centre plate can be the same shape as the entire skeg, and can be welded directly to this bar or you could cut the bar and allow the centre plate to rise into the hull where it can be braced and reinforced by a system of webs. These webs could also form part of the support for the rudder bearing. The thickness of the centre plate should be between 1/4" and 1/2" [6 and 12].

The leading edge of the skeg should have a pipe fitted which will be between 1" and 2" [25 and 50] diameter and for best results will be bent into a small fence arrangement forward of the skeg. Aerofoil shaped webs are now arranged, each side of the centre plate attached to the pipe leading edge, the centre plate and to a section of open-faced convex pipe just ahead of the rudder shaft. The convex

section used, must allow the rudder to turn without binding on the aft end of the skeg. The skeg is now plated with material at least the same thickness as used for the hull.

To install the plating you will need to make slots in the outer plate to allow the weld to be made between the plate and the webs. After fully plating the skeg, you should install a fillet on both sides, measuring say 3" to 4" [75 to 100] at forty-five degrees between the hull and the skeg. Fair off the forward end of the fillet that will be welded to both the hull and skeg plating.

RUDDER

Build the rudder in a similar manner to the skeg, except the leading edge will be the solid round bar or heavy walled tube rudder stock. The aft end is a flat bar between the two side skins. Take care when welding the fins and skin plate to the leading edge bar. You may wish to have an arrangement so you can remove the rudder without dismantling the bottom of the skeg or removing the skeg bearing or lifting the boat. You can arrange flanges bolted together to make removal of the rudder a simple matter. If you use flanges in the system, make sure they are of sufficient strength and have at least 5 bolts per flange and wire together all the bolts to prevent them coming loose.

WELDING THE HULL PLATE

When you have all of the plating tacked in position, now is the time to give your hull a final check over before going on to run the final welds. If you are not a competent and fully experienced welder, you should seek some assistance by way of hiring a suitably qualified person to complete the welding of the hull plate. As the intermediate stringers will not be attached to the plate at this stage, you may decide this is a good time to go inside the boat and tack weld the stringers to the plate.

It is not a good idea to weld the stringers to the plating until after the plate welding is completed. You may need to use some forces from inside the hull to make the plating fair, and having all the stringers welded to the plate may interfere with this process. A good panel beater can do wonders with a rubber hammer.

You must be careful not to introduce stresses and

distortion at this stage. The welding sequence is very important. Avoid anything that will cause excessive heat. Proper voltage and welding current, combined with the proper welding techniques, will go a long way towards keeping your plating fair. Improper joint size will cause overheating.

This is one time when MIG welding will come into its own. The lower current requirements combined with speed with which this method lays down the weld will all play their part in avoiding plate distortion. If you have used a plasma cutter, grinding wheel cutter or plasma cutter for sizing your plate, you will have avoided one of the main areas where heat distortion can make your job just that much harder. Weld congestion should be minimised. Never weld the hull plate continuously. Your choice of welding rods will be important, so make sure you choose the correct one for the job in hand.

When you are proceeding with the final welding, you must remove the tack welds as you go. Tack welds should never be left as part of the final plate welding. One of the most popular techniques used in welding the plate, is the back step. Welds of no more than 1 1/2" [37] for 1/8" [3] plate through to 3" [75] runs for 3/16" [4 to 5 mm] plate should be used for the plate sizes shown.

When it comes to welding runs, think small. Another benefit of MIG welding is that slightly longer runs can be used. Gaps of about the same length as the runs are left between each weld, these are filled in with the next series of welding runs, making sure to overlap the existing weld by say 1/2" [12]. Make sure the existing welds are fully cooled before you start to fill in the spaces. If you work around your tack welds, you can grind these off before running the final weld in that location.

It would be possible to write a complete book to cover the art of metal working and in particular the various welding techniques. Obviously it is not possible to cover the subject here in a meaningful manner; I have tried to remind you of the welding techniques that are important at any one stage of your boat building programme.

INSTALLING A RUBBING STRIP

Most plans will show a rubbing strip or some type and you will need one to protect your hull from the unavoidable contacts your boat will make with other craft, jetties and other immovable objects. You will

have several choices including a heavy rubber moulding that is usually attached by bolting to a specially installed steel strip, a timber rubbing strip that can be bolted to your hull or a split pipe rubbing strip that is welded to the hull plating. Our choice is the split pipe that is usually pipe of 2 1/2" to 4" [60 to 100] diameter depending on the size of your boat. This pipe is split up the centre and tapered at the forward end. The aft end is snaped off at forty-five degrees and the end plated over and sealed. The Split pipe is welded to the plating along the top and bottom. A good coating on the inside of the pipe will help to protect it from corrosion.

GRINDING THE WELDS

You may leave the grinding of the welds until you have turned the hull however as all the hull plating is readily accessible at this time you may decide to do this now. Anyhow this is a good time to discuss this subject. In boats built upright, you may leave the grinding until a later stage if you wish. In building commercial vessels and when building to some rules, it is forbidden to grind the underwater welds at all. They should be carefully examined for flaws, and any porosity, slag and other extraneous material removed by chipping or grinding. Make the welds good and no grinding takes place.

You may elect to grind the underwater welds, and if you do, take upmost care that you do not weaken the hull by over grinding. In welding above the waterline, you will want to grind for the sake of appearance. The same advice applies, on no account over grind to the extent that you weaken the weld. If your welding experience is limited, this is another area where some professional advice should be welcomed. If you have built using pre-prime coated material, now is the time to go all over your hull both inside and out, touching up the welded areas with primer. Firstly clean up the welds by wire brushing and apply at least two coats to the effected areas.

TURNING THE HULL

After you have completely welded up the exterior of the hull plating and you are satisfied that the hull is as fair as you can make it, now is the time to turn the hull, assuming you have built it upside-down. The methods described for turning a male moulded fibreglass hull can be equally successful in turning your steel hull. The choices include, building a crate type cradle around the hull and turning it one section at a time or employing a crane fitted with a spreader bar and two endless slings. In the crane assisted turnover, you simply revolve the hull within the endless slings, not forgetting to have suitable restraining arrangements so the turning operation does not get out of control. Once the hull is upright, or if you have built the hull right way up, the next job is to check over your structure to assure it is level in all planes. Remember, you will be building the decks and superstructure plus the interior, based on a level hull, so make sure you have just that.

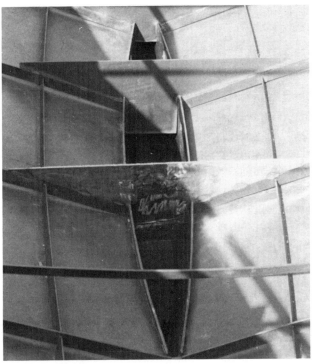

Web floors installed in ROBERTS 34. Built by Helge Andersson of Sweden.

CHAPTER THIRTEEN
STEEL - BUILDING DECKS AND SUPERSTRUCTURE

If you have used un-treated steel, you will need to grit blast and prime the interior of your hull. Some careful thought regards the sequence you will use for fitting out the interior and building the decks and superstructure, will pay dividends later. We suggest some options, but you should work out your own work schedule and make minor changes as you proceed. Be careful not to work yourself into a corner. Before you start to build the decks and superstructure, you may want to consider installing all of the bulky items that will need to be in the hull and which may be difficult to place after the decks and the superstructure are in place.

The engine, large tanks, bulkhead panels, the plywood sole and other similar bulky items may be installed before you go on with the building of the decks and before the cabin is finally closed up by the addition of the cabin top plating. Give the above

some serious consideration before you proceed further. Many items to be built within the hull, are much easier to construct before, rather than after the hull is closed, by the addition of the decks and superstructure.

FOAM INSULATION

Now is the time to consider if you are going to have the hull lined with one of the foams suitable for this purpose. You will need to install any foam insulation before you start work on furniture and joinery. There are two basic methods of lining the hull with foam, one is to use the spray in urethane foam that is installed wet, and allowed to expand over the stringers. This material is our choice as it really sticks to the inner hull surface. Make sure you choose a variety of foam that will not release

Engine bearers in ROBERTS SPRAY hull. A longitudinal steel web with lightening holes would improve this installation.

End view of installation shown above.

This builder combined steel side decks with plywood cabin structure.

Laminated timber deck beams, king plank, and underside of plywood deck on ROBERTS SPRAY.

harmful gases in case of fire. It should also be self extinguishing in event of fire. After application, you can dress off the foam, with a large sanding board.

The supplier usually has all the equipment to install this foam and charges by the cubic foot or pound or kilo or cubic metre. Make sure you get an estimate of the cost and do not just let the operator install the material without you having a good idea of the expected cost involved. With the spray in foam, there are arguments about whether you should, or need to paint the inside of your hull first. In my opinion if you are using the pre-prime coated material and you have cleaned up the welds and touched up the prime coating, which is sufficient preparation for the foam.

INSULATING WITH FOAM SHEETING

Another method of installing the hull with foam insulation is to purchase ready made urethane foam sheet. This material should be at least the thickness of the stringers or may be as thick as the frames. The thickness of the insulation may depend on where you are planning to use your boat, the more temperate the climate the less insulation you will need. You will certainly need some insulation if only to prevent condensation forming on the inside of your hull. If you use the sheet foam you will need

Steel decks and cabin on ROBERTS SPRAY built in England for BRUCE ROBERTS, U.K., Ltd.

Another view of Bernhard Nentwig's ROBERTS 53. Study the photographs carefully as they illustrate many stages in your building program.

to glue it the inside of your hull. The inside plating should be at least prime coated and painted before you install this type of foam. You may decide that if you are going to use spray or blow in foam, you would be better off to complete the hull decks and superstructure before calling in the operator. This means you will not be able to fit out you boat before installing decks etc. This is not a problem, providing you plan ahead.

PLYWOOD DECKS AND SUPERSTRUCTURE

Some builders may be tempted at this stage to think about installing plywood decks and superstructure. Our advice, forget it! Plywood has been used to successfully build boats of various types, but our opinion is, you should generally avoid adding a deck and superstructure to a steel hull. There will be exceptions such as with very small boats, however, in general, avoid plywood decks on steel boats. Our objections are based on thirty years of personal experience. It is very difficult to get a satisfactory joint between say the steel hull and the plywood deck or steel deck and plywood cabin structure. Yes, it can be done and in the case of a very small steel boat; it may be justified, but as a general rule don't. Various types of rot, are often found in plywood decks and superstructures, and when you mix materials you tend to exacerbate the problem.

If you are determined to install plywood decks and/or superstructure on you steel hull, then make sure you use a system that will effectively isolate the plywood from the steel hull. One method I have seen used, was to build a plate deck shelf that was in affect a 4" [100] wide strip of steel plate where the steel deck would normally join the hull. This plate formed the deck shelf and the plywood deck could overlay the steel this minimising the chance of fresh water getting between the plywood and the steel. You will need a bedding material such as one of the synthetic rubber compounds or another method of separating the plywood from the steel. The edge of the plywood will need protection and this can be arranged with a rebated timber toe-rail which could be through bolted and form part of the connection arrangement between the steel hull and the plywood deck structure.

ALUMINIUM DECKS AND SUPERSTRUCTURE

Here is an area where you may take your boat up-market and generally improve the performance, appearance and resale value. You need to have a good working knowledge of the aluminium before considering this option. If you select the aluminium decks and/or superstructure option, you will carefully consider the joint between the steel hull and the aluminum section of the structure. The traditional way was to use a barrier such as neoprene between the steel and the aluminium and using bolts isolated by way of sleeves, bolt the two structures together.

A more modern way to join steel and aluminum is by welding using the specially fused strip that has steel on one side and a special aluminium compound on the other. This fused strip may be used to successfully join the two materials that are welded on to the respective elements. The strip I am familiar with is made in Holland, however contact your local steel supplier for further information on this and other similar products.

FIBREGLASS DECKS AND SUPERSTRUCTURE

If you are thinking of a lightweight deck and superstructure arrangement, then you may wish to consider fibreglass as the material for these areas. Read the chapter on building fibreglass decks and cabin structures and see if these methods appeal to you. There is no valid reason the fibreglass decks and superstructure could not be installed on your boat. The core material would be discontinued before the solid glass was attached to a plate deck shelf as described for attaching plywood decks to steel hulls. If you are planning lightweight non steel deck and superstructure then fibreglass may well suit your needs.

DECK BEAMS

The deck material can be flat bar, angle or T bar. Each material has its benefits and drawbacks. Flat bar is light and easy to form, is not quite as strong as angle or T and lacks the flange on which to attach the inner lining. Angle is heavier but has a useful flange, same applies to T section. My choice is angle or T for deck and cabin top beams. We prefer flat bar or T for frames. If you are planning to use spray in foam then, any objections to angle disappear and as it is probably the least expensive, so why not use angle.

The deck beams can be bent using the Angle and

jack device we show elsewhere, or you can have the beams bent at your local metal shop. It is best to install the deck beams right across the hull even if you are going to have side decks. By installing the deck beams right across the hull you can better mark out the side deck widths and even plate the decks before you cut the beams to the width of the side decks. This sequence will make sure the beams all stay even at the edge where the side decks meet the cabin side. Imagine all those loose unsupported beam inboard ends if they are unsupported. The sections you cut from the centre between the side decks will later be re-bent to a greater camber and used for the cabin top beams. Re-bending to a greater camber will shorten the beams, this should not be a problem as the cabin side lay-in will offset the shorter length. After you have installed all the beams, mark out the side decks and note to which beam you will be bringing the fore and aft decks. It is better to finish the fore deck plating on a beam even if you cut it away later after the cabin structure is in place. In general it always easier to build on top of something than try to create a structure in mid air.

INTERCOSTAL STIFFENERS

Intercostal stiffeners are fore and aft stringers that are placed between, rather than slotting into the beams. Usually intercostal's in the deck are about the same spacing as the stringers in the hull. If your plans do not show intercostal's, you may need some, to help support the deck. Use the same material as you used for the hull stringers and about the same spacing. If you want the best job, snape the ends of the intercostal's taking about 25% off the bottom at the ends. If your deck has considerable sheer, you may want to bend the intercostal's to match the sheer so you will not pull the deck plating when welding the intercostal's to the underside of the deck. Use the same welding sequence as you used for the hull stringers.

BULWARKS

If you intend to have bulwarks on your boat, you will have fitted a deck stringer at the appropriate height. The frames above the height of the deck can be tapered to a width at the top to accept a stringer on to which a cap rail can be screwed. You may wish to top the frames and the bulwark plating at the sheer with a pipe rail or solid round instead of a

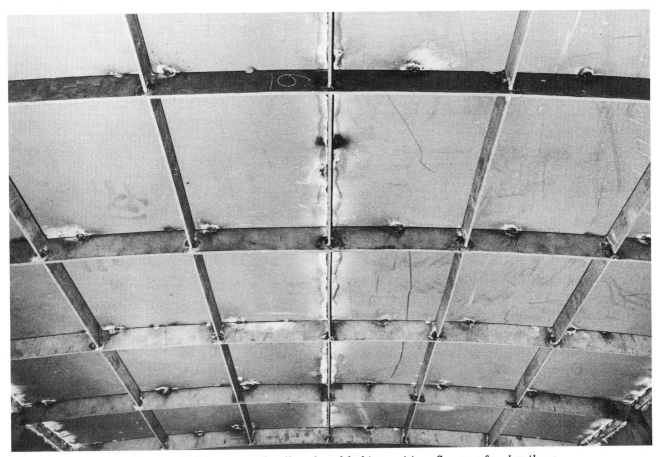

Cabin top beams and fore and aft intercostals all tack welded in position. See text for details.

timber cap rail. Anyhow, tapered frames above the deck will be the correct procedure. The frames may have a section of flat bar welded to make either an L or a T shape to the frame above the deck.

WATERWAYS AND FAIRLEADS

Finally do not forget to cut waterways on the outside of the bulwark stanchion between the frame and the hull plating and the deck so the water can flow behind the bulwark stanchion. Freeing ports or waterways will also be required to allow the water to clear the decks through the bulwarks. The freeing ports are situated at the lowest point of the sheer and the holes should be large enough to let water out without delay. Usually several freeing ports spread over the lowest area are better than one large hole. Reinforce the freeing ports around the edges. You will also need to install fairleads. These take the form of holes in the bulwark forward and aft, through which the docking or mooring lines are led from cleats on deck, to the dock or pier. The fairleads should be of adequate size for the lines that will occupy them and the edges should be reinforced with solid round bar.

MARKING OUT AND PLATING THE DECK

Once the deck beams and intercostals are in place, mark out the side decks using a long batten, to get an even fair line, where the cabin sides will meet the deck. Next plate the fore-deck, side decks and aft decks. Often the cockpit seats will be at deck level, so you may want to include this area in your total deck plating. Plating the decks will require similar skills as you have used for plating the hull. Patterning is recommended, never lay plate in place and trim by torch. You may now weld under the decks attaching the beams to the plating according to your welding schedule. Again do not over weld.

Now you may cut your deck beams to their correct length and while supporting the beams and the deck plating, install the cabin side carlin. The carlin will usually be a length of flat bar that runs along the inner edge of the beams tying them together. The carlin may be placed at an angle so the cabin sides can be welded to the carlin at the correct angle. The carlin may protrude above the deck plating by an amount so the cabin side plating can be welded to the outside of the carlin and on to the deck plating, making a one weld join on the outside and avoiding any rust traps. It is important to provide an easy

route for the water to flow off your hull and deck. Never create any indents where the water can lie and cause corrosion and rust.

BULKHEADS

At some stage about now, you will be marking out and installing your bulkheads and it is often easier if you let the bulkheads rise above the hull as a square and then mark out the side deck widths, the cabin lay-in and the cabin top camber on the plate or plywood before you attempt to shape the top of the bulkheads. It will depend if you have cutting equipment that can cut the bulkhead to shape above the deck line, after it is in place. An alternative is to carefully work out the shape of the entire bulkhead before you install it in the hull.

CABIN SIDES

After the bulkheads are shaped, the cabin sides may now be installed. You should have a pattern or measurements from which you will make a pattern. The pattern that may be plywood or Masonite, should be carefully checked in its correct position before you attempt to cut and fit the steel sides. The cabin sides will need some lay-in to look correct. Your plans should state the amount of lay-in. As a general rule the more modern the design of your boat, the more lay-in is required for your cabin sides. If in doubt, study other similar boats. One area where you will need to take great care is the forward

Steel foredeck on ROBERTS 44 built in Brisbane, Australia. Note bulwarks and bulwark cap.

Side deck beams, and part foredeck.

Jib tack fitting installed on ROBERTS 34.

Foredeck and partial side decks in place.

Side decks, cabin side framing and cabin top beams installed.

Foredeck, side decks, cabins sides.

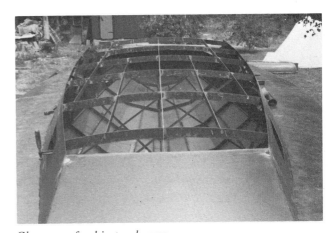

Close-up of cabin top beams.

end of the cabin structure. The intersection of the cabin front and the sides must be either parallel to the centre line or the top must lean inwards. Check your front from all angles, if the top appears to lay outwards it will look awful. If necessary, simply twist the forward sides inwards at the top and you will see the visual improvement for yourself.

THE CABIN FRONT

The cabin front will almost certainly lay back when viewed in profile and will usually have some curvature. If you do not have a specified round or curvature for the front you may use the same amount of round or the pattern for the cabin top beams as a guide. Too much curvature will look worse than too little. Once you have the cabin sides in place, next install the cabin front, considering the points mentioned above. When installing the cabin front, do not forget to allow for the camber on the top that will be required to match up with the deck beams. Usually you will need some reinforcing where the cabin sides will meet the cabin top. This can be a similar flat bar to the one used for the bottom carlin

Cockpit and coamings on ROBERTS 34.

Cockpit coamings and cockpit seating.

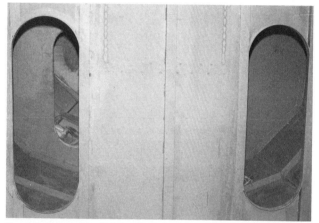

Steel bulkhead in ROBERTS 44 hull. Note rounded doorways and stiffening on bulkhead.

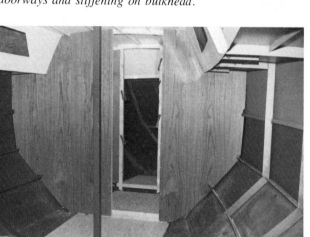

Bulkheads will need trim strips around edges and, exposed areas of hull should be lined.

Forward steel bulkhead in ROBERTS 44. Built by Dr. Larry Hall of Kentucky.

used at the intersection of the deck and cabin sides. Better still, use either split pipe or solid round to make an attractive rounded corner on the top corners of you cabin structure. The rounded appearance should be in intersections of the side to top and side to front.

THE BEVEL

A bevelled section makes an attractive intersection between the cabin sides and the cabin top. The bevel is one of my favourite architectural features and I note that a few boat manufacturers are incorporating the bevel between the cabin sides and top. The bevel can be any size but it is usually set at about forty-five degrees to the vertical and could measure across the face about 3" to 6" [75 to 50] depending on the size of the boat. The use of the bevel is also a great way to disguise the cabin height. If your design calls for a high cabin structure, then consider the bevel. For the record, the bevel when used in timber work is often called an "arras" meaning to take a small bevel say 1/4" to 1/2" [6 to 12] or so off the corner of a post, or other feature, to soften the corner in appearance and in fact.

CABIN TOP

Before you install the cabin top beams, please give final consideration to the items you will want inside the boat. Tanks, engine and associated equipment, large sheets of plywood for fitting out, and any other bulky items must be at least in the hull before you close off the top. This is a good time to mention access for the possible removal of the engine. I have seen builders make the most elaborate arrangement of hatchways etc., to be sure they can remove the engine if and when required. I think this is a waste of time, and sometimes you will build in the possibility of leaks. With a steel boat you simply cut out the panel to allow the engine to be removed and after the engine is reinstalled you weld the panel back into place, making good any beams etc.

At the same time as you are installing the top cabin side reinforcing, you will be installing the cabin top beams. Usually the cabin top beams will have more camber than the deck beams. The sections you cut from the centre of the deck beams will be now re-bent as cabin top beams. Once you have installed the cabin top beams, next install the intercostal's. Keep in mind any hatchways that can be incorporated into the pattern of the intercostal's. After you have all the beams and intercostal's in place, check over the whole cabin structure and install props and other bracing as necessary to maintain the shape until you complete the top plating sequence.

PILOT HOUSE

If your design includes a wheelhouse or pilot house structure, this will be built after the fore cabin. The fore cabin top should be extended back far enough, so the forward panels of the pilot house can be built on top of the fore cabin. Later you may want to cut away the section of the fore cabin top that is inside the pilot house or the top may act as a chart table or part of the arrangement to position the various instruments. Anyhow it will be easier to construct

Bulkhead need only be faced with fancy plywood where it is visible.

Quarter pipe used on cabin front and cabin top.

the forward part of pilot house structure over the fore cabin top.

HATCHES

Next fit the hatches. You may elect to purchase ready made hatches or you can fabricate your own from steel or other material. If your hatches are not

Flybridge decks need less camber than regular cabin tops. Note the bevelled edge of the overhang

Quarter of pipe used at pilot house corners.

Bevelled cockpit coaming on Roberts 53 built by A. Skjodt in Canada.

Note how pilot house is stepped in from fore cabin line, this takes away any boxy appearance.

steel, you will need to isolate the steel deck or cabin top from the other material. There is no reason you cannot leave most of the hatches out by simply plating over the whole deck and cabin top, leave one access hatchway and later simply cut holes in the deck and top to suit the hatches you require. You can easily reinforce the edges with the hatch coamings. This is one of the advantages of building with steel, you can make changes at almost any stage of the construction program.

LAID DECKS AND OTHER ALTERNATIVES

If you are building a boat of over sixty feet in length, then you may wish to consider the installation of laid timber decks. Many of you who are building smaller boats may want to install laid timber decks. Our first advice is don't! There are better ways of finishing off your decks, which will avoid the problems you will encounter when you try to install

a laid deck on a steel hull.

We would recommend one of the patterned non-skid decking material such as "Treadmaster" or one of the patterns available from "Vetus". These patterned materials are designed to be glued to the deck with an adhesive that is formulated especially for the purpose. Another method is to paint and sand your decks. In the case of painted or where the patterned materials are installed, always leave about 2" [25] clear space around all hatches, cabin sides, coamings, deck fittings, and deck edges. This clear area sets off the various features of your deck arrangement and mimics the way timber decks are laid.

LAID DECKS

If you install a laid timber deck, you should avoid making it too thick, as the additional weight will be a most unwelcome addition to your boat. You will

Example of well built steel decks, hatches, bases for fittings and staunchions - builder Mr. Flowers of Arapahoe, North Carolina, USA

On a steel boat do not extend the laid deck outside the rail, leave a waterway as shown

Ready made hatches can add a professional finish to any deck arrangement

need to either bed the timber in a mastic or an epoxy compound capable of gluing the timber to the steel decks. In the case of timber set in a sealing compound, the planks will need to be bolted or attached with studs that have been pre-welded to the steel deck. The planks are usually about 1 3/4" [45] wide and the thickness will vary between 1/2" [50] and 1 1/4" [30] and there should be no planking around the outer edges of the deck, which would interfere with the flow of run off water. You should

usually arrange a wider board around the cabin and hatches. There are many fibreglass production boats that are fitted with teak deck planking so you can copy the layout ideas, you will see on these boats.

Another method of installing teak or other timber decks over your steel deck, is to install a plywood sub-deck that is bolted or attached with studs to the steel and then install the timber planking over the plywood by screwing the planking to the plywood

Attractively laid out "Deckmaster" glued to steel deck of Roberts 44.

and using timber plugs to cover the screw heads. No matter that of the above methods you use, you must make hard decisions that will usually result in problems at a later stage. The problem is, no matter how careful you are with the caulking between the planks, water will eventually get under the planking. As there is no way for it to get out again, some corrosion problems must eventually occur.

GRIT BLASTING AND EXTERIOR COATINGS

Do not rush this section of your boatbuilding programme and you should undertake considerable research, before making a final selection of the protective coating for your boat. Do not be tempted to simply give your hull the once over with a sander or wire brush before you start the painting process. Unless you have built your hull from steel that has been grit blasted and pre- prime coated, you must grit blast before you paint.

Once you have completed the exterior of your hull deck and superstructure, it is time to think about applying the exterior coatings that will protect your boat for many years to come. If you have used pre-prime coated steel and you have been working under cover, all you need to do, is to wire brush and carefully clean up the welds and apply touch up coats of primer, before going on to apply the remainder of the finish coating. If your pre-prime coated areas have been exposed to the elements you will need to decide if you should grit blast back to bare metal, or simply touch up the prime coated area as required. Make sure you make the right decision, there in no point in applying several coats of

expensive paint over a doubtful base.

It is necessary to undertake the grit blasting and the initial coat of paint almost simultaneously. The grit blasting must be done on a fine dry day and you must install the first coating of primer within an hour, if not minutes after exposing the bare metal. When grit blasting, we are talking about back to bare metal with an all over shiny surface, ensuring that you have removed all of the foreign matter from the surface of the steel, before you attempt to apply any protective coatings.

METALLIZING YOUR HULL

Before we get into discussing the specific hull coatings, there is one alternate protective system that must be considered. Metallizing involves spraying the hull either outside or both inside and out with zinc or other similar compound. Special equipment is required to undertake this work and you probably can hire the equipment or hire a person to go with the metallizing outfit. Some builders who plan more than one boat have been known to buy their own set up. Before we go any further, I have to say that I am not in favour of this technique. One builder in the USA who has written extensively on steel boatbuilding, had great faith in this method of protecting a hull, and through his writings the system gained some popularity. There is considerable doubt that the metallizing is 100% successful. There have definitely been cases where the metallised coating has flaked off the hull taking the protective paint with it. It only takes a small area where the metallising is damaged to allow the water to permeate under the coating and cause it to lift off over a large area. If you are planning to metallize your hull, investigate the system fully, before taking the final decision to use this system.

There have been many coatings tried for protecting steel hulls. Do not be tempted under anycircumstances into using house type paints. Your paint job will have a very short life. Choose only those coatings especially formulated for marine use.

PROTECTING THE INTERIOR

The interior of your hull and exterior will have different needs so let us consider the interior first. Some materials are noted for their low cost but result in an unattractive finish, paints such as those based on coal tar or chlorinated rubber as best used where they will not be seen. Coal tar epoxy is a well-proven material that can be used in the lower part of the hull and anywhere in the interior that will not be exposed to personal contact. If you have installed spray in foam insulation, you will need only to paint those exposed areas, such as the bilge and any other parts that have been left un-coated by the foam.

The exterior of your hull will require a fine finish that will offer long lasting protection. A system of either Epoxy based or Polyurethane based paint, is usually preferred by quality steel boatbuilders. Most of these materials are best applied by a professional using the correct equipment for the particular system. As there is not space here to fully cover the subject, I am going to recommend you to International Paints Ltd. I have had thirty years experiences of dealing with this company and using their protective coating products. If you contact their local technical representative, you will receive advice on finish coating your steel boat. International paints have offices and technical back up services in many countries, so you probably can contact the right person.

Apart from lack of space there is another reason for not giving you specific advice on the choice of coatings, and that is improvements are ongoing in this area, so you should seek out the latest advice. There will also be other coatings manufacturers near you who could advise on their particular products.

The main piece of advice I can offer is this, always choose the products of one manufacturer only, never, but never mix the brands. Apart from the chances of incompatibility between materials made by different manufacturer, there will be the absolute certainty that if anything goes wrong, you will not obtain redress from one or any of these suppliers.

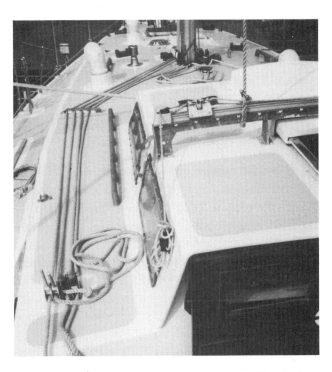

Above: Note how deck paint is stepped back from edges of sheer, hatches and deck fittings.
Below: Good protective coatings are essential - check out this Roberts 370 built in Finland

CHAPTER FOURTEEN
ALUMINIUM CONSTRUCTION

No matter how you spell it, Aluminium or Aluminum, this is one of today's premier boatbuilding materials.

Aluminium has gained in popularity in the past few years, not only as a medium for building commercial craft and fishing vessels, but also as the material favoured by many builders of large and not so large fine yachts.

If you are the builder, and you are considering using this material for you next boat; you should already have some experience in handling aluminium. Your experience may have been gained in a non boating field. The important thing is that you understand aluminium, and the specialised welding techniques required to successfully built a seaworthy boat. When considering construction techniques and work practices, aluminium is less forgiving than some other materials.

If you are having the boat professionally built then your decision may be based on a variety of reasons. You only need an overview of the material and a reasonable understanding of the points raised in this chapter. You will need a reliable boatbuilder, one who is fully experienced in handling the intricities of aluminium.

SELECTING A DESIGN

Aluminium is gaining in popularity, but as yet, there are not an abundance of plans available, that are designed especially for this material. There are many cases where individuals have attempted to build from plans designed to be used for other materials. Let me make it clear, right from the beginning, you should not try and build an aluminium boat, from plans designed for steel, fibreglass or wood; that is unless you have consulted with a designer, who has supervised the changes required to your construction plans.

In some cases it is possible to convert from one material to another; in other instances a complete re-design is called for. Only the designer of the original boat, or another equally qualified person, can determine, just what is needed for your chosen design to be built from aluminium.

After having provided suitable warnings, let me add that you will not necessarily need an expensive custom plan. Aluminium is a light weight material; you should not choose a design with a high displacement length ratio; nor should you seek out an ultra light design. Aluminium may be light in weight but the fittings, equipment, engine, stores, fuel, water and human crew still weigh the same.

The type of boat that most people are happy with, is one that can fulfil its intended role with ease. A boat where you have worry about the weight of every item you bring aboard, will not satisfy you for very long.

A design of moderate displacement can be adapted for aluminium construction. The main advice I can offer, is to make sure the construction follows accepted practices.

Aluminium is ideal as a building material for all types of planing hulls; it's light weight can be fully utilised in the V hull form.

The availability of sailboat designs which incorporate the Radius Chine building form has certainly caused a surge in the numbers of sailboats currently being built in aluminium. Building a round bilge sailboat in either steel or aluminium is a job for the expert metal boatbuilder; building a radius chine hull can be undertaken with confidence by any competent home builder.

ALUMINIUM - THE MATERIAL

Just like you will need a special plan to build an aluminium boat, you must also ensure you obtain the correct grade. For marine use the most often discussed grades of aluminium are the five and six thousand series. The five thousand series have the best all round properties for boat construction and its use is recommended for that purpose.

Aluminium with 5086 designation will be the material most often chosen to build a boat. There are several different numbers in the five thousand series that could be used. Aluminium with the 5086-H116 designation is recommended for framing and hull plating. The 5086-32 series is suitable for decks and cabin structures. Certain 6000 series aluminium are widely available as extrusions and some of these can be used for interior framing.

The five thousand series has excellent resistance to salt water, is ductile and retains a high strength when welded. In some cases you may choose aluminium with one designation for the hull plate and another for the frames and stringers.

You should discuss your final choice of material with the designer of your boat plus seek additional knowledge from your local supplier. If you are not already generally familiar with Aluminium you will need to undertake considerable study before you proceed further.

When it comes to purchasing the aluminium for your boat,one bulk buy is recommended. This material is very sensitive to quantity pricing so check around for the best deal.

Because of space restrictions, this book can only give you an overview of boatbuilding in aluminium. I hope you will at least gain enough knowledge, to decide if you should further investigate the benefits offered by this material.

I am only covering the welded aluminium. Boats can be pressed out of one single sheet; rivetted construction is still used in the manufacture of some small boats. Aluminium boats have been even formed by explosive techniques. The boat is formed in a mould with the assistance of a controlled explosion.

As I write this it brings to mind a visit I had in my U.S. office from a retired Swedish airline pilot who had previously built a boat to my design, but now thought he had a better way. Patents were mentioned and backers were being sought. The technique consisted of a series of interlocking aluminium strips, similar to the venetian blind slats we are familiar with in most countries.

The idea was to have an interlocking edge on each strip, and to use epoxy to permanently seal and join the strips. A twenty five feet [7.62 Metres] boat was built and tested; I recall the construction technique proved unsatisfactory in several areas, including the fact that the boat was extremely difficult to repair after striking a submerged object.

I relate the above, to illustrate just one of the dozens of construction methods, that have come in gone in the thirty years, I have been associated with designing and building boats. No matter which material you choose to build your dream ship, be wary of miracle, fast, cheap, or too good to be true boatbuilding materials and/or methods. If you have any doubts about the viability of a material or method, choose a well proven alternative.

Recently a new book has been published with its content totally devoted to aluminium and its uses for boat construction. The book is called "BOATBUILDING WITH ALUMINUM" This book can be obtained from any Bruce Roberts Design office.

FRAMING AN ALUMINIUM BOAT

Designers, builders and the various standards authorities have varying opinions as to the best layout of the framing. Some favour many frames with few stringers, others few frames with many stringers and just about every possible combination of the two arrangements.

The framing methods will vary depending of the type of boat being built. The strains imposed on a hull and other sections of the structure, vary between one type of boat and another. For instance the ballast keel of a sailboat imposes far different strains than those inflicted to the bottom of a high speed planing hull.

The selection of a framing arrangement will be an important part of the work the designer of your boat. Most of our own designs have a conservative mix of the two main framing members; the exact arrangement being determined, by the needs of the particular design.

Generally speaking, aluminium boats require more closely spaced frames and stringers than steel boats of similar size and type. The materials need to be of larger dimensions. For instance where a steel frame may be the same width throughout its length, an aluminium frame may need to be widened in certain areas, to allow it to do the same job as its steel sister.

In steel boats we generally recommend flat bar for both frames and stringers. In aluminium boats we almost always recommend T or L bar for the frames.

For stringers the ideal material is one that has a combination of flat bar with a bulb on the inner edge. This material is extruded and is sometimes available as a stock item for your local supplier.

Before you seriously consider building an aluminium boat, you may want to investigate the local availability of sizes of bar and plate, that you can obtain in the correct grade.

WELDING EQUIPMENT

As a minimum you will require a supply of 220 volt single phase 50 hertz electrical power connected to a DC inverter. The power source quoted is available in most households, as a standard item at the switchboard.

Either TIG, MIG or pulse arc are the most common types of welding used by the home builder or small boat yard. These three methods all use inert shielding gas and argon gas is usually used for this purpose. The purpose of using the gas is to create a gas envelope that protects the weld material from contamination.

I suggest you investigate the three choices of welding equipment and techniques as mentioned above; decide which will best suit your needs. Each method has its own benefits and drawbacks, discuss these with your equipment supplier.

You may be able to rent suitable welding equipment. Whether you buy or rent will depend on the size of your project and length of time you anticipate requiring the equipment. Check all the options with your welding equipment source.

Before you buy any welding system make sure it is tested at your site. You must be satisfied that the chosen equipment will be suitable for the job; and the only way to be sure, is to have the gear tested under actual working conditions at your building location. Most welding supply houses will be able to supply a qualified person to demonstrate the exact rig you are considering buying. Not only try before you buy but try AT YOUR SITE before you buy.

You will need a variety of equipment including electrical cables, welding gun and spool feeder. Of course you will require an angle grinder and other metal working tools as discussed in the chapters on steel construction.

Don't forget suitable protective and safety gear and equipment is a must. You will require full face welding hood with a number 10 or number 11 lens for welding below 200 amps. A suitable stainless steel hand held wire bush is required and this tool must be kept clean at all times. The brush is used to remove soot from the weld. Welding gloves, a leather apron and some arm protection are required.

BUILDING WITH ALUMINUM

Your building area will need to located in a draught free environment; consequently you must build an aluminum boat not only under cover but in an enclosed area.

As I have stated previously, this book does not attempt to teach you how to weld. Our aim is to give you an overview of the techniques required to build a boat from the particular material being considered.

Many of the tips outlined in the chapters on steel construction will apply here. We would not recommend a person who is inexperienced in the handling and welding of aluminium, to build an aluminium boat on his own. However, an inexperienced person could seek the assistance of, and work alongside a professional; and so acquiring the boat at minimum labour cost.

As boatbuilding materials go, aluminium is one of the lightest and cleanest. Working with this material is a pleasure. Aluminium can be sawn, planed and generally worked with similar tools, that are used for timber. The tools you need for fitting out will also have some uses here. A band saw and/or jigsaw, hand plane, files and rasps all have this duel usage.

Many aluminium boats are built upside down. The advantages and disadvantages of building this way as opposed to right way up are outlined in the chapters on steel construction. I have seen many aluminium boats built upside down and many built right way up. In my opinion, power boat hulls and radius chine sailboat hulls should always be built upside down.

I have recently seen advice being offered, that all of the watertight inside welds should be made before the outside of the plate is welded. This advice, if followed, may make you opt for building the hull upright.

ROBERTS 53 hull partially plated in aluminum by Canadian builder Bellavance Welding Ltd.

Preparing the building bedlogs or strongback, erecting the frames and installing the stringers, all follow similar procedures, to those outlined in the chapters covering steel construction. There will be some variations between the two techniques however these should be spelt out, in your building plans.

Do not forget to allow for limber holes in the frames and in other areas where you want the water to be allowed to drain to one or more collection points.

Where ever possible, when installing the plating on large flat areas, pre weld the sheets into one large sheet; a large portion of the hull structure is stiffened, before you tackle the more difficult curved areas. One instance of this is the bottom and sides, of a chine type power boat hull.

On radius chine sailboat hulls you may prefer to install the radius chine area first. As with all boat hulls, make sure you install both sides of the particular area of the hull at the same time. Under no circumstances complete one side of a hull before starting the other side. Failure to heed this advice will guarantee a twisted hull.

Photo shows stringer slotted into frame but not welded until after plating is installed. This allows for adjustments to fair up stringers etc.

It is recommended that you should weld up all of the plating into one unit before proceeding to weld the stringers to the plate. The welding sequences recommended for aluminium will vary from the accepted welding practices for steel, again I recommend you study the book "BOATBUILDING WITH ALUMINUM".

DECKS AND SUPERSTRUCTURES

One of the advantages of aluminium over steel is that it more easily forms into small radius sections. For instance when you are building the cabin or pilot house, it is far preferable to have rounded corners than the sharp edge of the side and front plates meeting at more or less a right angle. An attractive rounded corner always adds not only to the beauty

125

of your boat, but also to it's monetary value.

There are many areas of boat construction where you will be able to exploit the workability of aluminium. As mentioned above rounded cabin corners are more easily formed, cockpits and other well areas can be formed in three pieces instead of five; the rounded corners on the side-to-bottom join are a bonus. Seat backs, the seat and the seat front can be one piece connected with a small radius bend, that would be most difficult to accomplish with steel. In the chapters on steel construction I have recommended the frequent use of split pipe to achieve rounded corners on the superstructure and

Shoal draft hull being built in upright method

Typical solid web floors on ROBERTS design

Note how stringers have been pushed out of their slots to allow some shape to form in the bottom plating. ROBERTS 53 hull by Bellavance Welding Ltd.

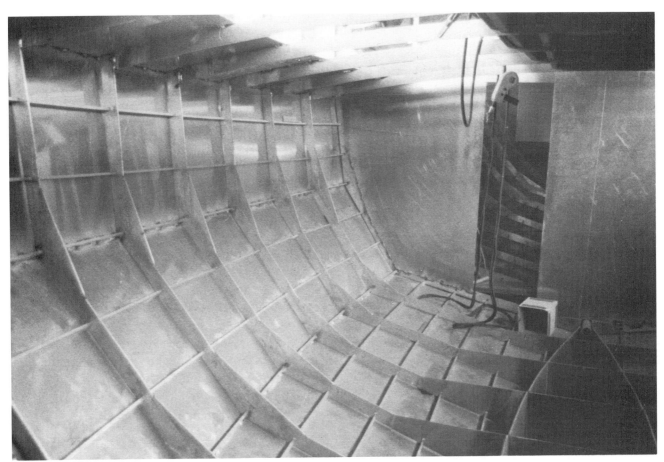

Interior of hull of ROBERTS 53 built of aluminum.

Deck being installed on a aluminum ROBERTS 53.

elsewhere; with aluminium you can take a much easier route to arrive at the same result.

As aluminium does not have the problem of rust, you can use more angle framing, not only in the superstructure, but also in the hull. The use of angle or T framing will make it much easier to attach the lining materials and interior joinery. Even if you are building a steel hull, you should give aluminium serious consideration as the deck and superstructure construction material.

The chapters on steel and fibreglass construction give many tips on deck and superstructure construction that can be useful when building in any material including aluminium. If you settle on aluminium as your building material, then do read the other chapters for helpful tips on setting up the various components.

SAILBOAT KEELS

Most aluminium sailboat keels are designed to have the ballast installed internally. This type of keel, no matter what the material, is generally referred to as an "Envelope keel". You may prefer to build the keel separately from the hull, installing the ballast before setting the hull on to the keel. If you follow this course, make sure you have some fool proof method of correctly lining up the keel and the hull. In our own designs, the web floors that go down into the keel are built as part of the total frame; this eliminates any chance of a misaligned keel. Some of our builders have built the keel as a separate unit and adapted the plans accordingly.

A better idea may be to leave off a section of plate around the keel area, so you can pass the ballast through, without it having to be lifted up and over the sheer. Do not pour LARGE QUANTITIES of molten lead directly into the keel cavity. I have seen steel and aluminium keels distort when treated in this way. The best method to install the ballast is either to pre-mould slabs of ballast; make them of a size you can lift; and lower these into the keel cavity; or use pre-cast pigs and install in a similar manner. You may then pour smaller quantities of lead carefully in and around the larger pieces of ballast without harming the basic keel structure.

As with any custom built boat, do not install all of the ballast before launching; keep say 25% of the recommended ballast amount for trimming purposes. Very few custom built boats are laid out internally

EXACTLY as the designer intended; give yourself some latitude in this area.

The leading edge of the keel may be suitably sized aluminium pipe or rolled plate. Check the radius of the leading edge of your keel, and consider if pipe or rolled plate, would be most appropriate.

From a sailing point of view, the most efficient intersection of keel and hull is a clean, near right angle. If the keel has several web floors extending down into the keel and up into the hull, then this more or less right angle join between the keel shin and the hull skin is satisfactory.

From a strength point of view, a better way would be to have an additional plate gusset at a forty-five degree angle between the keel sides and the hull skin. This angle could be rolled to form a smooth transition between the keel sides and the hull bottom. When you build the keel on your hull, keep this in mind; check with your designer to see if you can improve the strength in this area.

SAILBOAT SKEGS

The advice I offer here is similar to that outlined to builders of steel hulls. This part of your boat is so important I feel obliged to repeat most of the text here to make sure you treat skegs and rudders with the respect they deserve.

If the plans for your hull call for a separate skeg and rudder arrangement, you will need to assure yourself that the skeg will stay with the boat under all conditions. The skeg is probably one of the most vulnerable areas of your hull, so consider the installation in some detail. Most hulls have a substantial centre line bar and a centre plate for the skeg. The centre plate can be the same shape as the entire skeg, and can be welded directly to this bar or you could cut the bar and allow the centre plate to rise into the hull where it can be braced and reinforced by a system of webs. These webs could also form part of the support for the rudder bearing. The thickness of the centre plate should be adequate for the job; check with the designer of your boat.

The leading edge of the skeg may be pipe which will be between 1" and 2" [25 and 50] diameter and for best results will be bent into a small fence arrangement forward of the skeg. Aerofoil shaped webs are now arranged each side of the centre plate attached to the pipe leading edge, the centre plate,

ROBERTS 53 aluminum hull built by Bellavance Welding Ltd. of Canada

and to a section of open-faced convex pipe just ahead of the rudder shaft. The convex section, must allow the rudder to turn without binding on the aft end of the skeg. The skeg is now plated with material at least the same thickness as used for the hull. To install the plating you will need to make slots in the outer plate to allow the weld to be made between the plate and the webs. When the skeg is fully plated, you should install a fillet on both sides of the skeg, measuring say 3" to 4" [75 to 100] at forty-five degrees between the hull and the skeg, fair off the forward end of the fillet that will be welded to both the hull and skeg plating. The fillet may be rolled to provide a smooth transition from skeg plating to the bottom of the hull plating.

SAILBOAT RUDDERS

The rudder will be made in a similar manner except the leading edge will be the solid round bar or heavy walled tube rudder stock. The aft end will be a flat bar between the two side skins. Take care when welding the fins and skin plate to the leading edge bar. You may wish to have an arrangement so you can remove the rudder without dismantling the bottom of the skeg or removing the skeg bearing or lifting the boat. Flanges can be arranged and bolted together to make removal of the rudder a simpler matter. If you use flanges in the system, make sure they are of sufficient strength and have at lease 5 bolts per flange and that all of the bolts are wired together.

INSULATING ALUMINIUM HULLS

Your Aluminum power or sailboat hull deck and superstructure will need insulating against heat, cold, condensation and sound. I once sailed in an un insulated aluminium sailboat and I have never forgotten the experience. Yes, you will, have to insulate your aluminium boat.

The choices of insulation materials are much the same as those available to builders of steel boats. Polyurethane foam can be installed in sheet form or sprayed directly to the inside of the hull. The accepted practice, is not to treat the aluminium, prior to the insulation of the foam.

If you decide to use the spray in place foam, you would be advised to hire a contractor to undertake the work. If you hire a contractor, make sure you are familiar with the method of charging for the job and try and ensure you actually get what you pay for.

The nature of the equipment, and because it is next too impossible to measure what you have received, make it imperative that you stay on top of the situation.

The sheet polyurethane comes in several densities; three to four pounds per cubic foot is about right for your purpose. Sheets are sold in various sizes including 8' x 4' [2.4 x 1.22 metres]. This material is available in several thicknesses including 1", 2", 3" or 4" [25, 50, 75 and 100]. It is usual to insulate to the same thickness as depth of the stringers; but be effective at least 2" [50] should be considered a minimum. Where you plan to use the boat may guide you on the amount of insulation you require; extremes of temperature in either direction, call for additional insulation.

PAINTING ALUMINIUM HULLS

Strictly speaking, boats built from marine grade aluminum, do not need painting at all. The material is capable of coping with the ravages of the natural elements without protection. Many aluminium fishing boats have been successfully operated for many years in a totally unpainted state. However, cosmetics call for an attractive paint finish and fortunately there are now products on the market capable of providing this cover.

International Paints is again my choice for a selection of suitable aluminum coatings. This company, in which I have no shares or other financial interest, has proven most reliable in supplying paint products and other coatings for all types of boats.

Awlgrip Marine applications are highly thought of in the USA. If you can find a local supplier of paint products in whom you have faith who can supply all your needs then you make your own choice. ALWAYS PAINT YOUR HULL WITH THE PRODUCTS OF ONE MANUFACTURER. NEVER MIX BRANDS. If you do have any problems, each manufacturer or supplier will deny liability and blame the other company.

Preparation is the key, literally, to a successful paint job on your aluminum boat; or any other boat for that matter. If you do not adequately prepare the surface, the paint will not survive for very long in the marine environment. If you are looking for a high class yacht finish, then be prepared to use a reasonable amount of filler. Do not take the use of filler as an insult to your workmanship; accept that filler is required, and make sure you use and apply the correct type.

Epoxy based fillers are recommended, and micro balloons are one of the thickening agents. You should shop around for products that are produced for and/or recommended suitable for use on aluminium boats. With the rising popularity of aluminium as a boat-building material, more of these products are becoming available. You will need some technical assistance; so make sure you choose a product where the suppliers are able and willing to help and offer advice on the use of their product.

The preparation of your hull to receive its outer paint finish will in part depend on the product line you choose. In general preparation involves the following steps. First you will rough the surface of the aluminum, obviously not so rough as to cause surface scratches but sufficient to remove the normal aluminium shiny surface. You may use abrasive pads or by careful sanding. Never sand blast an aluminium hull. The next step will involve the use of an etching primer. Next follows a primer coat followed by several high build primer coats. Lastly you are ready for the finish coating.

Any system that will be successful will take many hours of work. No matter whether you are building yourself, or having the hull built; be prepared for a long and somewhat expensive job to give your hull a yacht quality finish. Remember, the finish will count in your favour, when one day you wish to recover your investment.

CHAPTER FIFTEEN
WOOD - BUILDING THE HULL

RECENT HISTORY

During the past thirty something years I have been associated with the building and designing of boats, wooden boatbuilding has changed in many ways. Until the late fifties, if you wanted to build a boat, you almost would always have chosen a timber hull. Viewed with suspicion by most boatbuilders, fibreglass was a relatively new material. Pleasure boats built of steel were definitely oddities, except in Holland and some other European countries, where they were as well accepted, as timber boats were in other areas. In the late fifties through to the mid sixties, Ferro Cement gained some popularity, however fortunately Ferro seems to have disappeared over the horizon.

At the end of the 1939 - 1945 war there was a considerable pool of technology for building timber boats using both cold and hot moulding techniques. During the war, were built thousands of patrol boats and many aircraft using various versions of these techniques. When the war finished there was a pent up demand for pleasure boats, and thousands of cold and hot moulded hulls were produced and many better built ones, remain in service to this day.

Until the early seventies, when Wood/Epoxy construction building techniques were just starting to appear, most wooden boats were either carvel planked and caulked in the traditional manner, strip planked and the method of laminated multi-diagonal plywood or veneer, using resorcinol or phenolic glues and silicon bronze and copper fastenings to complete the structure, was probably at its peak.

By the mid seventies fibreglass construction was well established, steel small boat construction techniques were becoming accepted in many areas of the world and the scene was set for the decline in the numbers of boats built of wood. The rise in popularity of Wood/Epoxy construction did play an important part in retaining the modest interest in wooden boatbuilding that exists today.

We notice that this continuing interest is not evenly distributed throughout the world. In certain areas like Germany, Scandinavia, parts of the USA, Canada and countries with their own timber resources, the interest in wooden boat construction is higher than in most other parts of the world.

Just when we thought that the arrival of Wood/Epoxy construction had made it possible to build a reasonably priced, long lasting timber boat, we have the latest negative factor to consider. It is no longer considered ecologically correct to use the species of timber that are most suited to boat construction.

If you, who feel that building and owning a wooden boat is worth the time and effort of the additional maintenance, as all timber boats do require more maintenance than boats built of alternate materials, the extra costs, as timber boats are expensive to build, and additionally the disapproval of certain members of the community, then for those of you, I continue this chapter.

COLD MOULDING

This method has been around for many years and as mentioned earlier, before the advent of fibreglass boats, both hot and cold moulding were very popular for building all types of hulls. With the resurgence of the interest in things traditional, and the fact that hulls built in this manner share with the Wood/Epoxy technique the benefits of light construction, make this technique worth your consideration.

STRIP PLANKING

As the differences between Wood/Epoxy and Cold moulding are somewhat blurred by the fact they share several of the same basic methods, so it is with Strip planking. Originally strip planking relied as much on the fastenings which edge nailed the planks together as it did on the glue. Today things have changed. If the correct epoxy resins are used between the planks, then you may consider this method as a Wood/Epoxy technique.

WOOD/EPOXY TECHNIQUES

This is the most popular timber boatbuilding method

in use today and Wood/Epoxy construction can be varied to suit the timber materials that are readily available in your area. The hull can be planked with several layers of 1/8" [3 mm] or similar thickness timber veneer and this can be combined with one layer of strip planking. You may prefer to build an all veneer hull. Good quality waterproof plywood can be used for the planking and depending on the materials you have chosen, you may wish to sheath the exterior with fibreglass cloth and epoxy resin.

There is more to the Wood/Epoxy technique than simply using the material as a glue. The idea is to saturate and/or seal the timber with the epoxy resin in such a way as to fully protect your boat both inside and out. The system does work and the boats do last much longer than timber boats built with other methods. Only you can decide if this is the method for you. The type of boat and its intended usage should have considerable bearing on your decision.

BUILDING THE FRAMES

Your plans may call for permanent frames or for the frames to be used only as removable mould formers, to be removed after the hull planking is complete. If you are having a boat custom designed, you may decide to have the permanent bulkheads utilised, as part of the setting up of the hull framework. If the frames are to remain in the hull, you will need to build them out of first grade timber and they are usually laminated to achieve the most strength for their size and weight. You may want to consider if your frames are going to incorporate any solid floors at this stage. Some plans leave the installation of the web floors until the hull is upright. Other designs call for the floors to be at least partially built with the frames.

If you are fortunate your plans will have been supplied with full size patterns and these can be laid on plywood sheets arranged to form a loft floor that is wider than the beam of your boat. The depth should equal the deepest frame and provide room for the keel patterns if they are included in the plans.

THE TRANSOM

You may install the transom either at the same time as the frames or later, after fully planking and turning the hull upright. Some plans, including our own, build the hull without the transom, in this case we include the frames past the transom position and the whole hull is planked before turnover. After the turnover the position of the transom is established and the transom installed just before the deck is to be installed. This method allows easy access to the hull until the last minute.

ASSEMBLING THE BASIC HULL

Once you have assembled the frames and stem, you may set up your hull either on a strongback or on a level floor depending on the arrangement shown in your plans. You may read the chapters in the fibreglass section of this book that deal with the setting up a male mould. The techniques of building the fibreglass male mould and setting up a Wood/epoxy hull have a lot in common.

After you set the frames up in their correct location, you should install the stem and stringers or battens, depending on whether it is intended that the frames and stringers stay with the hull or used only as a mould for the final laminated timber hull. Designers and builders disagree about whether you should leave the frames in the hull. In our own plans we have used both methods, sometimes as an option in

Set of frames for ROBERTS 29 built by Rick Bardell of California.

Transom fitted on ROBERTS 36.

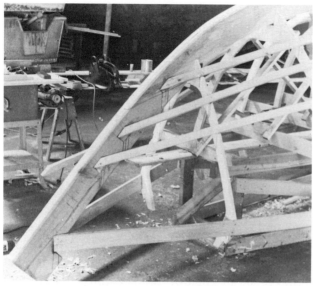

Stem will need considerable planing to allow plywood or veneer strips to lay flat across stem. An electric planer would be useful here and in other areas of molded plywood construction.

Battens used to check fairness of frames on ROBERTS 25 built by William Edwards. Note homemade clamps used to laminate deck shelf.

the same design.

In recent years we have leaned towards designing our Wood/Epoxy hulls to be built over a temporary mould and the reinforcing added from inside. The idea of a lightweight shell, with a clean interior, ready to receive laminated web floors, laminated bulkhead grounds and other interior joinery, does have considerable appeal. A smooth interior is less likely to trap moisture, in a way that will promote rot. Today we build most modern timber hulls upside down and the hulls are turned upright after the planking is completed. You may install the transom at any stage before the deck is added. Usually the stem, the keelson, the deck stringer or deck shelf and transom if installed at this stage, will all remain with the hull when the hull isremoved from the mould former. Often if the frames are to be removed, this is done after turning the hull upright.

FAIRING THE BASIC STRUCTURE

Once the frames, stem, keelson, stringers and deck stringer are in place, you will need to fair off the keelson and stem and other areas that need bevelling to receive the planking. Be careful not to over bevel any one area, if you do make a mistake, you can glue a piece of timber on to the affected area and simply re-bevel to the correct angle.

Use a batten to check over your basic hull structure and to check you have the bevels at the correct angle to receive the veneer or plywood planking. In a chine plywood hull the setting up procedure will be

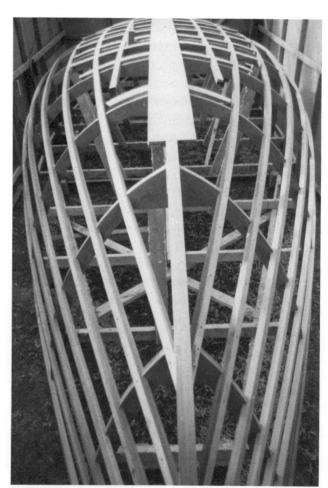

ROBERTS 36 ready for final fairing and planking in plywood or veneer strips.

similar except the chine logs or chine stringers will certainly stay with the hull even if the frames are removed. In fact it is more usual to leave the frames in a chine hull.

Laying on first lamination. Photo shows the late Hedley Nicol, an early advocate of molded plywood construction.

Two men working together or husband and wife team can make the job proceed much more quickly.

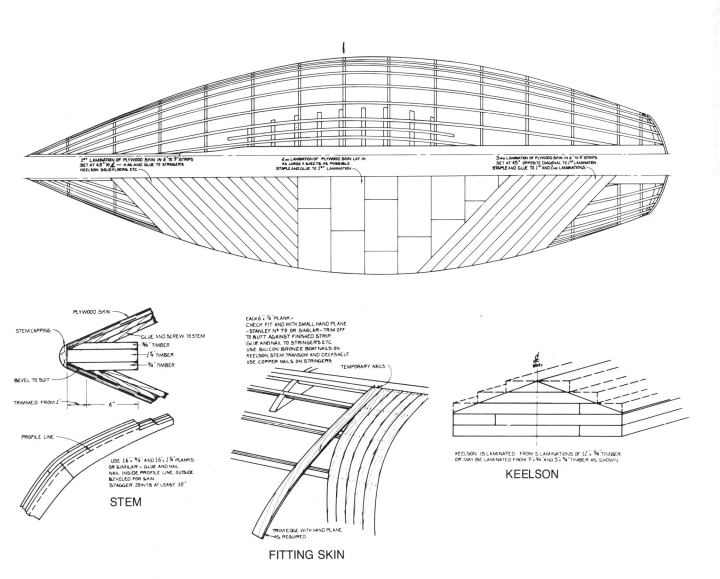

1ST LAMINATION OF PLYWOOD SKIN IN 6" TO 9" STRIPS
SET AT 45° TO ℄ — NAIL AND GLUE TO STRINGERS
KEELSON SOLID FLOORS ETC.

2ND LAMINATION OF PLYWOOD SKIN LAY IN
AS LARGE A SHEETS AS POSSIBLE
STAPLE AND GLUE TO 1ST LAMINATION

3RD LAMINATION OF PLYWOOD SKIN IN 6" TO 9" STRIPS
SET AT 45° OPPOSITE DIAGONAL TO 1ST LAMINATION
STAPLE AND GLUE TO 1ST AND 2ND LAMINATIONS

PLYWOOD SKIN

STEM CAPPING

GLUE AND SCREW TO STEM

¾" TIMBER
1¼" TIMBER
¾" TIMBER

BEVEL TO SUIT

TRIMMED FROM 2"

6"

PROFILE LINE

USE 16" x ¾" AND 16" x 1¼" PLANKS
OR SIMILAR - GLUE AND NAIL
NAIL INSIDE PROFILE LINE, OUTSIDE
BEVELED FOR SKIN
STAGGER JOINTS AT LEAST 10"

STEM

EACH 6" x ¼" PLANK -
CHECK FIT AND WITH SMALL HAND PLANE
- STANLEY N° 79 OR SIMILAR - TRIM OFF
TO BUTT AGAINST FINISHED STRIP
GLUE AND NAIL TO STRINGERS ETC.
USE SILICON BRONZE BOAT NAILS ON
KEELSON, STEM, TRANSOM AND DECKSHELF.
USE COPPER NAILS ON STRINGERS.

TEMPORARY NAILS

TRIM EDGE WITH HAND PLANE
AS REQUIRED

FITTING SKIN

℄
BOA

KEELSON IS LAMINATED FROM 5 LAMINATIONS OF 12" x ¾" TIMBER
OR MAY BE LAMINATED FROM 9" x ¾" AND 3" x ¾" TIMBER AS SHOWN

KEELSON

INSTALLING THE PLANKING

The next decision is how are you are going to install the hull skin. Generally speaking, your hull shell will be between 1/4" [6 mm] for say an eighteen foot boat, up to a thickness of two inches [50] for a sixty-foot vessel. We recommend for the smaller and lighter skinned hulls, an all timber veneer laminate . For say a 3/8" [9 MM] hull skin, three layers of 1/8" [3 mm] veneer would be ideal. Once the total thickness required is over say 5/8", [15 mm] you may consider a combination of strip planking and veneer. You could have an all strip planked hull, but we prefer at least one layer of veneer to finish of the exterior. Your plans should advise you as to the recommended hull skin for your boat. Always, we recommend one or more layers of fibreglass cloth set in epoxy as the final exterior finish.

If you are building an all veneer hull, you should use 1/8" [3 mm]or better still 3/16" [4 mm] plywood for the first layer. The veneer is usually too soft to bend evenly when not totally supported as often happens when laminating over stringers or battens. The plywood will bend much more evenly and provide a better base for the layers of veneer that make up the remainder of the hull skin. If you are building a chine plywood hull, your decision may rest between installing the planking in one or more layers. In some powerboat hulls, we recommend that you install the plywood planking in two or three or more layers, because often it would be virtually impossible to install the thicker plywood at one time.

ROUND BILGE HULLS

For round bilge hulls, the first layer will usually be installed in strips varying in width from 4" [100] to 18" [460]. The strips or panels will usually be installed at the 45 degree diagonal. The width of the strips will vary depending on the shape of the hull, tight bilges make for narrower strips, and will vary depending on which section of the hull the strip is being installed. Up near the bow will be the easiest area and the strips will be wider there. Only trial fitting on your hull will tell you how wide the strips should be, on the various areas of your hull.

No matter where you start the planking on your hull, make sure that you install both sides simultaneously, under no circumstances plank all one side before starting on the other, as you will end with a twisted hull if you do not heed this advice. For best results,

apply one strip on one side and then another on the other side working your way along both sides of the hull in this manner.

TRIMMING THE PANELS

You will find that each strip or panel has to be fitted next to its neighbour. It is not just a matter of cutting the sheets of plywood or veneer into strips and laying them side by side at a 45 degree angle. You will discover that as the panels are laid around the hull, they twist slightly and each new panel will not lay flush against the adjacent strip. Fortunately, it is a simple matter to spile off the material where the edges overlap the existing panel. The excess can be trimmed off with a small hand plane, or if the overlap is considerable, it can be removed using the band saw or similar.

Now reinstall the panel or strip on the hull. Make sure you get a good fit, because if you force the panels into place by pushing them sideways into positions where they will not want to lay, you will never achieve a smooth hull finish. Any forcing to make a fit, will result in a hull that will have a series of lumps and bumps that remain when you install the subsequent layers of veneer; the fit of the first layer is very important. The whole idea of using plywood for the first layer, is set up a smooth skin to receive the rest of the timber laminate. It is possible to use an all plywood lay up. Good quality, void free plywood is important if you plan to use plywood throughout.

Glue and nail the first layer to the stem, keelson and the deck stringer. If the intermediate stringers are to stay in the hull, then the panels can be nailed and glued to the stringers as well. If the stringers or battens do not stay with the hull, then you staple the panels to the stringers without glue, and use pads under the heads of the staples to facilitate the removal of the staples before installing the next layer. There is no need to edge glue the panels, however on subsequent layers the glue will seep through and create a bond between the edges.

TAPING INSIDE THE HULL

Before you start to install the second layer of veneer, you should tape inside, between the panels of the first layer. One inch [25] wide tape should do nicely. This taping will stop the glue seeping through the joins in the panels and running down the inside the hull.

Second layer of veneer is installed at 90° to first layer.

Almost completed ROBERTS 34 hull built in Brisbane, Australia.

When you have completed the installation of the first layer of the panels, the next step will depend on required number of layers for your hull. If the plans call for the installation of three layers, it is often possible to install the middle layer in quite large sections and you can install this layer any way the larger panels will fit. Make sure the larger panels lay neatly in place, without having to deform the panel or force down the edges. If you find that the larger panels will give you a problem, revert to diagonal strips as used for the first layer. If you apply the second layer in strips, then install it on the opposite diagonal to the first layer.

CHOICE OF ADHESIVE

We assume you are using epoxy adhesive between the laminations, however epoxy does have some disadvantages compared to some other adhesives. For instance some other glues including resorcinol, may not have the ultimate strength of epoxy resins, but are more forgiving when it comes to working in less than ideal conditions. To make the most of the qualities of the true Wood/Epoxy techniques, you should be working in an environmentally controlled area. Temperature is important as is the absence of high humidity. You will need to decide how your building site will measure up and choose your adhesives accordingly.

MARK STRINGER LOCATIONS

It is always wise to mark the positions of the stringers, deck stringer or shelf and keelson on each subsequent layer of veneer panels. This will give

you the location of the keelson and the stringers etc., as you are nailing the first layer in place. When installing the first layer and even when installing subsequent layers of veneer, it may be necessary to have a person inside the hull with a "dolly" to make sure you are getting a good tight fit as you nail or staple the veneer or plywood to the stringers, stem, deck shelf and keelson. Any bouncing or spring back as you nail or staple, will often prevent a good join. A person equipped with a "dolly" stationed inside the hull can do wonders in making sure all your fastenings are doing their jobs.

The marked stringer locations will give you the positions through which to staple or nail the second layer to the first. You may either nail the first layer to the keelson etc., or staple the first layer and nail through both the first and second layers, so getting more of the layers actually nailed to the important keelson, deck stringer and stringers if they remain with the hull. The areas between the stringers should be stapled together in a close pattern to make sure the glue can do its job. It is obvious that you will want a perfect bond between the various layers of veneer that make up the hull skin. A good pattern of staples will apply the correct pressure to ensure a good bond between the layers. It is recommended you employ a "dolly" wielding assistant.

SELECTING THE FASTENINGS

In the past we have considered two types of staples, one is the common galvanised wire type, the other could be stainless or silicon bronze. We have always recommended that you remove steel or galvanised staples and the stainless or silicon bronze staples could be left in the hull. Current thinking is that it is best to remove all staples so it is pointless using the more expensive variety.

Some builders laminate the final layer in a fore and aft direction. Unless you are going to finish the hull clear, I don't think it matters which way you install the various layers, if you have a good bond between the various veneers. A balanced lay up is essential and by balanced, I mean all the layers do not run in the same direction. The plans you are using may give you the exact directions as to the procedure and sequence for applying the hull skin, then follow your plans.

FAIRING AND FINISHING THE HULL

Once the hull has been completely laminated, then the next job will be to fair off the stem and fit a trim strip. Next dress off the bottom of the keelson to accept the laminated timber keel and the skeg. Raw end grain of the plywood should always be covered by a timber facing, at the stem, the trim strip will take care of that requirement. In other areas of your boat you should always work towards covering the end grain especially in the case of plywood or veneer. The timber keel can be laminated in position and can be reinforced with copper bolts.

Next give your laminated hull a good check over and dress off any unfair areas using similar techniques to those used to finish a fibreglass hull. We recommend you give the hull, keel and the skeg a sheathing of fibreglass set in epoxy resin. My opinion is that one layer of 1 1/2 oz [450 g/sm] mat followed by one layer of 10 oz [300 g/sm] cloth

and surfacing tissue makes a very strong and durable protective outer layer for your moulded plywood or veneer hull. You can benefit by reading the chapters on finishing a fibreglass hull.

TURNING THE HULL.

Next job will be to turn your hull upright, please read the chapter covering the subject of turning over fibreglass hulls. Once the hull is upright and levelled on all planes, you are ready to go on with the fitting out of the interior and the installation of the decks and superstructure.

SOLID FLOORS

One point you may want to consider early in the construction programme, it may be easier to fit the solid floors during the framing up of the hull, rather laminate them in place later. Our plans have used both methods and each approach has its advantages. Again your plans should guide you as to the best sequence for your particular design.

It is usually preferred in chine type hulls, to attach the floors to the frames in such a way they can be faired off with the stringers and the rest of the framing and then the hull skin can be laminated directly on to the floors. On round bilge hulls involving a "bolt on keel", then it may be best to laminate leaf spring type floors into the hull after turning the hull upright.

EPOXY SATURATION

If you are using the Wood/Epoxy technique, it is necessary that every part of the boat that is exposed to the air, is saturated with the epoxy resin. You will need to plan for this saturation at every stage of the building programme. Make sure that the application of the resin is undertaken before you close off an area with interior joinery and make it difficult if not impossible to complete a proper job of saturating the timber.

TRADITIONAL AND NOT SO TRADITIONAL STRIP PLANKING

Before leaving the subject of building your hull we must give some consideration to the traditional strip planking technique. In some parts of the world where traditional boatbuilding methods are still widely practised it may be worth considering this method. I understand that this boatbuilding

Roberts 43 built in Brazil using wood epoxy techniques as described in this book

technique evolved in some areas of the USA because of the availability of certain small sizes of timber off-cuts. At the time when this method was widely used, not only in the USA but in other parts of the world, the epoxy and other superior adhesives were not available.

If you are thinking of using traditional timber boatbuilding techniques, then we think, this is the pick of those methods. Strip planking is easy to execute and it is not necessary to secure the timber in single long lengths. The basis of strip planking is timber that is cut to 3/4" to 1 1/4" [20 to 30] thickness and can either be square in section or a little deeper for example 3/4" thick x 1 1/4" deep [20 x 30]. The planks are "edge glued" one on top of the other. Traditionally, strip plank boats are built upright, however I have seen this type of hull built upside down. There was at least one builder who preferred to build his hulls inside a set of female mould frames.

FRAMING

You will require temporary framing, consisting of sawn frames similar to those used for any mould. It is usual to rebate the stem and the keel and the planks let into this traditional boatbuilders rebate, which provides a place for the hull planking to join the keel and stem. Sometimes when the hull is built upside down, the method is to install the strip planking up to the keelson and a laminated keel is fitted in the manner described earlier in this chapter.

The planks are fitted one on top of the other and are edge nailed and glued one to the other. This method of construction provides a strong hull that needs the minimum of interior framing. The planking timber may be dressed with square edges or may be machined to a concave section on the top and convex on the bottom. This machining of the planks, allows them to lay one on top of the other and to follow the curve of the hull frames, with a minimum of dressing of each plank.

The traditional method is to dress off the top of each plank after it has been installed to provide a surface square off the frame on which to lay the next plank. Either method is satisfactory, although as the planking will usually not go on up the hull in an even manner, it will be necessary to spile in extra planks in certain areas. Some advantages of the specially milled timber are lost when you have to spile in, or fit short lengths to even up the progress

Stem for ROBERTS 44 built in Turkey.

Note the size of keel timber being shaped for ROBERTS 44.

of the planking.

KEELS ON WOODEN BOATS

For sailboat builders, there is one very important disadvantage common to strip plank and other timber methods including plywood is; you will need aseparate keel casting of either lead or cast iron as ballast. I have seen some attempts to build timber hulls, where the ballast was incorporated in an envelope strip plank keel. This was the exception rather than the rule and does not seem a popular solution with either designers or builders of timber boats.

If you are building a strip plank hull following the traditional techniques, you will set up your ballast keel and the timber keel and work upright from there. The mould frames are set in place with the stem and transom. The planking starts at the keel with the first plank let into the rabbet and the remainder of the planking installed as described above.

PLANKING THE HULL

The first plank is called the garboard and this plank may need to be somewhat wider that the rest of the strip planks. As the garboard plank sets the stage for the rest of the planking, it is best if it is wide enough to be shaped on the bottom and to have a level top face and this starts the strip planking off level. As the strip planking proceeds up to the bilge area, it will often be necessary to taper the planks or lay in a

few stealers in the centre of the planking. You would finish with the planking too dished in a fore and aft direction by the time it reached the deck level. The idea is to reach the deck level with one long continuous plank, rather than a series of short ends of planking towards the bow and stern of the hull.

The methods you use to ensure that the planking is level when it reaches the deck, will depend on the design you are building. In general, the beamier the design, the more stealers you will need to ensure a neat and efficient planking job.

STOP-WATERS

Make sure you install adequate stop-waters where the timber joins in the keel and stem cross the rabbet line and this will avoid troublesome leaks at a later stage. If you have not had experience using traditional boatbuilding methods, it is important you seek out this knowledge before you start building a boat using these methods. There are several

Planking proceeds from sheer upwards on ROBERTS 22 hull.

excellent books available that cover the subject of traditional timber boatbuilding in detail. Check out your local library first.

Before you start the planking you will have decided whether you are going to be using square edge planking or the convex, concave variety. As mentioned earlier, the planks can have a greater depth than thickness. It is a fact that the planks bend into place better if they are rectangular in section rather than square. Usually the depth is best at 1.5 times the thickness.

FASTENINGS

Regarding the choice of nails and glue used to fasten the planks one on top of the other, as with other forms of timber boatbuilding you have the same choices as outlined in the earlier parts of this chapter. There are two basic choices for the adhesive, epoxy or resorcinol. As for the nails, you can use either galvanised steel or silicon bronze. The galvanised variety are much cheaper and they are buried in the timber. Their main function is to hold the timber together until the glue is set so it may be wasteful to pay the considerably extra cost for silicon bronze nails for this job. As with many decisions you must make during the building of your boat, the depth of your pocket will have a bearing on your final choice.

INTERIOR FRAMING

Once the hull has been completely planked and cleaned off, then the temporary framework may be removed and any laminated frames that are specified in the plans, can be installed. Generally there are laminated frames where the bulkheads are to be attached to the hull and in some larger designs, a series of laminated frames may be specified throughout the hull. Sometimes the setting up, frames or formers, are laminated frames that remain with the hull. This system of permanent frames is usually reserved for boats of over fifty feet [15 metres].

Any intermediate floors not previously installed as part of the setting up process, are now laminated in place. The bulkheads may be installed and it is often best to leave them standing up square well above the sheer so that the plywood can be marked out with the side deck width, cabin lay-in and cabin top camber. The interior may be roughed out at this stage and any large items such as engine, tanks and large panels of plywood required for the interior, should be in the hull before you start work on the decks and superstructure.

The cabin sole may now be installed, keeping in mind you will need access to the area of the keel bolts and in any case, it is always prudent to have removable sole panels, certainly on the centre line and anywhere else where the removable panels are practicable.

Steel box keel being fabricated for ROBERTS TRAILER/ SAILER 24. Full size patterns give shapes for keel webs.

Almost completed keel.

ROBERTS TRAILER/SAILER 24 hull built with molded plywood by Carl Alexander.

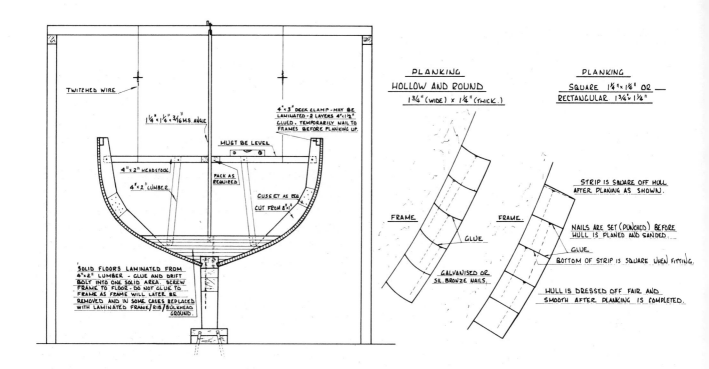

PLANKING
HOLLOW AND ROUND
1¾" (WIDE) x 1¼" (THICK.)

PLANKING
SQUARE 1¼" x 1⅛" OR
RECTANGULAR 1¾" x 1⅛"

STRIP IS SQUARE OFF HULL AFTER PLANING AS SHOWN.

NAILS ARE SET (PUNCHED) BEFORE HULL IS PLANED AND SANDED.

BOTTOM OF STRIP IS SQUARE WHEN FITTING.

HULL IS DRESSED OFF FAIR AND SMOOTH AFTER PLANKING IS COMPLETED.

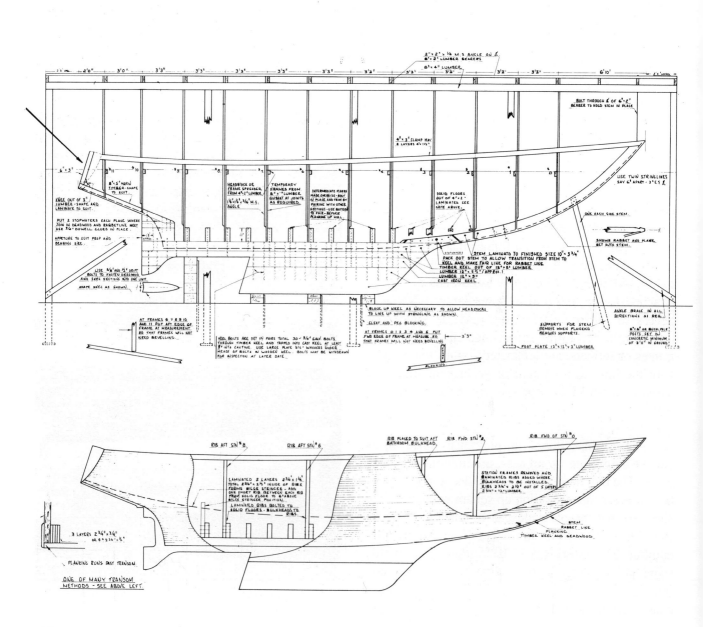

CHAPTER SIXTEEN
WOOD - DECKS AND SUPERSTRUCTURE

If you have built your hull from a technique involving timber, you will most likely want to build your decks and superstructure using timber and plywood. Your first job will be to equip yourself with a camber pattern for the decks and another for the cabin top. If you are working with full size patterns, your plans may show these items full size. These master camber patterns will serve in many areas of the construction from this point onwards. Make a careful copy of your camber patterns. If you cut your patterns from sturdy plywood or wide boards, you can have both male and female patterns and this can be handy at times. You will be using the patterns to transfer the cambers on to many areas of the decks and superstructure.

BULKHEADS

You should have left your bulkheads stand up square above the hull sheerline. Now is the time to mark out the width of the side decks, mark the camber right across the boat, this way you will get an even camber. Later you will mark the amount of the cabin side lay-in, and the height and camber of the cabin.

All these things are marked out on the appropriate bulkheads. Now is a good time to check the headroom as designed. Do not be tempted to increase the headroom unduly. An inch or two [25 to 50] of extra headroom may be acceptable, however before you increase the headroom, check if it is possible to lower the sole. Never increase the headroom on any boat without first consulting the designer. You may adversely effect the stability of your boat if you make changes on your own volition.

Anyhow, if you require the headroom to be increased by any amount over 3" [75], it must be done in increments, say partly by lowering the sole, partly by raising the freeboard of the hull and partly by increasing the height of the cabin sides. As I have already stated, it is a job for the designer to consider all aspects of changing any design especially when the changes affect the stability of the boat.

Next mark out the cabin top camber and the lay-in of the cabin sides and you now have a sectional view of the decks and cabin structure. The cabin top camber is usually larger than the camber used for the decks. Another hint, too much camber is more harmful than too little. Do not be tempted to increase the camber to get extra headroom, you may not be able to work on the decks or cabin top in any sort of a seaway without the possibility of sliding overboard.

Laminated transverse cabin top beams fitted to ROBERTS 29.

For timber/plywood – glass deck install beams on edge as shown. Follow curve of sheer.

CAMBER

For decks a camber of 3% to 5% of the beam is usual, I like to keep close to 3% for decks and for cabin tops 5% of the width of the cabin top is the maximum we recommend. Cambers have reduced in recent years as more modern methods and materials and higher freeboard makes it unnecessary to have the larger cambers that were fashionable in the past. For power boats fitted with a flybridge, the cabin top should have a maximum camber of 3%.

DECK BEAMS

At this time you will need to decide if you are going to use transverse or longitudinal deck beams. In the days of wooden boats, all deck beams had to be installed transversely because the deck planking ran fore and aft. Now we have plywood deck planking, where the "planking" runs in all directions. You may now decide to install longitudinal deck beams. You plans should clearly show whether transverse or longitudinal deck beams are required. You may wish to install a combination of longitudinal and transverse beams. While as you are installing the beams you will frame up for the cockpit, coamings and install the framing for the hatch openings.

If you are planning a laid timber deck on top of the plywood sub-deck, then you should install transverse timber deck beams so that you will able to through fasten the timber deck planks if you wish.

One method of laying deck beams for timber, plywood-glass deck.

Even if you use longitudinal beams and later decide to install a laid deck, you have the option of using the diagonal or herringbone pattern for your laid deck. If you are planning a plywood deck and/or timber deck, you will have installed a timber deck shelf.

Here are a few useful pointers. Most hulls have some sheer, meaning they are lower in the middle than the ends. If you take your camber pattern and mark out all the bulkheads, lining up the pattern centre line with the centre line of the hull, then install a longitudinal beam, notching it into each bulkhead the same amount, this beam will then take

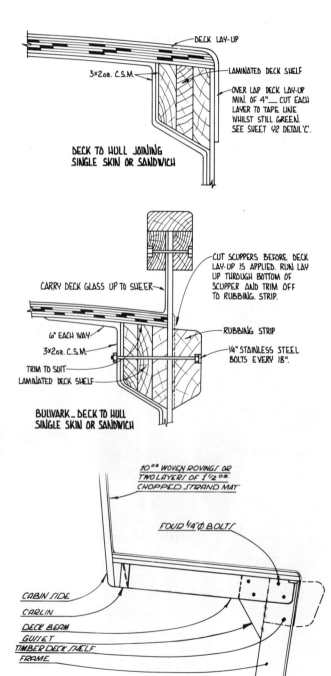

Joining steel hull to plywood deck.

Combination of longitudinal and transverse deck beams in ROBERTS 36 built by Rhea Adams of Florida.

up the proper sheer in all parts of the hull. Provided you always use the same master deck pattern for the decks and your cabin top master pattern for the cabin tops, the sheers and cambers will all work out without giving your boat any strange appearance when viewed from any angle.

You can attach a transverse beam to each bulkhead, both at the deck line and cabin top, this applies no matter if your main deck framing is transverse or longitudinal beams. There is always a transverse beam at each bulkhead, which thickens up the

bulkheads. Anyhow you will need some longitudinal beams, one for the cabin top in way of the mast step and one in the fore deck, known as the king plank, in way of the positioning of the mooring bits, anchor winch or fore-deck cleat. Fore and aft king planks can be wider and shallower and can be checked into the transverse beams.

In you are installing transverse beams, these can either be sawn or laminated. A typical beam may be 1 3/4" wide by say 2 3/4" [45 x 70] deep. This beam can be made up of laminations of 1 3/4" wide

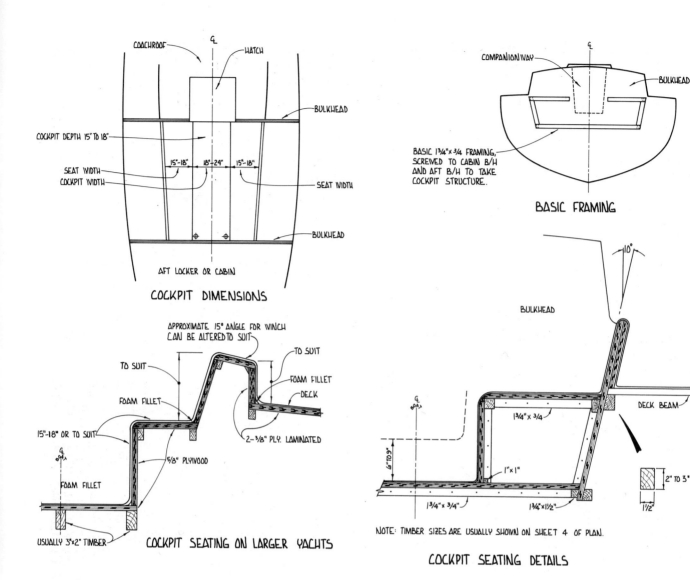

COCKPIT DIMENSIONS

BASIC FRAMING

COCKPIT SEATING ON LARGER YACHTS

NOTE: TIMBER SIZES ARE USUALLY SHOWN ON SHEET 4 OF PLAN.

COCKPIT SEATING DETAILS

by 1/2" [45 x 12] with one thicker layer to made up the odd amount. The layers of timber are set up in a jig made to the same camber as the master pattern. Usually laminated beams will spring back a small amount so you may want to make the camber slightly larger, if you do this, make the beams before you cut the bulkheads and use one of the sprung beams to make a new master deck camber pattern. In any case, builders often make up the beams well in advance, these beams are laminated one every week and set aside until needed. The longer you can leave the beams in the jig, the less spring back you can expect.

The camber pattern is part of a large circle. Now, say you have a beam that is five feet [1.52 m] long and you need a shorter beam, always cut the shorter beam from the centre of the longer one. The reason for this is when the beams spring back they tend to flatten out at the ends, so always take sections of beam from the centre as you want your camber to remain constant for the full length of the boat. If you

are using longitudinal beams, make sure they are set into the bulkheads and any transverse bulkhead top beams, so they are at right angles to the surface of the beam. This will avoid you having to dress off the top of the longitudinal beam to accept the plywood decking.

Use plenty of rounded corners on the cabin structure. You can work solid timber posts into the corners. You will need to cover all end grain of the plywood and it is not a good idea to have any timber end grain exposed to the elements. As mentioned in previous chapters, the bevel can be an attractive alternative to the round when it is used on cabin structures, coamings and similar areas.

Once you have installed all the framing for the deck, check it over and dress off any unfair areas. Make use of a batten laid diagonally across the surface of the deck framing, to make sure you have no lumps or hollows, which will give you problems when you start to install the plywood deck planking. A final reminder, I trust by now you have already installed all of the larger items in the hull.

PLYWOOD DECK PLANKING

When you are satisfied the framework for your deck is complete and faired, you can now go on to install the plywood deck planking. You will already have decided, how many laminations of plywood will be needed to make up the total thickness required. If your boat is under thirty feet [9 metres], then two layers of 1/4" [2 x 6 mm] plywood should do the job. A 3/4" [20 mm] deck can be three layers of 1/4" [3 x 6] and so forth. The first layer is nailed and glued to the deck framing and the second and subsequent layers are glued and stapled to the first. If you have air equipment, an air stapler can be a wonderful tool to apply the layers of plywood deck planking, which are to be stapled and glued to the first layer.

Do not over nail the first layer to the beams. Some builders have the mistaken idea that more is always better, not so. Remember the nails are only effective until after the glue has cured. In the case of the staples, these are removed after the glue has cured and before subsequent layers of plywood are installed and of course removed from the last layer. You can imagine the number of nails your beams would be asked to receive if you installed closely spaced nails in all the layers of the plywood deck. Your plans may even specify a nailing pattern, so many nails to the inch and so forth, if so, follow the recommendations as outlined by the designer of your boat.

COMPLETING DECKS AND SUPERSTRUCTURE

You will need to cover the plywood decks as they cannot be left unprotected and simply painting them would not offer sufficient protection, even if you are using the Wood/Epoxy techniques. You have some choices including the traditional method of covering the decks with painted canvas. I once helped an experienced boatbuilder to cover his decks with canvas and I must say I would not like to employ this method today, when there are more long lasting and easier treatments available.

LAID DECKS

A laid deck can be structural or decorative. For a laid deck to be considered as contributing to the

View of laid deck over ply/glass as fitted on ROBERTS NORFOLK 43.

Pitch or synthetic rubber caulk may be used between deck planks. Hatches are planked to match deck.

structural strength of the vessel, the planking would need to be at least 3/4" [20] thickness and the planks should be set in mastic and screwed to the beams underneath. The screws heads are at least 1/4" [6] below the surface of the planking and protected with timber plugs. If you use a structurally

147

Overall photo of laid deck on ROBERTS 43.

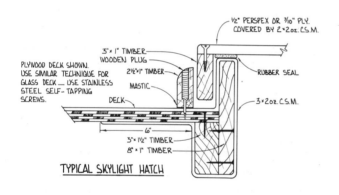

½" PERSPEX OR ⅜" PLY.
COVERED BY 2×2oz. C.S.M.

3"×1" TIMBER
WOODEN PLUG
2½"×1" TIMBER
MASTIC

RUBBER SEAL

PLYWOOD DECK SHOWN.
USE SIMILAR TECHNIQUE FOR
GLASS DECK — USE STAINLESS
STEEL SELF-TAPPING
SCREWS.

DECK

3×2oz. C.S.M.

6"

3"×1½" TIMBER
8"×1" TIMBER

TYPICAL SKYLIGHT HATCH

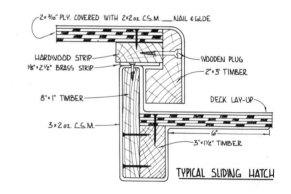

2×⅜" PLY. COVERED WITH 2×2oz. C.S.M. — NAIL & GLUE

HARDWOOD STRIP
⅛"×2½" BRASS STRIP

WOODEN PLUG
2"×3" TIMBER

8"×1" TIMBER

DECK LAY-UP

3×2oz. C.S.M.

6"

3"×1½" TIMBER

TYPICAL SLIDING HATCH

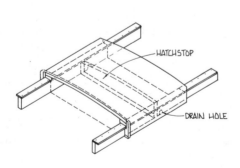

HATCH STOP

DRAIN HOLE

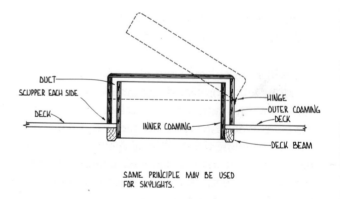

DUCT
SCUPPER EACH SIDE

DECK

INNER COAMING

HINGE
OUTER COAMING
DECK

DECK BEAM

SAME PRINCIPLE MAY BE USED
FOR SKYLIGHTS.

LEAK PROOF HATCH

effective laid deck, you may reduce the plywood deck to compensate for the strength of the laid deck. You would also want to reduce the weight.

If you are intending to install a laid deck, it will need

to look like a traditional installation, no matter if it is only intended as a decorative deck with the non-skid bonus that this type of deck can offer. Generally the planks are 1 3/4" wide and the thickness will vary as described elsewhere. The king plank, which is the plank that runs up the centre line of the fore-deck and the covering board, which runs around the outer edge of the deck, should all have a width of two to two and one half times the width of the regular deck planking. A margin plank will be fitted to the areas around the cabin side, deck intersection and the area around each hatch.

Before you decide to tackle the installation of a laid deck, be advised that it is a very labour intensive operation, and either you or your hired labour will take several days to install even a modest sized laid deck.

The planking may be laid one of several ways, fore and aft parallel to the centre line, or may follow the curve of the sheer, or may be divided between the first two alternatives, or may be installed diagonally at a forty-five degree angle. Anyhow, the ends of the planks will need to be nibbed either into the king plank, the fore end of the covering board or elsewhere depending on your chosen lay out for the planking. Usually the edges of the planks are rebated out say 1/8" to 1/4" [3 to 6 mm] to twenty -five percent of their depth, the planks are then set close together, set in silicone rubber such as Dow Chemical Silastic and the top rebates filled with either coloured epoxy or silicone rubber.

All laid decks must be fastened through to the deck beams. For traditional laid decks, use silicon bronze screws with the heads set below the surface, so you can install a timber plug to hide the screw. Special tools are available for cutting these plugs. I have seen laid decks fastened with silicon bronze nails with a washer slipped under the head. The heads were set below the surface as for screw-fastened decks, and timber plugged.

Usually glued, a non structural laid timber deck can be as light as 1/4" thickness; glued to the plywood deck with epoxy resin. A thickened black epoxy putty is used between the beams to resemble traditional laid deck planking. A thorough sanding job gives the total decorative laid deck an attractive appearance. When installing a laid deck, you will need to select the timber carefully, we prefer teak. Avoid the temptation to finish the deck bright, which is either varnished or coated with a shiny epoxy or other finish. It may seem obvious that a deck should not be shiny and in turn slippery, however I have seen decks finished in this manner.

SHEATHING PLYWOOD DECKS AND SUPERSTRUCTURE

A well proven method of protecting your plywood decks and superstructure is to sheath them with fibreglass cloth set in epoxy resin. Polyester resins have been used for sheathing but they have proved to be unreliable. Sheathing installed using polyester resins, will often lift and part company with the plywood after a few years, or in extreme cases after a few months.

When we are speaking of the fibreglass sheathing of timber or plywood decks and superstructure, we always recommend epoxy resins for this purpose. The best fibreglass sheathing is one layer of 1 1/2 oz [450 G/sm] followed by one layer of 10 oz [300 G/sm] fibreglass cloth.

When preparing to sheath the plywood decks and superstructure, you should fill all the nail and staple holes and any other blemishes. All holes should be filled flush with the face of the plywood. All corners must be rounded to accept the fibreglass mat. Use epoxy putty to create a concave radius to allow the fibreglass sheathing to smoothly progress from cabin sides to decks, coamings to decks and pilot house fronts on to cabin-top and around hatch coamings.

After you are satisfied the decks and superstructure are ready to receive the fibreglass sheathing, give the whole area a coat of epoxy resin and allow this resin to cure to a stage where you are satisfied that the moisture content of the plywood has not inhibited the bond between the plywood and the resin.

Any excessive moisture content in the plywood will prevent you achieving a lasting bond between the fibreglass and the plywood decks and superstructure. Naturally you will have chosen a dry day when there is low humidity, to undertake the sheathing of your decks. If satisfied you are going to achieve a good bond, then go on to install the fibreglass sheathing using normal fibreglass installation techniques.

Even if you plan to install a laid fibreglass deck over the plywood, it may be advisable to install at least one layer of fibreglass between the plywood and the laid timber deck. Fibreglass will form an excellent sealer for the cabin sides and other areas where you would not be installing the laid decking. If you follow our advice on the above matters, you should have a totally waterproof deck that will last indefinitely.

If the fibreglass is to be the final deck surface, then you will need to incorporate a non-skid element into the fibreglass. This may be done in any one of several ways, including sprinkling clean, dry fine sand into the final resin coats. Now is a good time to read the chapters on finishing fibreglass.

Sheet plywood can be used extensively throughout the building program. Bulkheads, cabin soles, interior joinery, and the decks are often built from sheet plywood, no matter which material is chosen for the hull structure. Note the camber pattern lying on the framed cabin top.

CHAPTER SEVENTEEN
INTERIOR JOINERY

Once you have installed the bulkheads and the sole, the techniques used to fit out the interior of a steel, fibreglass or timber boat, are all very similar. Always, a considerable amount of the joinery is attached to the bulkheads and the sole. Where the joinery is attached to the hull, you must make special provision for this attachment, depending on the hull material.

SUGGESTED JOINERY DIMENSIONS

The measurements for the human frame have gradually changed over the past many years with the population generally growing taller as the years pass. When I first started to build and later design boats, a berth with an overall length of 6'-2" [1.88 metres] was considered adequate. Today, the same berth would be expected to measure around 6'-6" [1.98 metres]. Here are a few measurements that I would consider relevant today.

Single berths should be 6'-6" [1,98 m] or minimum of 6'-4" [1.93 m] long and 2'-6" [7620 mm] wide.

The width may be narrower at the extreme head and foot, the main width requirement is at the shoulders. Double berths should be 4'-6" [1.37 metres] wide although two friends can manage with 4'-3" [1.29 Metres]. Most of you will be familiar with the various measurements of Queen and King size beds and today I am often called upon to include these large size berths, especially when preparing plans for power cruisers. Queen size berths are usually 5'-0" [1.52 metres] wide and 6'-6" [1.98 m] long. The space between upper and lower berths should be 21" [533], seats should be 18" [457] wide and between 12" and 18" [305 and 457] from the sole. The higher the seat the less foot room is required. Seats require 3'-6" [1.07 m] headroom and 24" [610] frontage for comfort. If seats face each other then 30" [762] foot room, although this is sometimes difficult to obtain in small boats. More time is spent sitting than standing so seating comfort requires a fair amount of consideration.

Clothes lockers should be at least 16" [406] in width or depth with a height of 40" [1.016 m]. Ice

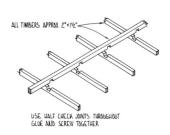

ALL TIMBERS APPROX. 2"×1½"

USE HALF CHECK JOINTS THROUGHOUT
GLUE AND SCREW TOGETHER

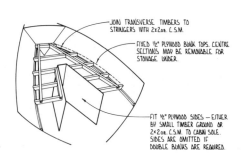

JOIN TRANSVERSE TIMBERS TO
STRINGERS WITH 2×2 oz. C.S.M.

FIXED ½" PLYWOOD BUNK TOPS. CENTRE
SECTIONS MAY BE REMOVABLE FOR
STOWAGE UNDER.

FIT ½" PLYWOOD SIDES — EITHER
BY SMALL TIMBER GROUND OR
2×2 oz. C.S.M. TO CABIN SOLE.
SIDES ARE OMITTED IF
DOUBLE BUNKS ARE REQUIRED.

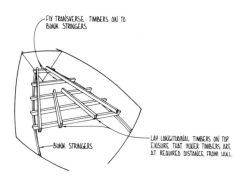

FIX TRANSVERSE TIMBERS ON TO
BUNK STRINGERS

BUNK STRINGERS

LAY LONGITUDINAL TIMBERS ON TOP.
ENSURE THAT INNER TIMBERS ARE
AT REQUIRED DISTANCE FROM HULL.

NOTE
INTERIOR JOINERY AND FURNITURE IS
BEST BUILT WITH ⅜" AND ½" PLYWOOD.
USE FANCY FACED PLYWOOD WHERE
VARNISHED OR CLEAR FINISH IS DESIRED.
SOLID TIMBER TRIM CAN BE USED AS RE-
QUIRED. IF POSSIBLE BOND FURNITURE
AND JOINERY TO HULL STRUCTURE.
SCREW AND GLUE TO BULKHEADS ETC.

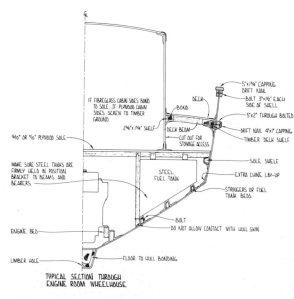

TYPICAL SECTION THROUGH
ENGINE ROOM WHEELHOUSE

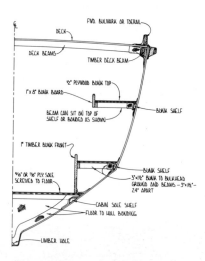

TYPICAL SECTION THROUGH A CABIN

boxes should be as large as the space available permits and have a minimum lining of 3" [75] of insulation. A well-built ice box is a creditable alternative to a freezer. The minimum size for a sink is 10" x 10" x 6", but larger is preferable. The sink should have at least 15" clear space above. Deep sinks are to be preferred especially in a sailboat as the heeling can considerably reduce the working depth. If you are going to be sailing with your female mate, please ask her advice about laying out the galley. The standard height for tables is 28" [711] above the sole or 12" [305] above the top of the seats. 24" x 18" [610 x 457] of table space is required for each person.

Galley work benches and sinks should be at least 15" to 18" [380 to 457] wide and 36" [914] above the sole. Drawers should be no more than 9" [228] deep and the maximum dimensions should not be more than 30" x 20" x 9" [762 x 508 x 228]. If the

drawers are narrow, say 8" [203] then the depth may be increased to say 15" [380]. You can see the object is to not make drawers so big, which they can be made to hold too heavy a load, which may take charge in a seaway. Make sure you include safety catches or special slide arrangements, so the drawers stay closed in rough weather. The maximum pitch for ladders should not exceed 60 degrees, and long ladders should have less pitch than short ones. Steps should rise 7" to 9" [178 to 228] per step and each step or tread should be at least 7" to 10" [178 to 225] deep. Hatches should be a minimum of 18" x 18" for ventilation but should be more so they can be used in an emergency. All the heights given, assume you have standing headroom in your cabin.

SAVING CASH

Try and think of ways you can save money on your fitting out programme. For instance, the mould from

Dinette arrangement in pleasureboat version of ROBERTS TRAWLER 48. – Builder Ken Mills.

King size double berth in owner's suite of ROBERTS TRAWLER 48.

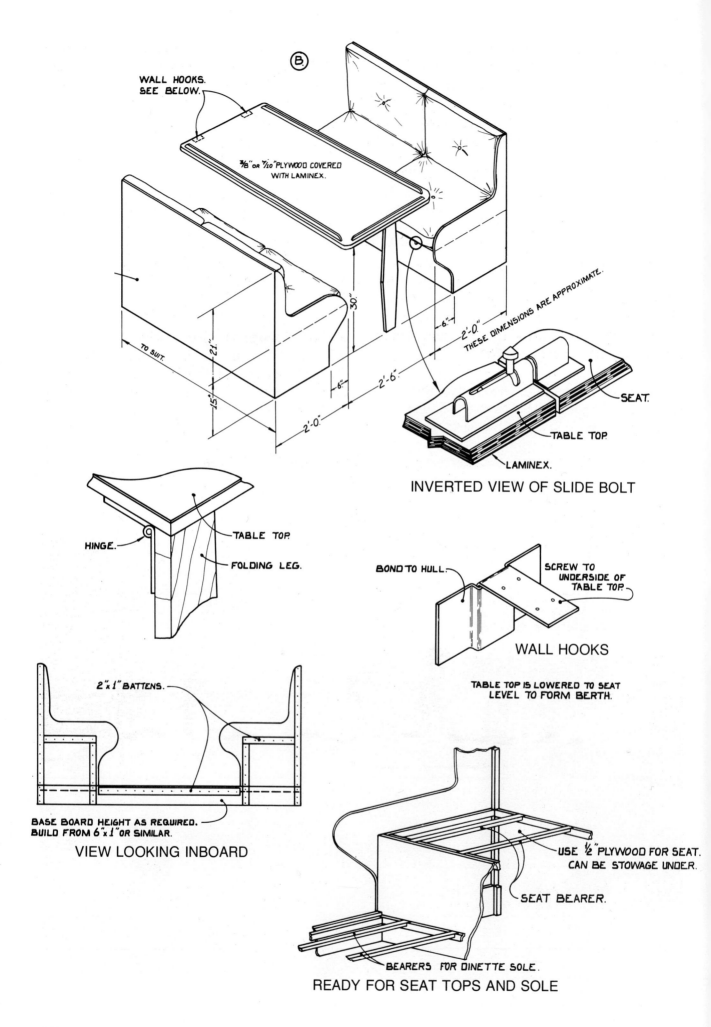

(B)

WALL HOOKS.
SEE BELOW.

³/₈" OR ⁷/₁₀" PLYWOOD COVERED
WITH LAMINEX.

TO SUIT.

30"

21"

15"

6"

6"

2'-0"

2'-6"

2'-0"

THESE DIMENSIONS ARE APPROXIMATE.

SEAT.

TABLE TOP.

LAMINEX.

INVERTED VIEW OF SLIDE BOLT

HINGE.

TABLE TOP.

FOLDING LEG.

BOND TO HULL.

SCREW TO
UNDERSIDE OF
TABLE TOP.

WALL HOOKS

TABLE TOP IS LOWERED TO SEAT
LEVEL TO FORM BERTH.

2"x1" BATTENS.

BASE BOARD HEIGHT AS REQUIRED.
BUILD FROM 6"x1" OR SIMILAR.

VIEW LOOKING INBOARD

USE ½" PLYWOOD FOR SEAT.
CAN BE STOWAGE UNDER.

SEAT BEARER.

BEARERS FOR DINETTE SOLE.

READY FOR SEAT TOPS AND SOLE

154

your fibreglass hull should supply some timber that can be re sawn to the dimensions you need for framing up interior joinery. If you plan ahead, you can use certain size timbers for the mould and setting up, that can be either re sawn or used as they are for another purpose at a later stage.

I understand Henry Ford had the batteries delivered in wooden boxes that were specified, so the timber would exactly match the dimensions needed to make the T model floor boards. Tongue and groove flooring can be a very inexpensive and rewarding fitting out timber. Second hand timber can also be very useful. In my own early days of boatbuilding, we used to build all the fibreglass male moulds out of reclaimed house timber. Some recycled timber is much better quality than you could possibly find as new stock in your local timber yard.

For the construction of the saloon table, we would recommend the use of two sets of stainless steel or aluminum tubes sized so one fits inside the other. The larger tube has a thumb screw fitted to position the height of the table as required. Alternatively the table can be hung from a bulkhead leaving the sole

space clear. With a reasonable amount of planning, a table of this type can yield as much useful space as a fixed table.

UPHOLSTERY

You can make at home the bunk and settee cushions; with the use of a household sewing machine, or they can be purchased from your local tent or bedding supplier. An upholsterer can upholster the dinette and settees directly to the plywood bases, however this sleek job will come at a much higher cost.

LINING MATERIALS

It is more difficult to fit out the interior, if you intend all the hull surfaces to be on display. A wide variety of lining materials are used to cover the basic fibreglass or steel hull. Quite often a wooden hull is deliberately left on display with dramatic effect. Lining materials can include vinyl, foam backed carpet or heavy cloth. Cork tiles give a dated appearance and are not my choice ;you may use mirror tiles if they are in the right place. I have seen ceramic tiles used in galley and stove areas,

Interior of ROBERTS MAURITIUS 43, "Valerie Ann III" built by Ken and Val Johnson of Vancouver.

especially in traditional boats. Depending on what finish you use, you can run all your wiring and plumbing behind the lining.

Traditional boats are often fitted with a batten interior lining. The battens, usually of light coloured timber, are 1" x 1/2" [25 x 12] and finished as a D shape on the top. Often called "ceiling,"space these battens about 25% of their width apart. This allows for ventilation behind the lining, a most important requirement in wooden boats and a recommended feature in all craft.

Around the edge of the lining, trim strips or quad or other cover strips can be used to hide any joints and in fact the cover strips can be a feature in themselves. A vinyl, Laminex or Formica deck-head with teak cover strips is most attractive and relatively easy to fit. If you use a Laminex type material, this should be first glued on to thin plywood.

If you have the financial resources, you may wish to specify a truly professional lining material like the vinyl foam "Somyvl". This material is made from expanded PVC and comes with an inlaid or printed pattern. This type of material is completely flexible and has a closed cell structure, particular suitable for lining the interiors of boats. These specialised lining materials fit easily around corners and projections and can be bonded to almost any surface.

Section of head in ROBERTS 43. Note toilet built up and outboard makes space available for shower in front of toilet. Folding footrest makes the arrangement practical.

It is usual to leave the lining installation until the boat is almost completed. This allows you to install at last minute, plumbing and electrical wiring without disturbing your finishing materials.

READY MADE JOINERY

You may consider the use of ready made interior joinery, such as pin rails, shelves, locker doors, drawer fronts, handrails, special timber mouldings, etc., which can be purchased ready made, from teak or similar high quality timber. These are not cheap, but will give your boat a professional finish, which may pay handsome dividends when you sell the boat at some future date.

You may decide to make some patterns and have special bronze or other fittings cast at the local foundry. You can save huge amounts of money if you plan and are prepared to do the finishing yourself. It is permissible to use brass fittings for interior cabinet handles, ring pulls and similar, but

Interior of aft cabin on ROBERTS 43. Note adequate head-room between berth and cabin top.

never use brass outside of the interior. Bronze is the requirement for cast fittings that are to be exposed to the elements.

Unfortunately space restrictions do not allow me to cover the fitting out with the amount of detail that the subject requires. At a later stage I hope to devote an entire book to the subject, until then, you can find several alternate publications that will be of great assistance in this area.

Finally, it is a mistake to start using your boat before the fitting out is complete. It is almost impossible to use a boat and make a good job of fitting out the interior simultaneously. If you must succumb to the temptation, then make sure you fit-out one area completely before starting on another. Take your time with the fitting out process, you will never regret it.

OTHER CONSIDERATIONS

During the fitting out stage, there will be many things to consider, such as fire fighting equipment, drainage of bilge water to collection points via limber holes, bilge pumping system, proper ventilation, safe electrical installation etc. Many of these items are subjects of complete books in their own right and so are too complex to be covered here. Read everything on the subject that you can get your hands on.

Interior of Robert 43 built by Gene and Seeth Trimpert

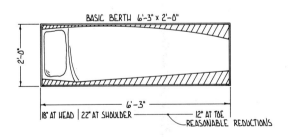

BASIC BERTH 6'-3" x 2'-0"

2'-0"

6'-3"
18" AT HEAD | 22" AT SHOULDER — 12" AT TOE
REASONABLE REDUCTIONS

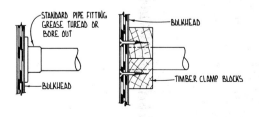

STANDARD PIPE FITTING GREASE THREAD OR BORE OUT

BULKHEAD

BULKHEAD

TIMBER CLAMP BLOCKS

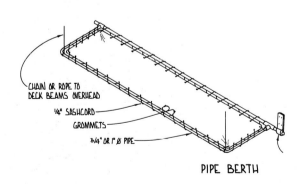

CHAIN OR ROPE TO DECK BEAMS OVERHEAD
¼" SASHCORD
GROMMETS
¾" OR 1" Ø PIPE

PIPE BERTH

CHAPTER EIGHTEEN
BALLAST

When thinking of ballast one usually thinks of sailboats, however some displacement hulled power boats can benefit from the addition of ballast. One will often find ballast in fishing trawlers and similar vessels. No matter what type of boat you have that requires ballast as part of the basic design, now is a good time to undertake this work. The ballast may be lead or scrap steel or a combination of the two. It is important you follow the information given in your plans, as incorrectly ballasting your boat may cause you untold problems once the boat is in service.

SAFETY FIRST

Please reread the notes of safety and safety equipment that are outlined throughout the various chapters of this book. You will need masks when working with lead. We do know of one builder who worked with lead ballast in a confined area and the gases given off by the melting lead made him quite ill for a time. Do not work with lead or any noxious material in a confined space.

Lead ingots make good ballast if your pocket allows.

This ballast is tractor track pins set in resin putty and cost builder only the transport of the scrap. Many BRUCE ROBERTS designs call for scrap steel ballast.

Always arrange adequate ventilation to your immediate work area. If you are installing ballast in the keel, naturally you are working in a somewhat confined space in the bottom of your hull. You can arrange extra ventilation by using fans, vacuum cleaners or other devices to move the contaminated air from your immediate working environment.

INSTALLING THE BALLAST

Often you would be wise to install only 70% of the recommended ballast before you launch the boat. If you think your boat is overweight, then install 60% at this time. You can install the remainder after the boat is in the water and this has the benefit of allowing you to finally trim the boat using the remainder of the ballast. The boat should be trimmed after launching with all of the interior completed, reasonable stores aboard, tanks half full and the normal complement of crew aboard.

As a rule, no two boats of any one design are exactly the same, which is the whole point of building a custom boat. As long as you use common sense in the building and ballasting of your boat, you should not have a problem with the performance of your boat. Experience has taught us that there is a wide variation between boats built to the same basic design. Here are a few tips regarding the items that may effect the ballasting of your boat.

Keep a check on the weight of your keel building material. This keeping of records is especially important in the case of a steel boat, as the weight of the keel plate is considerable. Allow this as part of the ballast weight calculation. Never install more than 70% of the recommended the ballast before launching and this 70% should include the weight of the keel itself. You will find it much easier to trim the boat properly if you take our advice on this point. Always install the initial ballast in the forward 60% of the keel; in boats with very long keels, take the length into account and install the ballast in the forward 50% of the keel.

As a rule, always balance the choice of the rig with the choice of draft. Taller rigs need deeper draft than a lower aspect sail plan. If you want the shallowest draft possible, always consult the designer of your boat regarding a low aspect sail plan. You can usually have the same or even additional area if required, but the lower aspect rig will help with all considerations of offsetting the proposed shallower draft.

WEIGHT EDITING

It is impossible for the designer of any boat to know how the builder keeps track of the weight of materials used to build his boat. Only the builder knows what has been added to the basic construction as advocated by the designer. Builders often add to the structure in the usually mistaken belief, which "It will make it stronger".

If you want your ballasting to be correct and as efficient as possible, keep accurate records and generally follow the designer's recommendations as closely as possible. In any case, it may be worth having your hull weighed before adding the ballast. The weighing can often be undertaken by the crane this is used to move the boat, or by calling at a weigh-bridge on the way to a potential site. By doing some planning ahead, often the ballast can be installed just before launching.

If you are using bolt on ballast, you do not have the luxury of only installing part of the ballast, naturally

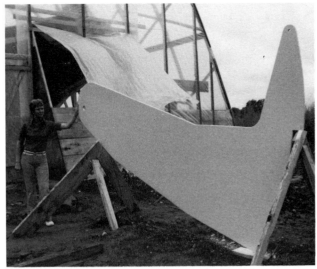

This size of centerboard has to be considered part of the ballast so weight of plate should be allowed for when installing the rest of the ballast. The centerboard pictured is from a ROBERTS 53, centerboard version.

the total recommended ballast must be in the original casting.

If after launching your boat reaches the designed waterline before you have all the ballast installed, don't panic. Your boat may sail quite well as long as you can install the majority of the ballast. Sailing trials will answer any questions in this area. Remember this possible problem when you are building, keep unnecessary weight out of your boat. Do not overbuild.

There are a variety of methods used to install ballast. The one we use most frequently, is to place the ballast in the envelope keel. We build the keel as part of the hull structure and specially design it to receive and hold the ballast. The ballast may also be cast separately and bolted either directly to the hull or to a sub or stub keel.

CASTING KEEL BALLAST

In the days when I was learning boatbuilding, all separate bolt on keels were cast in the boat yard. Today the modern bolt-on keels are often so complex in shape and the area available to bolt them on to the hull is so small ;these keels can only be cast by experienced professional keel makers. If your bolt on keel is of the non complex variety, then you can cast the lead in a timber or sand keel mould. In the case of timber moulds, you will find that the 1" to 1 1/2" [25 to 35] thick timber used to construct a properly braced keel mould will do the job.

This builder, Ian Goodson of Brisbane, made a pattern of the inside of his keel and then made a plywood mold in which he cast lead for the section of keel on his ROBERTS 36 hull.

Kim Johnson made this Roberts 246 cast lead keel, moulded in a concrete mould, cast around a western red cedar plug.

Normally from the hull, you make a copy of the bolting pattern that considers the position of the web floors, keelson arrangement and other factors about where the bolts are to end in the hull. Using this pattern, bolts are placed in the keel mould so when the lead is poured, they will remain in the correct position. The ends of the bolts that remain in the lead are either L shape or are welded with a connecting plate, or employ some similar arrangement so they remain in the lead under severe operating conditions. In a sand mould, you will need to ensure that the sand is kept absolutely dry, moisture and molten lead can have a violent reaction.

BALLAST IN FIBREGLASS KEELS

In fibreglass boats, the keel is usually of the envelope type. Increase the laminate in the area of the keel to accommodate the strains caused by the inclusion of the ballast.

Web floors are recommended and these webs should continue down into the ballast, to at least twenty-five percent of the depth of the ballast. Install the lead in pig form and then smaller pieces of lead can be added to fill the voids. You could consider lining the keel spaces with sheet lead, installing pigs and then pouring a very small quantity of molten lead into the voids.

BALLAST IN STEEL KEELS

In steel boats, the ballast is almost always contained in a nenvelope keel. There will be web floors that go down into the keel to strengthen the hull to keel structure. In the event your design calls for lead ballast, this can be sometimes poured directly into the keel, however this must be done carefully, as the heat of the lead will distort the plating of the keel, if you pour in too much at one time. If you install the lead in pigs or sections you have specially moulded, then you can put in small quantities of molten lead to fill the voids.

MAKING PATTERNS

In our own boats we recommend the builder makes patterns of the area to receive the ballast. The patterns should be a maximum of 2" [50] thick and not so large in area that you cannot handle the material yourself. Taking that thought to its natural conclusion, you should make patterns that will translate into moulded pieces of lead that weighs no more than 70 or 80 pounds. The idea is to install the lead in layers, but with no voids between the layers and/or around the edges. The cheaper variety urethane foam or other suitable material can be used to make patterns.

LEAD BALLAST

You can sometimes obtain scrap lead locally at a reasonable price. Your local scrap merchant is likely to be pleased to quote you, as the amount you require will make up a reasonable order. Some builders have obtained a considerable amount of scrap lead by collecting the used tire weights from their local garages or tyre centres. Another source of scrap lead can be from old batteries, however the practice of piling them up and then burning to release the lead would be frowned upon today, and definitely very unfriendly to your neighbours. When installing your lead ballast, you must work hard to achieve 700 pounds per cubic foot [3416 kilos per cubic metre] You can use an old cast iron bath or similar receptacle to melt the lead. As lead has a low melting point, it is easy to work with, once you accept the weight factor and plan all the handling with that in mind.

SCRAP STEEL BALLAST

Some designs may allow you to use scrap steel ballast. The best materials for this purpose are old pins from the tracks of crawler tractors. Ask around at your local heavy equipment suppliers or other places which sell and service this type of machinery. Cut lengths of railway track, steel balls from rolling mills, steel punchings and lengths of steel rod are all possible scrap steel ballast. The ballast material is packed into the keel as carefully and as tightly as possible and then it is sealed in place as described below. Install the scrap steel ballast so you can achieve a density of 350 pounds per cubic foot, [1700 kilos per cubic metre].

ENCAPSULATING THE INTERNAL BALLAST

Keeping the ballast where you install it is most important. It is easy to imagine the chaos that would ensue if your ballast moved about during some

Home made lead melting device. Lead must be installed in bars and only consolidating amounts of lead melted into the keel in this manner.

particularly bad weather. Fortunately, it is relatively easy to install the ballast materials in such a way, which it remains in its proper position. The materials you may consider to turn your separate pieces of ballast material into one homogeneous mass are, fibreglass polyester based resin putty, better known as "bog", molten lead, cement or epoxy putty.

The polyester resin putty is a good material for encapsulating the ballast in a fibreglass keel. The putty will need to be thin enough to pour in place between the ballast and you should not pour in too much at any one time as this material can generate excessive heat as it cures. After the ballast is finally set in place, you can apply a laminate equal to the basic hull laminate, over the top of the ballast, to finally seal it in position.

Use the pour-in molten lead only in steel hulls where it is easier for the keel material to dissipate the heat. Anyhow, only install a small amount of the molten lead at once, allowing each pour to cool before adding additional molten lead. As mentioned earlier, place as much of the lead as possible in the keel in large pieces and only use the molten lead to fill the voids and consolidate the lead ballast. You can weld a complete steel plate sub sole over the ballast, this will then provide a clean bilge with all the benefits that provide.

SUMMARY

It is important that the ballast has all the features that are needed to allow it to achieve the correct result. It must be as tightly packed as possible. After the ballast is fully installed, there must be no voids remaining and any voids apart from being wasted space that should be occupied with ballast; are likely to cause problems in other ways once the boat is in service. Any water that can get down into the ballast will surely have a detrimental effect on your keel structure. This applies to keels made of any of the boatbuilding materials discussed here, so make sure that your ballast is properly installed, Permanently secured and sealed from all inside and outside elements.

CHAPTER NINETEEN
FITTINGS AND USEFUL CHARTS

Chester Lemon fitting rubbing strip to his ROBERTS 44.

In keeping with our "Build for less" philosophy, we recommend you manufacture as many of the fittings as possible. It will be found that most of the items that go to make up the deck fittings and associated gear can be made by you, the builder, if you have time, inclination and the economic need. I find that traditional boats, such as the Spray series and displacement hulled power boats, often look best if you fit them out with the type of fittings you make yourself. Conversely, I have spent considerable time on a very modern Robert's sailboat built in Sweden, on which almost every fitting was manufactured by the owner. Economic necessity was the driving force here. The forty-four foot [13.41 metres] modern sail boat was built for a total cost of US$25,000 and sold two years later for US $95,000. The prices are not relevant today, but the spread between the cost and resale price achieved tell their own story.

As the fittings represent one area where you can spend some serious money, you should consider just what you can make yourself. As mentioned earlier, making patterns for fittings that can be cast at your local foundry is a good start. Buying stainless steel strap and cutting and drilling it to make your own chain plates and other fittings, is another area worth exploring. You can manufacture all your mast fittings and you can make the mast itself from a light pole of suitable grade aluminium. I have seen boats that have successfully circled the world totally

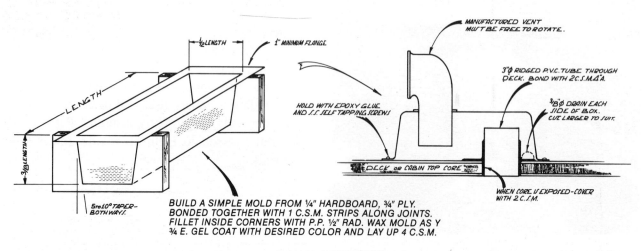

BOX VENTILATOR

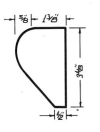
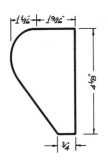
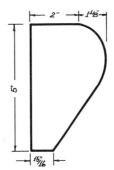

PROPORTIONAL SECTIONS FOR RUBBING STRIP MOLDINGS. MAKE PATTERN TO SUIT.
SIZES GIVEN ARE FOR VESSELS 35 TO 45 FEET.

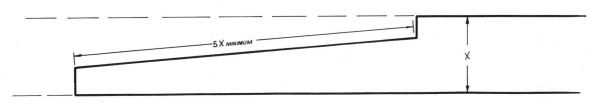

SCARF FOR JOINTING RUBBING STRIP.

Fabricated galvanized mast head fittings.

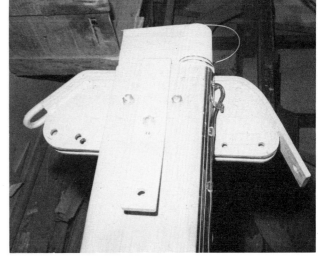

General view of masthead.

All fittings made by the builder, D Johnson of Canada.

Mast fittings may be made by the builder, or by a local metal shop.

equipped by their owner builders in the manner described here.

You can manufacture your own bowsprit, pulpit, push-pit, stanchions and any other fitting that you may made from simple pipe work. These fittings do not have to look inferior to the factory made alternate item. If you have the time, you can make an excellent job of manufacturing all these items. Assuming you cannot weld, then you can bend, shape and prepare the article and then hire a competent welder to assemble the fitting. You will still save an enormous amount of money over professionally made articles of similar quality.

Cleats can be made from wood, cowl and other ventilators of fibreglass, bow fittings can be made of stainless steel plate and as stated earlier, you can make most of the fittings yourself if you have the time and the interest. Building a boat should be fun and it should be affordable. Which means you

probably can afford to build the boat and not feel you have to sell it soon after you complete the project because you have overspent.

These pulpitt rails were made by the builder of this Roberts 44.

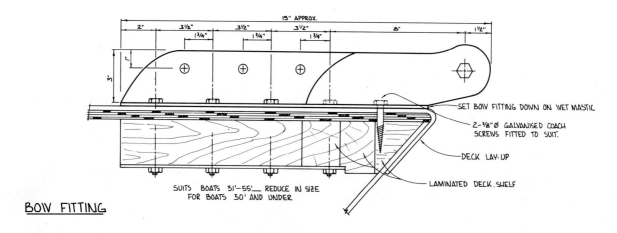

BOW FITTING

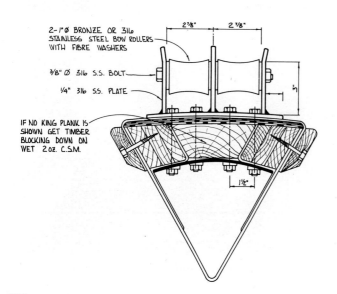

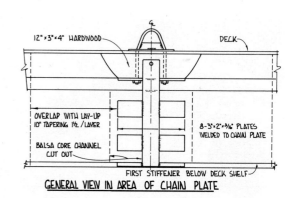

GENERAL VIEW IN AREA OF CHAIN PLATE

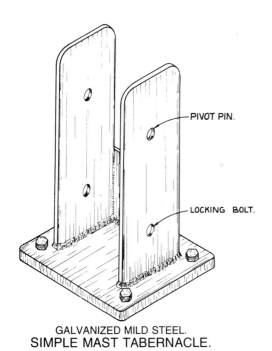

GALVANIZED MILD STEEL.
SIMPLE MAST TABERNACLE.

- PIVOT PIN.
- LOCKING BOLT.

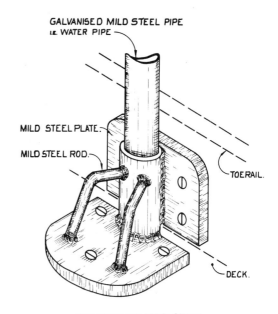

GALVANISED MILD STEEL PIPE
ie. WATER PIPE

MILD STEEL PLATE.

MILD STEEL ROD.

TOERAIL.

DECK.

GALVANIZED MILD STEEL.
STANCHION TOERAIL BRACKET.

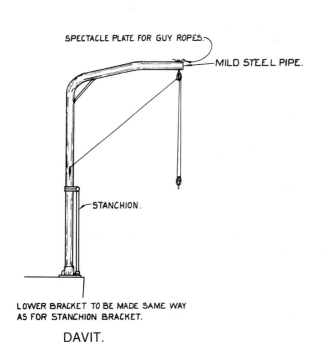

SPECTACLE PLATE FOR GUY ROPES.

MILD STEEL PIPE.

STANCHION.

LOWER BRACKET TO BE MADE SAME WAY
AS FOR STANCHION BRACKET.

DAVIT.

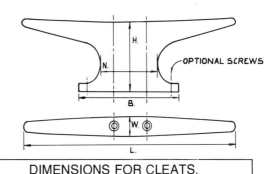

H.

N.

OPTIONAL SCREWS

B.

W.

L.

DIMENSIONS FOR CLEATS.					
CIRCUMFERENCE OF ROPE	OVERALL LENGTH L	BASE LENGTH B.	WIDTH W	HEIGHT H.	NECK LENGTH N.
3/8" - 1/2."	6" - 8".	5".	3/4".	1 3/4" - 2".	2" - 2 1/2".
1/2" - 3/4."	9" - 11."	6" - 7."	1" - 1 1/4."	2" - 2 1/2."	2 1/2" - 3 1/2".
3/4" - 1 1/4."	12" - 16."	8" - 12."	1 1/2" - 1 3/4."	2 1/2" - 3."	4" - 5".

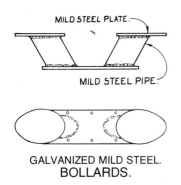

MILD STEEL PLATE.

MILD STEEL PIPE.

GALVANIZED MILD STEEL.
BOLLARDS.

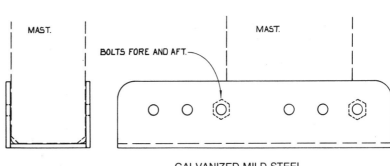

MAST.

MAST.

BOLTS FORE AND AFT.

GALVANIZED MILD STEEL.
SIMPLE MAST STEP.

FUEL CONSUMPTION CHART

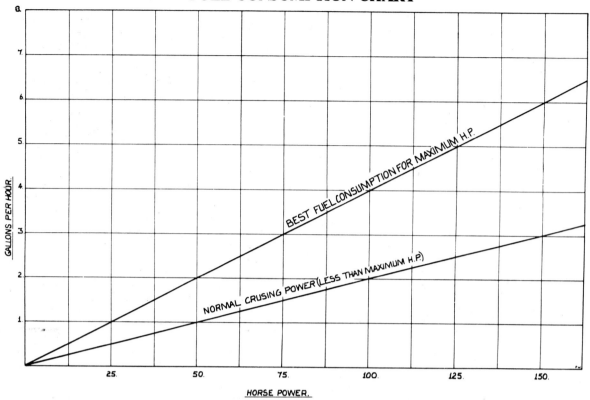

WATER CONSUMPTION CHART

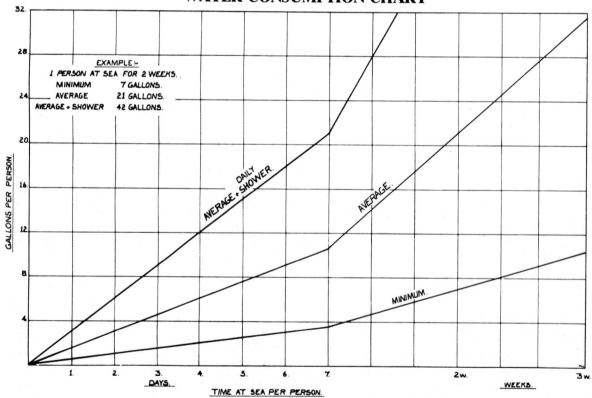

Water purifying tablets should be carried by all cruising yachts — 1 cu. ft. = 6¼ gallons of water.

TIMBER GLUE CHART

APPLICATION	WATER RESISTANT GLUE JOINT	APPLICATION	WATER RESISTANT GLUE JOINT
...STICS METAL AND ...L TO WOOD	EPOXY	DOWELING	PLASTIC RESIN GLUE / POLYVINYL GLUE
...MINATING HEAVY ...MING MEMBERS	CASEIN GLUE	LOOSE FITTING JOINTS / RELATIVELY ROUGH SURFACES	PLASTIC RESIN GLUE / CASEIN GLUE HEAVY MIX
...D-WOOD JOINTS / ...RED JOINTS / ...ARPH JOINTS	POLYVINYL GLUE / CASEIN GLUE HEAVY MIX	PLYWOOD TO DECORATIVE PLASTIC LAMINATES	CASEIN GLUE / CONTACT CEMENT / PLASTIC RESIN GLUE
...GENERAL GLUEING OF ...D AND SOFT WOODS	PLASTIC RESIN GLUE / CASEIN GLUE / POLYVINYL GLUE	POROUS MATERIALS SUCH AS LINOLEUM AND CANVAS TO WOOD	PLASTIC RESIN GLUE / CASEIN GLUE / CONTACT CEMENT
...NEERING INLAYS / ...BINET WORK	PLASTIC RESIN GLUE / POLYVINYL GLUE	HARDBOARD TO PLYWOOD, WOOD OR ITSELF	PLASTIC RESIN GLUE / CASEIN GLUE / POLYVINYL GLUE / CONTACT CEMENT
...DING OILY WOODS / ...AK, PITCH, PINE, OSAGE, YEW	CASEIN GLUE SPONGE SURFACE WITH DILUTE CAUSTIC SODA SOLUTION ONE HOUR BEFORE GLUEING.	PARTICLE AND CHIPBOARDS TO WOOD	PLASTIC RESIN GLUE / CASEIN GLUE / CONTACT CEMENT / POLYVINYL GLUE

...TAINLESS STEEL MONEL AND COPPER NICKEL IN MARINE USE

MATERIAL	APPLICATION	YIELD STRENGTH	TENSILE STRENGTH	ELONGATION % IN 2"
...2 S.S.	RAILS, TRIM CABLE, HARDWARE	40 KSI	90 KSI	50
...4 S.S.	GALLEY HARDWARE	42 KSI	84 KSI	55
...5 S.S.	BOLTS NUTS SCREWS FASTENERS	35 KSI	85 KSI	50
...o S.S.	GENERAL USE PREFERED IN SALT WATER	42 KSI	84 KSI	50
...o L.S.S.	PREFERED CHOICE FOR WELDING	34 KSI	81 KSI	50
...-4 PH S.S.	PROPELLER SHAFTS	175 KSI	205 KSI	15
...NEL ALLOY 400	PUMP PARTS, WATER BOXES, VALVES, TUBING	35 KSI	80 KSI	45
...NEL ALLOY K-500	VALVES PUMP SHAFTS / HIGH STRENGTH APPLICATIONS	130 KSI	160 KSI	22
.../30 COPPER-NICKEL	PIPE, TUBING, WATER BOXES ETC.	25 KSI	60 KSI	45
.../10 COPPER-NICKEL	PIPE, TUBING, WATER BOXES ETC.			

...ERAGE SIZES OF BRONZE THREADED NAILS ...R TIMBER PLANKING AND DECKING

...ICKNESS OF PLANK	NAIL GAUGE	NAIL LENGTH
	Nº 14	1¼"
	Nº 12	1½"
	Nº 10	1¼"
	Nº 10	1¾"
	Nº 8	1½"
	Nº 8	1¾"
	Nº 8	2"

NAIL SPACING FOR PLYWOOD PLANKING AND DECKING

PLYWOOD THICKNESS	NAIL GAUGE	NAIL LENGTH	SPACING — EDGES OF PLY.	SPACING — BEAMS & FRAMES
¼"	Nº 14	⅞"	1½" TO 2"	3" TO 5"
⅜"	Nº 12	1¼"	2½" TO 3½"	4" TO 6"
½"	Nº 10	1½"	3½" TO 4½"	5" TO 6"
⅝"	Nº 8	2"	4"	6"
¾"	Nº 8	2¼"	4"	6"

...UGE OF ...CREW	DIAMETER 'B' DRILL FOR SHANK	DIAMETER 'C' DRILL FOR THREAD
6	⅛"	1/16"
7	⅛"	1/16"
8	5/32"	1/16"
10	3/16"	3/32"
12	7/32"	⅛"
14	15/64"	5/32"
16	9/32"	3/16"
18	5/16"	3/16"

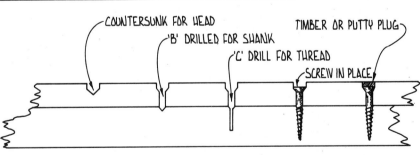

USEFUL SCREW SIZES — LENGTH	½"	¾"	1"	1¼"	1½"	1¾"	2"	2¼"	2½"	2¾"	3"	3½"	4"	4½"	5"
USUAL GAUGES	6	6	8	8	8	10	10	10	12	12	12	14	14	14	16
		8	9	10	10	12	12	12	14	14		16	16	16	18
					12										18

ROBERTS 43 Pilot House version, custom built in Sydney, Australia using single skin over male mold technique for the hull and timber and plywood construction for the decks and superstructure.

CHAPTER TWENTY
SELECTING A DESIGN

METHODS AND MATERIALS

The builder should decide the material that suits him best. The materials such as fibreglass, steel, timber veneer, plywood, aluminium and sometimes a combination of two or more of these materials, presents a confusing set of choices for the intending builder. Fortunately there are many considerations that may help you to make a final choice about which material will be best choice for your boat. You will be guided first, by your personal preference. Let us hope this is tempered with other points such as the availability and cost of materials and the conditions under which the boat will be built.

As the choice of material is closely associated with the choice of design, let us consider the options. I prepared the following chart in 1968 and it has been updated in view of the development of the various materials. My own preferences have changed, add to this the wealth of experience and input from builders of our designs. You will complete the chart using your own likes and dislikes.

While giving consideration to the choice of materials, you will no doubt be looking at a selection of suitable designs. It is natural to choose the design at the same time as you settle on the material that best suits your talents and abilities. If you do not have any previous practical experience at anything, then either fibreglass or steel construction offers the easiest learning curve.

One point to keep in mind when you are selecting a plan, is that it costs as much to build a bad design as it does to build a good one. You must be very careful when you are selecting a design and do not begrudge the designer his fee. Please do not build from scaled up lines plans you may find in various books. If you find a design in a book or magazine that appeals and the plans are no longer available from the original designer, contact another reputable designer to ask if he can prepare plans for a similar design. There was never a design that could not be improved, even mine !! So ,please never build from inadequate plans, lines plans that have been copied from reduced drawings or from plans in which you do not have the utmost confidence. There are dozens of reputable designers from whom to choose, many with well-known specialties. Please reread the first sentence of this paragraph.

One of your biggest decisions will be choosing the right size of boat to suit your particular requirements. You should be very careful in selecting the size of boat you are going to build. First, as a boat gets longer the size squares. For

MATERIAL	COST	EASE OF CONSTRUCTION	SPEED OF CONSTRUCTION	SHELTER REQUIRED	CLIMATIC EFFECTS	PREV. EXP. WITH MATERIAL	PERSONAL CHOICE	MAINTENANCE	RESALE VALUE	AVAILABILITY OF MATERIALS (CHECK YOUR AREA)	TOTAL POINTS OUT OF 100
ALUMINUM	7	8	7	8	10	7	8	8	9	10	82
FIBERGLASS	8	10	10	7	7	10	10	9	10	10	91
PLYWOOD	8	8	9	8	8	9	9	7	8	10	84
STEEL	9	9	9	10	10	7	9	8	9	10	90
STRIP PLANK	7	7	7	8	8	8	9	7	8	8	77

instance, a twenty five feet [7.62 m] boat is one and one-half times bigger than at twenty feet [6.10 m] boat, and a fifty five feet [16.76 m] is twice as big as a forty four feet [13.41 m] boat and so forth. Give that fact some thought before you make a final decision.

Your intended usage is another important factor. Are you really going to live on the boat full time, are you really going to sail around the world, would you be better off settling for a smaller boat now and building a larger one if your plans remain the same when you retire? Do you really want a very fast planing power boat? Would you be happier and actually get more use out of a comfortable family type, less expensive to run, semi-displacement cruiser?

Some of right questions I have raised here are so elementary that you may wonder why we bother raising them, however as we have now sold over fifty thousand sets of plans and seen over fifteen thousand of our boats actually in service, we have seen every conceivable reasoning used to justify a decision that may be totally incorrect for the person concerned.

INVOLVING THE FAMILY

If you want your family to be involved in your boating project, then you must consult their wishes in the early planning stages. Consult your lady on the type of galley and other facilities planned in the proposed design. Do not depend on your children or their friends being interested once they reach their teens, they will almost certainly have interests that do not necessarily include boating with their parents.

Building your own boat does have its own rewards. Jim Kirby and family sailing his Roberts Spray 40 off the coast of Mexico.

Do not build to accommodate more than the occasional guests and finally, providing you use common sense, ignore all the above and build the boat you want.

PREVIOUS EXPERIENCE

We know of many people who have built boats without any previous experience at building anything !!! I personally know of one fellow who made a child's chair and simply nailed it together, not realizing that glue would help to make the article a permanent structure. From this modest beginning, this person went on to successfully build three boats in the thirty-foot range. We have documented details of hundreds of seaworthy boats built by people who had no previous boat building experience. If you have the desire, some free time and a little money, then you can do it.

If you are a professional boatbuilder with the experience of building many boats, then you will only need the minimum of plans and building instructions. However I assume most of you who are reading this book, do not fall into this category, so I slant my advice to those with modest, or no previous experience. Let us consider what you will need in a plan to enable you to build your boat. Some designers provide full size patterns and some do not. Some of those who do not provide full size patterns make all kinds of excuses why you are better off without patterns. It used to be, that those designers just did not have the facilities or even the lofting experience to offer patterns. This was proven often as the designers in question later offered patterns after forcefully stating for some time that they were not needed.

Today most designers work with computer assisted yacht design and drafting programs, which are all capable of generating full size patterns in a fraction of the time it used to take us to loft the patterns by hand. Now there is no excuse. Demand full size patterns, do not be put off by ineffectual excuses by the designer concerned. You will save several days and maybe weeks of labour, if you have full size patterns and avoid the necessity of lofting your own.

LOFTING

Never simply loft the frames full size, without drawing out the complete set of water lines, buttock lines and all other elements of your boat full size. If you are planning to take the plunge and loft your own boat, you will need a loft floor the length of your hull, and a few inches either end. It is possible to undertake what is known as contracted lofting, this is where you draw the overall length to less than full scale but you draw the beam and the depth to full scale. You can loft accurate frames using this method but you lose some advantages of lofting full size in that you cannot take off some patterns for other parts of the hull that are not full size. You can of course re- loft the particular parts separately, but this offsets the advantages of using contracted lofting in the first place.

Different designers have differing ideas about what constitutes a set of plans. There may be no right or wrong set of drawings, however below we have listed what we consider offers you the best chance of building a good quality well finished boat. The list of drawings that make up your plan package should include the following, not necessarily in the order we show here.

Sheet 1A

General arrangement drawing, which includes sail plan if applicable, hull, deck and superstructure profile plus a deck plan.

Sheet 1AA

Accommodation plan, accommodation profile, material list for all versions and material options.

Sheet 2

Lines plan, shows hull sections, profile including all water and buttock lines, plan view including all water lines and buttock lines. All frame spacings, stern or transom detail, keel measurements, rudder and skeg should all be included and all dimensions are clearly indicated.

Sheet 3

This sheet will be a reduced drawing, representing what you can expect to see, when you lay out the full size patterns. We call this sheet the key to full size patterns.It acts as a key when arranging the patterns and will enable you to readily understand just what the patterns contain. Hopefully this sheet will help you to resist the temptation of trying to lay out the patterns on your living room floor.

Sheet 4

Here you will be shown how to manufacture and assemble the frames, plus form up the stem and other parts of the basic framework. This sheet also shows how to set up all these items on a strongback or a system of bedlogs. You will now have formed the basic shape of your hull.

Sheet 5

This sheet will show the installation of the stringers and deck shelf plus covering the framework with the sheathing material and generally finishing the outside of the hull. In a steel hull, this sheet would be about plating.In a fibreglass hull, the sheet would deal with the applying of the laminate and so forth. Fairing the basic hull would be covered in this sheet also.

Sheet 6

Now we move inside the hull and start installing the floor webs, bulkheads, engine beds, and all interior stiffeners.

Sheet 7

This sheet may show detail of the various items covered in sheet 6. Often it takes two sheets to cover webs, bulkheads, engine installation and locating the tanks.

Sheet 8

This is the engineering sheet and covers making the rudder, building the tanks, sterns and rudder tube details plus propeller shaft detail and other information that could be considered as engineering. Items such as stanchions, swim platforms and similar items may also be on this sheet.

Sheet 9

We now move on to the forming and installation of deck beams, side decks, fore-deck, aft deck, cockpit construction and all deck framing details.

Sheet 10

Patterning and making the cabin sides, cabin front and plating and planking or laminating the decks depending on which material we are covering in the particular plan.

Sheet 11

This may cover such items as chain plates, deck fittings, additional rudder construction details and similar information.

Sheet 12

This sheet may show an alternate version of the basic design, additional material lists for that particular design and detailed measurements for the interior joinery.

Sheets A,B,C,D,E,F,G & H

These are the full size pattern sheets that are laid together wall paper fashion to make up the full set of patterns. The sheets all require generous overlays and clearly indicated reference marks, to insure their accuracy. Patterns can be on special plan printing paper or Mylar film. Paper patterns are satisfactory and we have records of several thousand boats built using these type of patterns. If you are affluent or just plain picky, then you can spend the extra and obtain your full size patterns on Mylar film.

This one-off fibreglass Waverunner 48 was built in under twelve months by two non-orofessionals.

This is what it's all about. ROBERTS 44 "Honeymead" anchored in beautiful cove in French Polynesia.

Roberts Waverunner 65, several currently being built in fibreglass and steel

Roberts 53 sailing in San Francisco Bay

In addition to the above, our own plans are accompanied by a special book of extra plans giving details of items you can manufacture yourself and so keep your building costs to a minimum. The plans we have supplied to over fifty thousand builders have gone through over twenty-five years of evolution, not revolution as we move slowly when it comes to accepting new techniques. For instance, the Radius chine steel or aluminum boatbuilding technique was well proven by professional builders before we released to the general market. If you wish to contact the author, you may do so by contacting my U.K. Agent, Mr Philip Sheaf, "Orchards", Schoolhouse Lane, Easton, near Woodbridge, Suffolk, IP13 0ES, England, U.K.

ROBERTS ADVENTURE 22, an ideal design for building in fiberglass or molded plywood.

ROBERTS 36 built in Brisbane. Australia.

This ROBERTS 44 was custom built by Chester and Norma Lemon with fiberglass using the single skin over male mold technique. A system of longitudinal foam/glass stringers plus fiberglass ribs and web floors make this hull extremely strong and suitable for offshore cruising. This particular boat has already covered 30,000 miles.

This ROBERTS 45 was owner-built using one-off fiberglass techniques.

Custom built ROBERTS TRAWLER yacht built in Surfers Paradise. Queensland. by Ken Mills.

ROBERTS TRAWLER YACHT 48 built in Surfers Paradise. Queensland. by Ken Mills.

After the first few one-off examples proved popular, fibreglass moulds were made for this Roberts Longboat 21 and to date over two hundred and fifty boats have been built from this one set of moulds.

Roberts 53 - "Henrike". This boat was built as a training ship for the sea scouts of Finland who are happy with the 9 knot performance of this steel hull yacht.

ROBERTS SPRAY 40 custom built in double chine steel.

TOM THUMB 24

FRAMELESS STEEL

Tom Thumb 24 as her name denotes, is no giant. She is but a little over seven metres long; she is, however, designed to be built of steel. That means she displaces a considerable 7,900 pounds [3,590 kilos]; the waves think twice before throwing her around.

She is frameless; with her almost 9'-6" [2.92 metres] beam and her cambered cabin top, renders Tom Thumb a very large interior. Headroom is 6'-3" [1.90 metres] and her plumb ends gives her a long waterline and a surprising turn of speed.

Her hull speed is six knots and already examples of this design have exceeded that figure. She is definitely, for her size a very a fast lady. She has many admirers; over sixty examples are sailing the seven seas and quite a few oceans as well. Many of her owner/builders, have taken the trouble to write and tell us how they have rated her performance against other earlier loves. So far, she has passed these tests with flying colours.

You will like her interior. A fully enclosed head and workmanlike galley are just two of Tom Thumb's features that are unusual in a mini cruiser. The addition of four berths, a separate hanging locker and plenty of additional stowage, round out a very adequate interior.

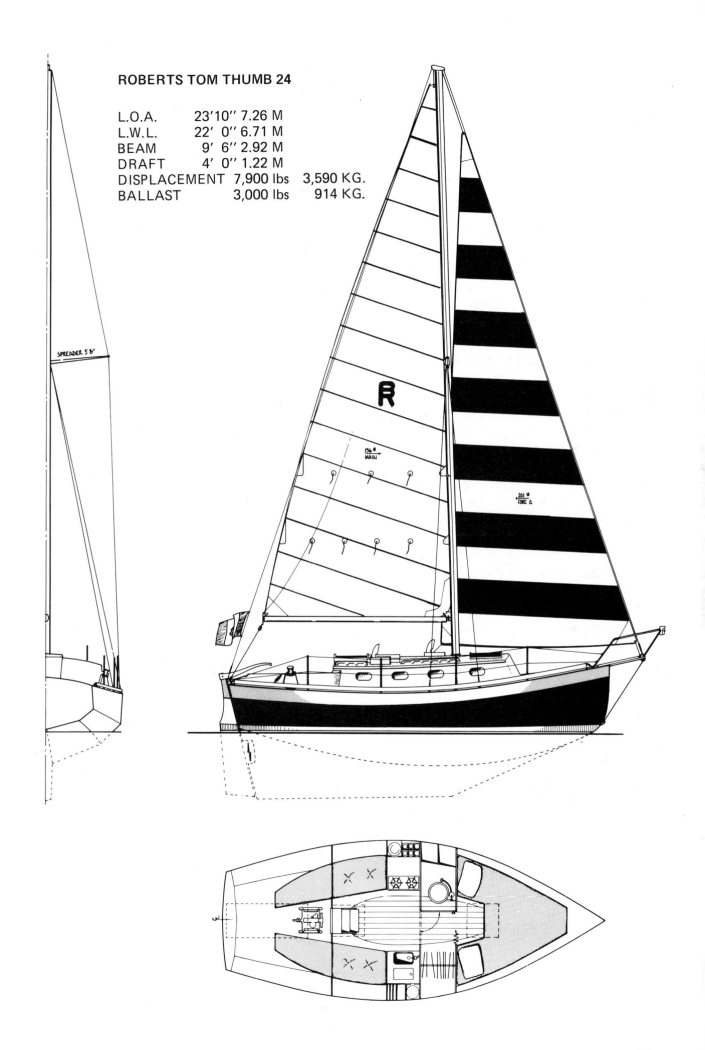

ROBERTS TOM THUMB 24

L.O.A.	23'10''	7.26 M
L.W.L.	22' 0''	6.71 M
BEAM	9' 6''	2.92 M
DRAFT	4' 0''	1.22 M
DISPLACEMENT	7,900 lbs	3,590 KG.
BALLAST	3,000 lbs	914 KG.

SPREADER 3'6"

136 #
MAIN

201 #
FORE △

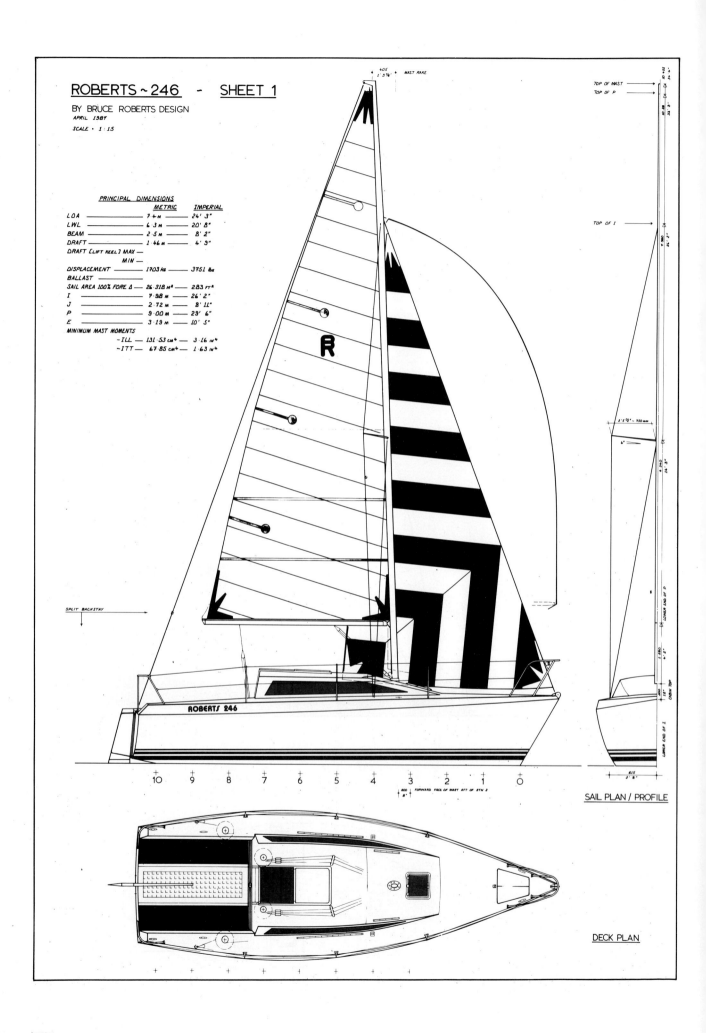

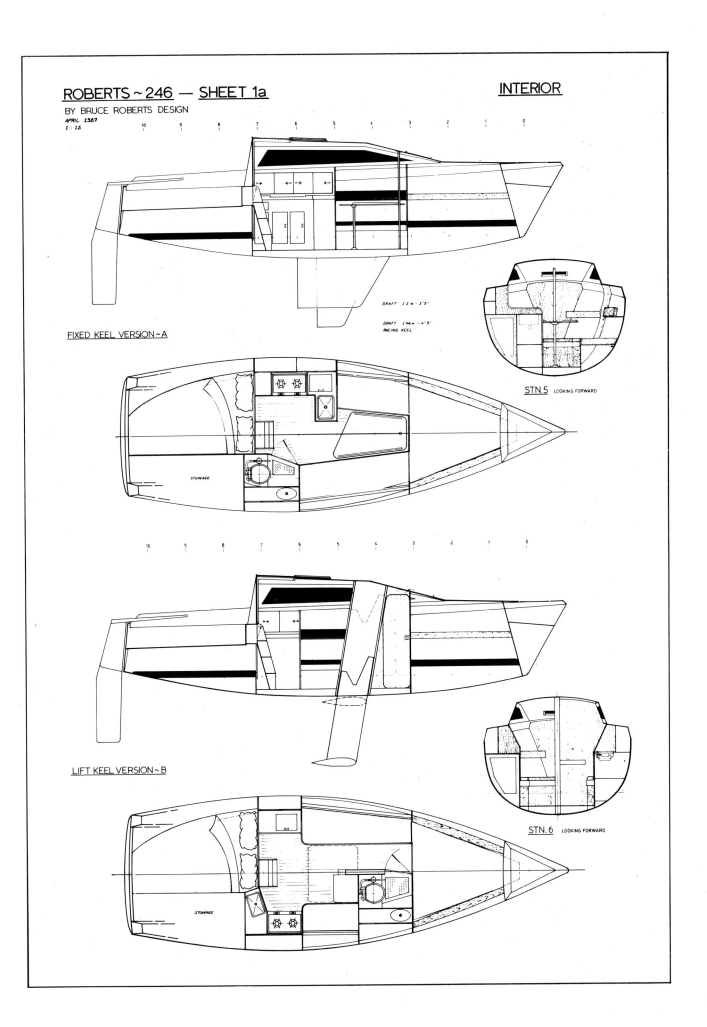

ROBERTS ~ 246 — SHEET 1a

INTERIOR

BY BRUCE ROBERTS DESIGN

APRIL 1987
1 : 15

FIXED KEEL VERSION ~ A

DRAFT 1.5 m - 3'9"

DRAFT 1.46 m - 4'9"
RACING KEEL

STOWAGE

STN.5 LOOKING FORWARD

LIFT KEEL VERSION ~ B

STN.6 LOOKING FORWARD

STOWAGE

185

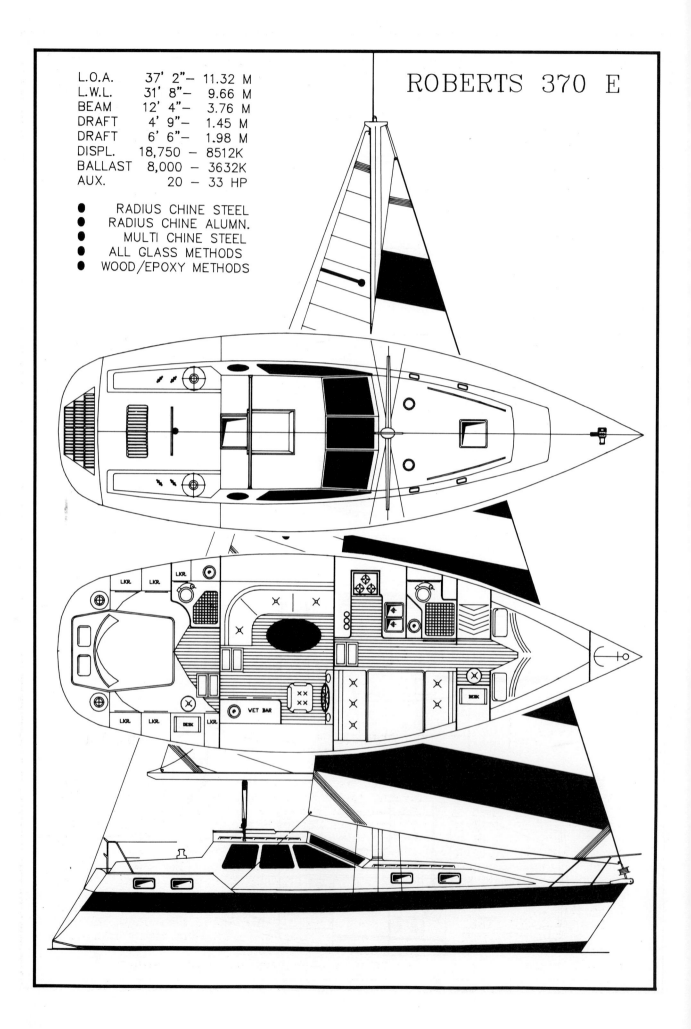

L.O.A.   37' 2" – 11.32 M
L.W.L.   31' 8" –   9.66 M
BEAM   12' 4" –   3.76 M
DRAFT   4' 9" –   1.45 M
DRAFT   6' 6" –   1.98 M
DISPL.   18,750 – 8512K
BALLAST   8,000   – 3632K
AUX.   20 – 33 HP

● RADIUS CHINE STEEL
● RADIUS CHINE ALUMN.
● MULTI CHINE STEEL
● ALL GLASS METHODS
● WOOD/EPOXY METHODS

ROBERTS 370 E

ROBERTS 370

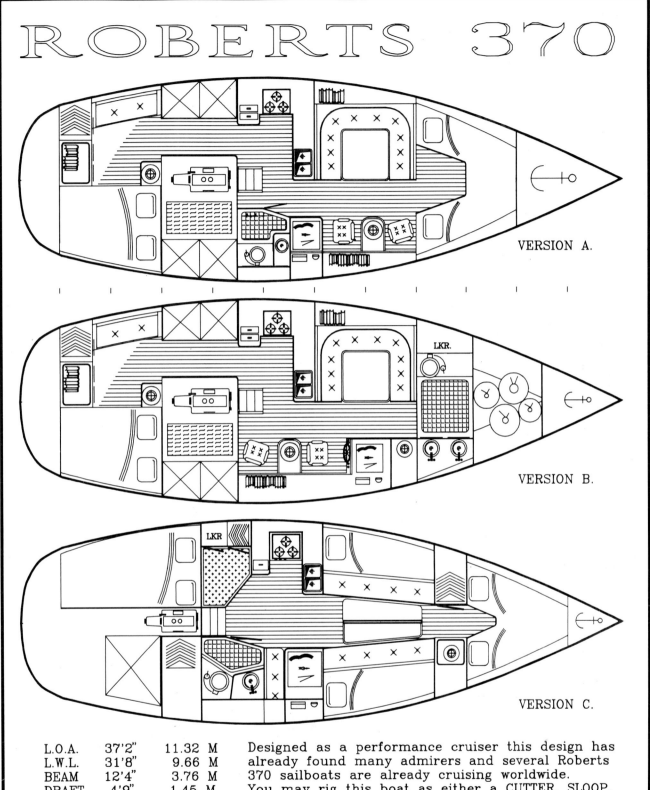

VERSION A.

VERSION B.

VERSION C.

L.O.A.	37'2"	11.32 M
L.W.L.	31'8"	9.66 M
BEAM	12'4"	3.76 M
DRAFT	4'9"	1.45 M
DRAFT	6'6"	1.98 M
DISPL.	18750	8512 K
BALST.	8000	3632 K
AUX.	20	TO 33 HP

- FIBERGLASS
- RADIUS CHINE STEEL
- DOUBLE CHINE STEEL
- ALUMINUM
- WOOD/EPOXY

Designed as a performance cruiser this design has already found many admirers and several Roberts 370 sailboats are already cruising worldwide.
You may rig this boat as either a CUTTER, SLOOP, or KETCH and she will perform well with your choice of sailplan.
You have a choice of draft and the boat can be built with shoal or deep keel to suit your cruising grounds.
You have a wide choice of building materials, the large scale SUPER STUDY PLANS have material lists for all construction methods, plus other information about this popular design.
Call your us about custom interior layouts.

ROBERTS 345

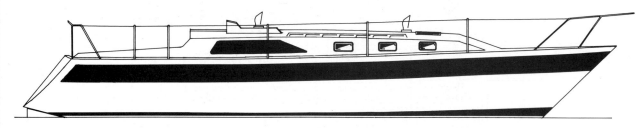

L.O.A.	34'5"	10.50 M
L.W.L.	28'9"	8.76 M
BEAM	11'7"	3.52 M
DRAFT	4'3"	1.3 M
DRAFT	5'9"	1.75 M
DISPL.	10,500	4762K
BALLAST	4,850	2200K
AUX. PWR.	20 — 33 HP	

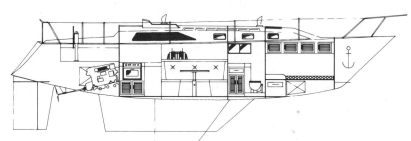

PLANS AND PATTERNS :

- FIBERGLASS
- WOOD/EPOXY
- RADIUS CHINE STEEL
- MULTI CHINE STEEL
- ALUMINUM

The Roberts 345 has been available for some time as a Multi Chine Steel design. The great sucess of this boat and the many requests for plans and patterns in other materials has been met as shown. Good boatbuilding.

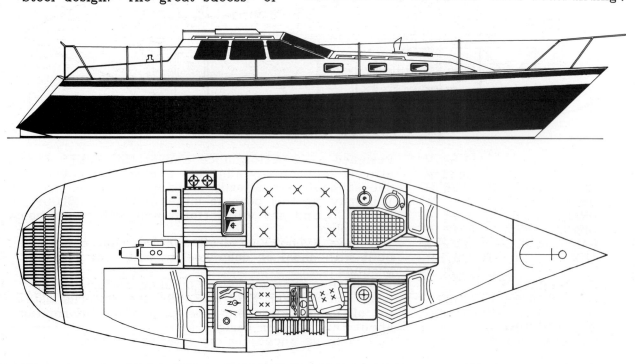

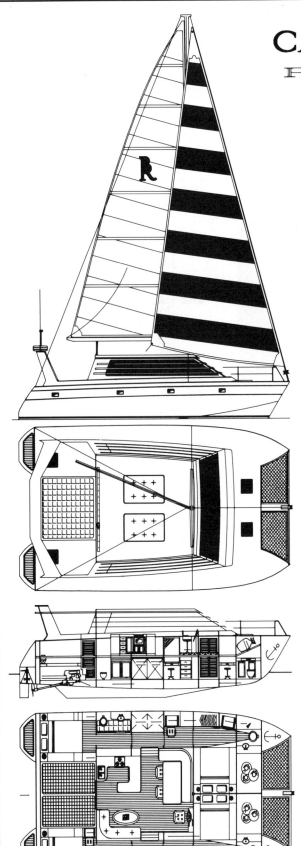

CAT THIRTY NINE
POWER SAILER

L.O.A.	39'–10"	12.1	M
L.W.L.	36'–6"	11.1	M
BEAM	23'–6"	7.16	M
DRAFT	3'–6"	1.07	M
DISPL	22,000 LBS	9979	K
SAIL AREA	731 SQ FT	223	SQ M

FEATURES FIBERGLASS "PANEL" CONSTRUCTION.

DESIGNERS COMMENTS:

THIS CATAMARAN IS DESIGNED TO BE BUILT USING THE BRUCE ROBERTS FIBERGLASS PANEL CONSTRUCTION TECHNIQUES.

THE FIBERGLASS PANEL CONSTRUCTION TECHNIQUE IS BEST SUITED TO CHINE TYPE HULLS. THE METHOD IS VERY SIMPLE TO USE AND PERFECT FOR THE IN-EXPERIANCED BUILDER.

ALL OF THE LOFTING IS DONE IN THE COMPUTER AND PATTERNS ARE SUPPLIED FOR THE FEMALE FRAME FORMERS. SPECIAL PRE-SCALED DRAWINGS ARE SUPPLIED FOR EACH HULL PANEL MAKING IT SIMPLE FOR THE BUILDER TO LAMINATE ALL OF THE HULL AND SUPERSTRUCTURE ON A FLAT TABLE. THE PANELS ARE SET INSIDE THE PRE-ERECTED FRAMEWORK AND LAMINATED TOGETHER SIMILAR TO THE PLYWOOD "STITCH AND GLUE" METHOD.

THE PANEL METHOD IS NOT NEW, WE HAVE USED IT TO BUILD ALL TYPES OF VESSELS FOR 30 YEARS. WHAT IS NEW IS THE ABILITY OF THE COMPUTER TO ACCURATLY LOFT THE PANELS AND MAKE SUPER ACCURATE PATTERNS FOR THE FORMERS.

THE ROBERTS CAT 39 SHOWN HERE IS A "POWER SAILER" CONFIGERATION. THE WORD "POWER SAILER" IS USED TO DESCRIBE A MODERN VESSEL THAT IS DESIGNED TO PERFORM EQUALLY WELL UNDER SAIL OR POWER.

AN ALL SAIL OR ALL POWER VESSEL WOULD HAVE SUPERIOR PERFORMANCE UNDER THE CHOSEN PROPULSION SYSTEM BUT FOR FAMILY USE THE "POWER SAILER" CONCEPT HAS A LOT TO RECOMMEND IT.

TWIN ENGINES CAN BE VARYING SIZE FROM 2 X 50 HP TO 2 X 250 HP.

IT IS POSSIBLE TO RE-DESIGN THIS CATAMARAN WITH A WITH A BIAS TOWARDS SAIL PERFORMANCE, CONTACT THE DESIGNER FOR ADDITIONAL DETAILS.

NOTE INSIDE STEERING. OUTSIDE STEERING MAY BE AT THE AFT END OF THE COCKPIT OR BULKHEAD MOUNTED JUST AFT OF THE CABIN (FORWARD END OF COCKPIT), A SCREEN OR DODGER MAY BE FITTED TO PROTECT THE HELSMAN.

LARGE SCALE STUDY PLAN PACKAGES ARE AVAILABLE FOR THIS DESIGN AND FOR ALL OTHER BRUCE ROBERTS PLANS, SEE PRICE LIST OR CONTACT YOUR NEAREST BRUCE ROBERTS DESIGN OFFICE FOR FULL DETAILS.

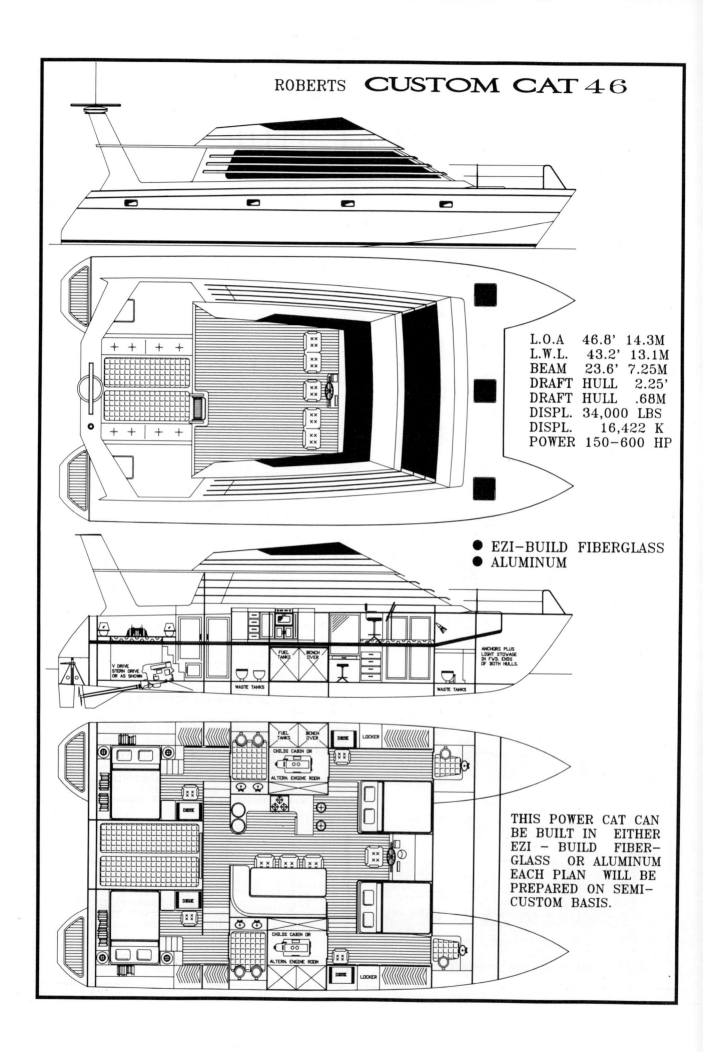

ROBERTS **CUSTOM CAT 46**

L.O.A	46.8'	14.3M
L.W.L.	43.2'	13.1M
BEAM	23.6'	7.25M
DRAFT HULL	2.25'	
DRAFT HULL	.68M	
DISPL.	34,000 LBS	
DISPL.	16,422 K	
POWER	150–600 HP	

● EZI-BUILD FIBERGLASS
● ALUMINUM

THIS POWER CAT CAN
BE BUILT IN EITHER
EZI - BUILD FIBER-
GLASS OR ALUMINUM
EACH PLAN WILL BE
PREPARED ON SEMI-
CUSTOM BASIS.

This new version is for those who are interested in a Cruiser that offers maxium comfort for two couples.

If you are looking for a Sailboat that could be used for Luxury Charter or one that is suitable as a live—aboard for two couples then we recommend you consider this design.

Plans and Full Size Patterns are available to build the Roberts 434 in:

- All Wood/Epoxy Methods
- All Fiberglass Methods
- Radius Chine Steel
- Round Bilge Steel
- Multi Chine Steel

ROBERTS 434 D

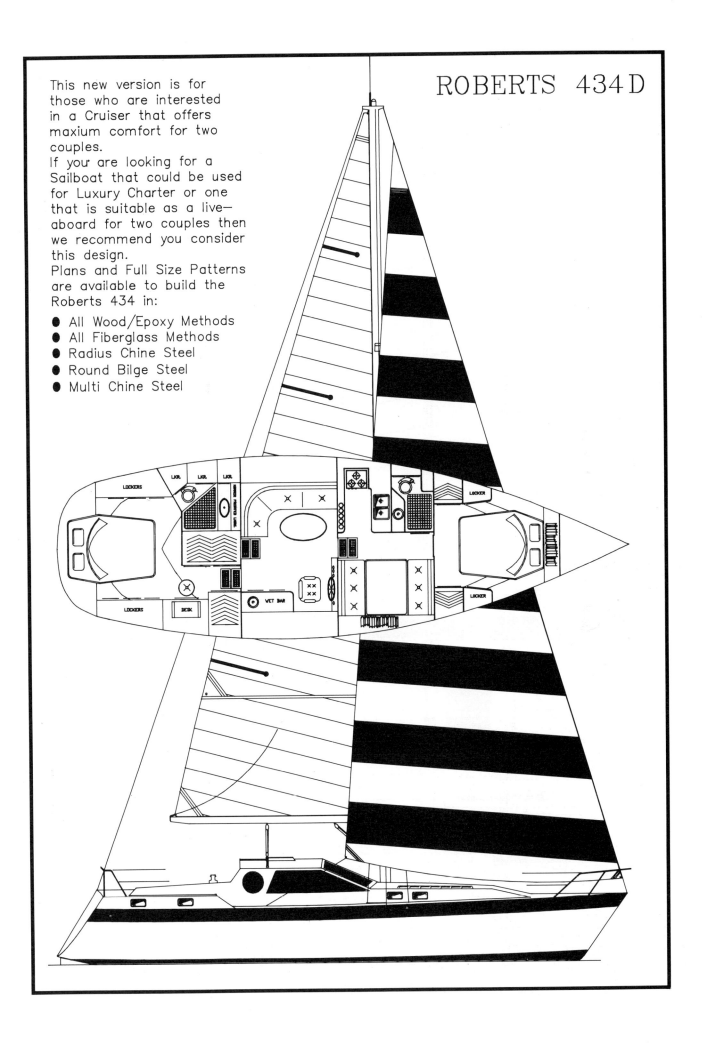

NEW YORK 46

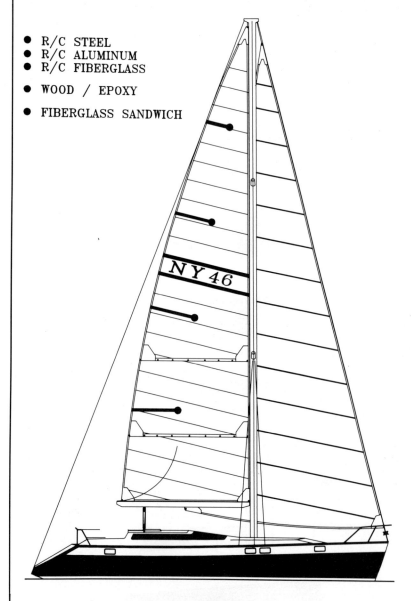

- R/C STEEL
- R/C ALUMINUM
- R/C FIBERGLASS
- WOOD / EPOXY
- FIBERGLASS SANDWICH

L.O.A.	46'-10"	14.28 M
L.W.L.	43'-5"	13.24 M
BEAM	12'-6"	3.81 M
DRAFT	7'-6"	2.29 M
DISPL.	42,972 LBS	19,492 K
BALST.	12,750 LBS	5,783 K
SAIL AREA	1200 S.F	111 S.M
AUX. POWER		85 HP
D/L RATIO		235
S/A DISPL. RATIO		16.5

THE NEW YORK SERIES:

The New York Series has developed over the past few months from an idea given to us by two of our builders who are separated by over 3,000 miles yet came up with the same requirements although for very different usage.

Major Pat Garnett is attached to the Sultan of Oman's army and already has built several of our boats in the Middle East including a Spray 33, Waverunner 44 as a fisheries research vessel and a Radius Chine Steel Roberts 434 which Pat sailed around the World in the near record time of 218 days.

Pat Garnett requested us to design a new concept for a 65' (60' L.W.L.) R/C steel boat to make another attempt on the record for a non-stop single handed circum-navigation. The Omani 65 is the result of our combined efforts and this boat is currently being built in Oman.

At almost the same time another Custom Design enquiry arrived from Bo Lindstrand, a Swedish born New York businessman and although the boat was intended for family use the performance requirements and general concepts were the same as for the Omani 65. So the New York 65 was born.

These two designs show such promise that we have decided to use the new concepts as a basis for three new designs namely the New York 65, New York 55 and New York 46. We plan to offer both "Slimline" (Minimum beam hulls for Superior performance and "Wide Body" hulls for those who seek all the comforts of home while insisting on excellent sailing qualities

A choice of keel types allowing for various draft options, alternate sail plans etc., will allow these designs to be customised to suit most requirements.

Contact Bruce Roberts for additional details and prices for Customised versions of these plans.

NEW YORK 46

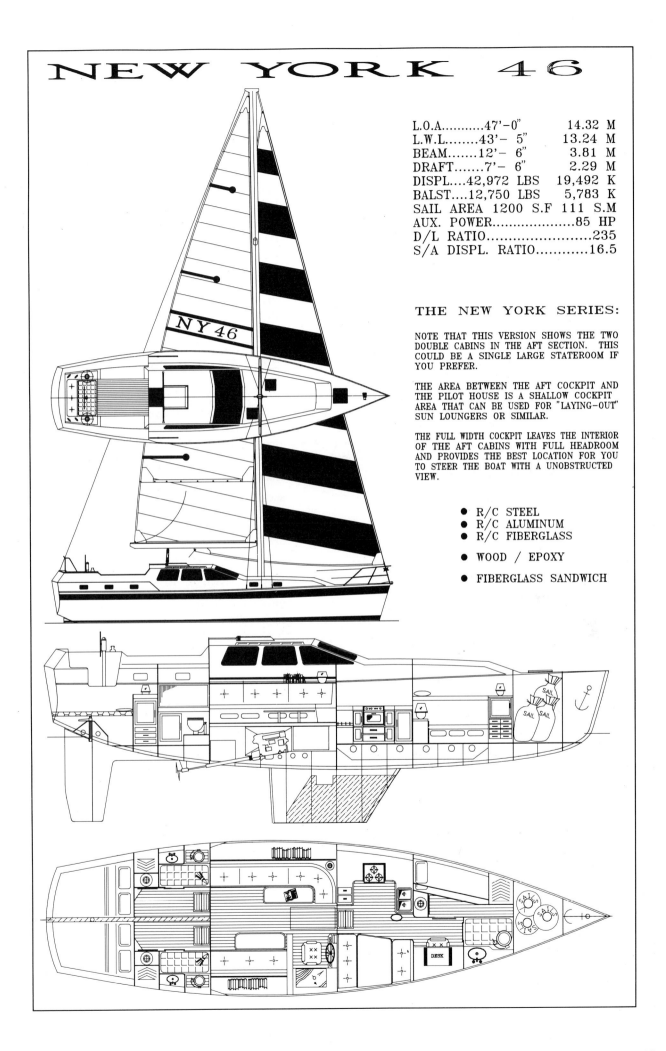

L.O.A.	47'-0"	14.32 M
L.W.L.	43'-5"	13.24 M
BEAM	12'-6"	3.81 M
DRAFT	7'-6"	2.29 M
DISPL	42,972 LBS	19,492 K
BALST	12,750 LBS	5,783 K
SAIL AREA	1200 S.F	111 S.M
AUX. POWER		85 HP
D/L RATIO		235
S/A DISPL. RATIO		16.5

THE NEW YORK SERIES:

NOTE THAT THIS VERSION SHOWS THE TWO DOUBLE CABINS IN THE AFT SECTION. THIS COULD BE A SINGLE LARGE STATEROOM IF YOU PREFER.

THE AREA BETWEEN THE AFT COCKPIT AND THE PILOT HOUSE IS A SHALLOW COCKPIT AREA THAT CAN BE USED FOR "LAYING-OUT" SUN LOUNGERS OR SIMILAR.

THE FULL WIDTH COCKPIT LEAVES THE INTERIOR OF THE AFT CABINS WITH FULL HEADROOM AND PROVIDES THE BEST LOCATION FOR YOU TO STEER THE BOAT WITH A UNOBSTRUCTED VIEW.

- R/C STEEL
- R/C ALUMINUM
- R/C FIBERGLASS

- WOOD / EPOXY

- FIBERGLASS SANDWICH

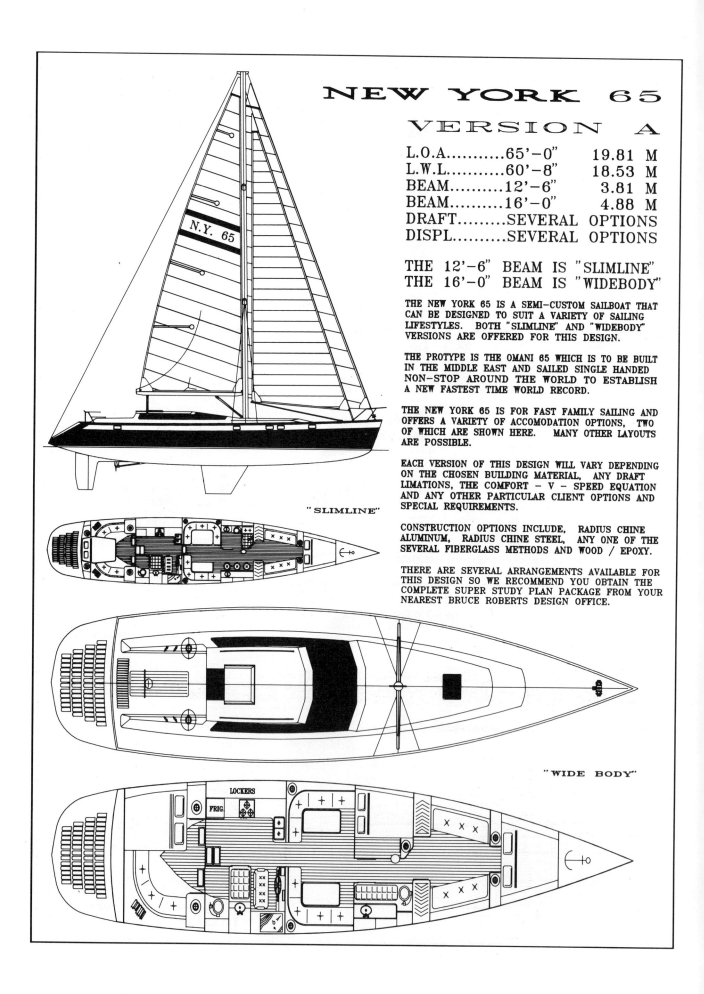

NEW YORK 65

VERSION A

L.O.A.	65'-0"	19.81 M
L.W.L.	60'-8"	18.53 M
BEAM	12'-6"	3.81 M
BEAM	16'-0"	4.88 M
DRAFT	SEVERAL OPTIONS	
DISPL	SEVERAL OPTIONS	

THE 12'-6" BEAM IS "SLIMLINE"
THE 16'-0" BEAM IS "WIDEBODY"

THE NEW YORK 65 IS A SEMI-CUSTOM SAILBOAT THAT CAN BE DESIGNED TO SUIT A VARIETY OF SAILING LIFESTYLES. BOTH "SLIMLINE" AND "WIDEBODY" VERSIONS ARE OFFERED FOR THIS DESIGN.

THE PROTYPE IS THE OMANI 65 WHICH IS TO BE BUILT IN THE MIDDLE EAST AND SAILED SINGLE HANDED NON-STOP AROUND THE WORLD TO ESTABLISH A NEW FASTEST TIME WORLD RECORD.

THE NEW YORK 65 IS FOR FAST FAMILY SAILING AND OFFERS A VARIETY OF ACCOMODATION OPTIONS, TWO OF WHICH ARE SHOWN HERE. MANY OTHER LAYOUTS ARE POSSIBLE.

EACH VERSION OF THIS DESIGN WILL VARY DEPENDING ON THE CHOSEN BUILDING MATERIAL, ANY DRAFT LIMATIONS, THE COMFORT – V – SPEED EQUATION AND ANY OTHER PARTICULAR CLIENT OPTIONS AND SPECIAL REQUIREMENTS.

CONSTRUCTION OPTIONS INCLUDE, RADIUS CHINE ALUMINUM, RADIUS CHINE STEEL, ANY ONE OF THE SEVERAL FIBERGLASS METHODS AND WOOD / EPOXY.

THERE ARE SEVERAL ARRANGEMENTS AVAILABLE FOR THIS DESIGN SO WE RECOMMEND YOU OBTAIN THE COMPLETE SUPER STUDY PLAN PACKAGE FROM YOUR NEAREST BRUCE ROBERTS DESIGN OFFICE.

"SLIMLINE"

"WIDE BODY"

LOCKERS

FRIG.

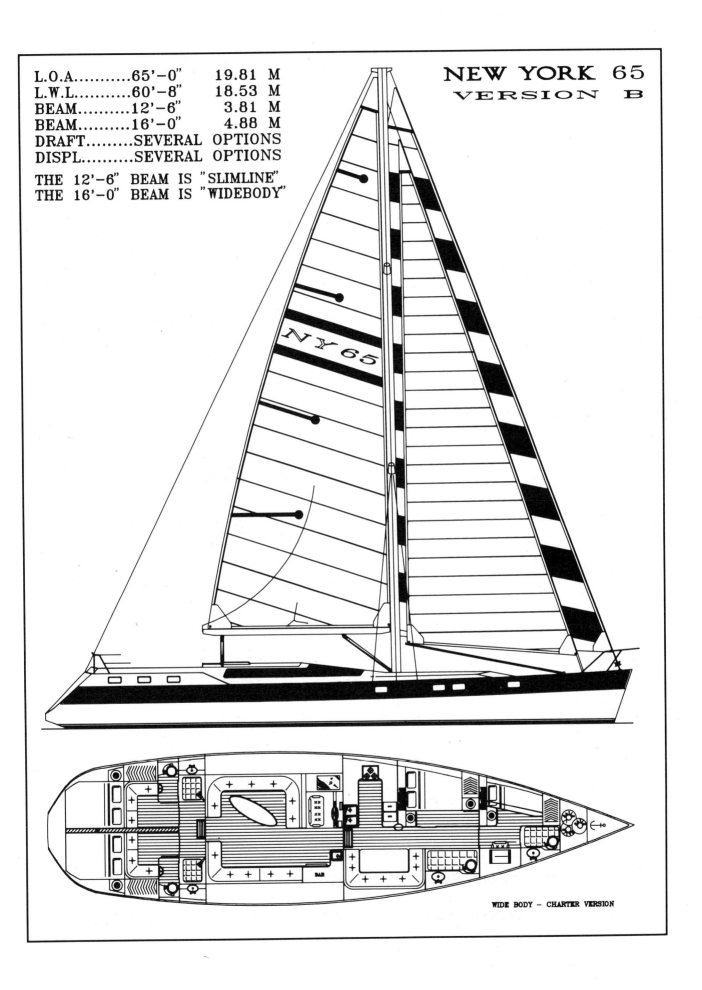

L.O.A..........65'-0"   19.81 M
L.W.L..........60'-8"   18.53 M
BEAM..........12'-6"   3.81 M
BEAM..........16'-0"   4.88 M
DRAFT........SEVERAL OPTIONS
DISPL.........SEVERAL OPTIONS

THE 12'-6" BEAM IS "SLIMLINE"
THE 16'-0" BEAM IS "WIDEBODY"

NEW YORK 65
VERSION B

NY 65

WIDE BODY — CHARTER VERSION

ROBERTS 53

- BALSA SANDWICH F.G.
- FOAM SANDWICH F.G.
- C-FLEX FIBERGLASS
- RADIUS CHINE STEEL
- R.C. ALUMINUM
- MULTI CNINE STEEL
- M.C. ALUMINUM
- ROUND BILGE STEEL
- R.B. ALUMINUM
- WOOD/EPOXY

VERSION H
Note two Pilot House
window styles shown,
you choose   how to
Customise your boat.

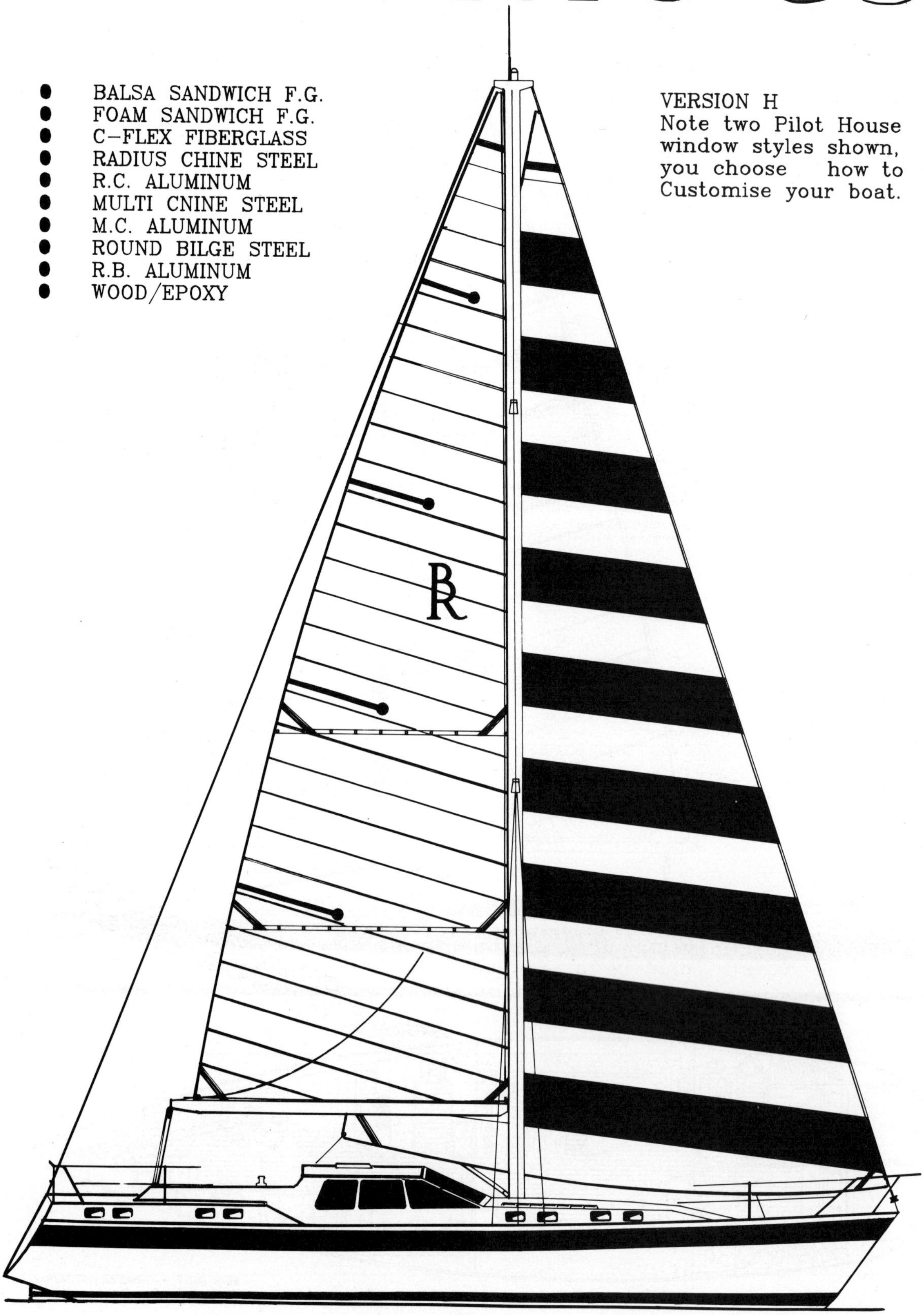

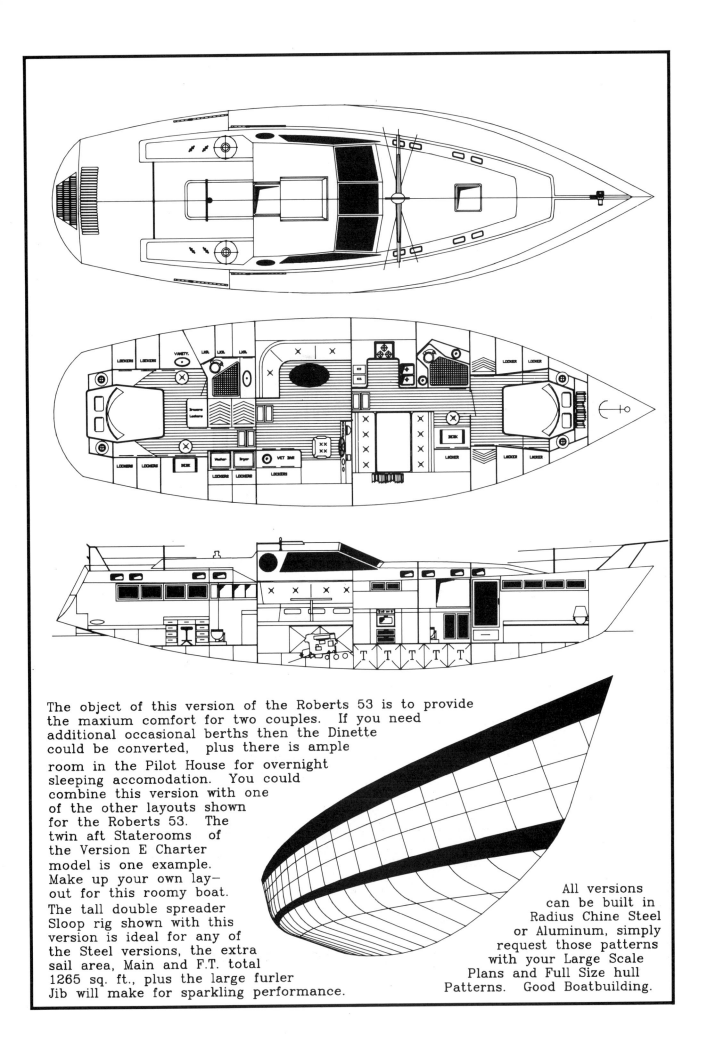

The object of this version of the Roberts 53 is to provide
the maxium comfort for two couples. If you need
additional occasional berths then the Dinette
could be converted, plus there is ample
room in the Pilot House for overnight
sleeping accomodation. You could
combine this version with one
of the other layouts shown
for the Roberts 53. The
twin aft Staterooms   of
the Version E Charter
model is one example.
Make up your own lay-
out for this roomy boat.
The tall double spreader
Sloop rig shown with this
version is ideal for any of
the Steel versions, the extra
sail area, Main and F.T. total
1265 sq. ft., plus the large furler
Jib will make for sparkling performance.

All versions
can be built in
Radius Chine Steel
or Aluminum, simply
request those patterns
with your Large Scale
Plans and Full Size hull
Patterns. Good Boatbuilding.

ROBERTS SPRAY SERIES

The story of Captain Joshua Slocum and his sloop, *Spray*, is standard reading for any cruising yachtsman and the Captain's book, *Sailing Alone Around The World*, makes fine reading. Over the last 70 years, it has been the inspiration for many of those who go to sea in small boats.

Some years ago, our design office was approached by a *Spray* enthusiast who wanted to know if we could prepare plans for the *Spray* to be built in fiberglass. It so happened, while we were considering this request, another approach was made by an English yachtsman who had just completed a voyage from England to Australia and who wanted plans for a cruising vessel similar to the *Spray*.

It was a challenge; so we researched and came up with sufficient information to convince us that the proposition was practical. Work was started on the plans. About this time, we were fortunate in securing a copy of Ken Slack's book, *In The Wake Of The Spray*, which provided a wealth of information. Ken, an Australian, had included a detailed analysis of most aspects of the *Spray*, which was of great help.

For those of you who are not already familiar with the original *Spray*, perhaps this is a good time to re-cap some of the exploits of this fine boat, and lay to rest some of the misconceptions and half-truths that have been written about her over the past 70 years. In 1892, Joshua Slocum, at age 51, was given an aging and decripit sloop the *Spray*. The Captain spent the next few years rebuilding the

vessel. He removed the centerboard and replaced almost every piece of timber in the hull and deck. All of the materials used were collect around Fairhaven, Massachusetts, where the vessel had lain in a field for several years.

The *Spray's* lineage is clear when one examines photographs of old and still-sailing examples of the North Sea fishing boats than have worked off the coast of England and France for at least 150 years. Slocum's *Spray* was reputed to have served as an oyster dragger off the New England coast. Slocum sought to improve the sea-worthiness of his acquisition by adding freeboard, so that the vessel would be better suited to the deep water sailing that he obviously had in mind.

After a year of commercial fishing on the Atlantic coast, and generally proving the worth of his new boat, Slocum decided to undertake a voyage that even today is not undertaken lightly.

Slocum's trip proved a resounding success. Not only did he achieve what he set out to do, that is, circumnavigate the world singlehanded, but he proved the many fine features of the *Spray* and that is what we are considering here.

Building replicas of the *Spray* is certainly not new. Although ours were to be the first foam/glass versions, many copies of the *Spray* had already been built in other materials. The first known replica was built in Rochester,

Bow of ROBERTS SPRAY 33 built in California.

England in 1902. This slightly enlarged *Spray* — 42 feet overall — was built by Gill of Rochester and sold abroad to a German buyer. The history of this replica makes interesting reading. She was renamed *Heimat* and was sailed extensively in European waters, making voyages to Norway, and spending a lot of time sailing in the Baltic. During the course of her career, *Heimat* became *Jurand,* and was sold to two Polish owners. Her history extends right through into the second World War when she was captured by the German navy and used as a training school for the Luftwaffe. She was re-captured at the end of the war by the R.A.F. It is believed she was then towed back to England, where she disappeared into obscurity. Another replica was the *Pandora,* which was built in Perth, Australia, in about 1908. This vessel sailed from Australia to New Zealand and then on to Pitcairn and Easter Island. From Easter Island, the *Pandora* sailed for Cape Horn, arriving off the Horn in January, 1911. A week later, she was struck by a huge wave that rolled her over completely. It is an interesting point to note that the vessel was self-righting. She did come up the right way after being capsized. In the Faukland Islands, repairs were made to the *Pandora* and she crossed on to St. Helena, and on to New York.

Several other *Spray* replicas have been built in Australia, and this is not surprising considering that Slocum spent a considerable amount of time in both Melbourne and Sydney. The *Spray* caused a great deal of interest in the yachting fraternity in those cities.

In the United States, many replicas have been built. The late John G. Hanna, well-known naval architect of Duniden, Florida, designed modified versions of the *Spray,* which were built in sizes ranging up to 100 feet. Another well-known U.S. boatbuilder/designer, Captain R.D. (Pete) Culler, built two *Sprays,* one for his own use, and another for Gilbert Klingel. Captain Culler owned his *Spray* for 23 years and in various writings, both he and Mrs. Culler spoke very highly of the *Spray's* sea-worthiness and comfort.

The list of successes and virtues of the many *Spray* replicas that have been built is far too long to be listed here. In fact, some of the voyages and comments of owners and builders of *Sprays* make almost as interesting reading as does the voyage of the original.

For those that are interested in reading further about the *Spray* and the early replicas, I recommend the book, *In The Wake Of The Spray* by Ken Slack.

It is a fact that the *Spray* as Slocum sailed her, would be most unacceptable to the cruising yachtsman of today. Firstly, Slocum's accommodations were basic. He had the after-cabin fitted out with two berths, a sea chest, and book racks. The forward section of the vessel was used as a cargo hold, and nowhere were there provisions for the modern cooking and toilet facilities which are considered essential by today's yachtsmen.

Because of the volume provided by the SPRAY's hull, it was a simple matter to arrange several alternate accommodation plans to allow for the varied tastes of today's cruising fraternity.

During the design stage, it was decided that instead of having the over-sized cut-water at the bow, it would be preferable to fair in the forward sections above the waterline, and hopefully to improve the appearance. These minor changes would in no way adversely affect the sailing.

These plans and full size patterns include Cutter, Ketch or Gaff Schooner. You can choose to build in Airex Foam, C-Flex Fiberglass, Steel or Wood/Epoxy.

The ROBERTS SPRAY 33 is a proportional reduction of the original SPRAY, and the resulting dimensions have proven to provide an excellent version of this well proven design.

The draft of 4 feet was achieved by slightly deepening the keel from the original SPRAY 40 lines. This is the line with our latest modifications to the larger SPRAY, that is, adding a few inches to the depth of the keel. We have found the additional keel depth has greatly improved the SPRAY's performance, while not adding any detrimental features to the boat's overall handling and performance characteristics.

The Bermudan cutter rig balances very well and drives this hull at maximum hull speed in any sort of breeze. It has been found the SPRAY hull is very easily driven, and the performance is creditable under actual cruising conditions. I don't think anyone would suggest the SPRAY is a boat for round-the-buoys racing, however, experience has taught us that as a long-distance cruising boat the SPRAY has much to offer. In many cases, we have documented evidence of SPRAY's actually outperforming more modern designs on point-to-point cruises. This is partly acheived by the fact that the SPRAY can carry her full working rig longer and stand up to a breeze when other boats are reducing sail.

Because of the volume of this hull, there is more than adequate stowage space for all the water, fuel, and general stores that are required for long-distance passage-making. It is a known fact there are two schools of thought when it comes to selecting a cruising boat. One school prefers the medium-to-light displacement cruiser of more modern type. While this type does offer fast cruising at minimum cost, it tends to require that the boat be longer overall to accommodate the necessary fuel, water and stores without completely destroying the sailing lines of the boat. In the case of the heavier displacement, more traditional boat, a shorter boat can be used to achieve the same results. This is, good load carrying ability which is absolutely essential for serious off-shore cruising. We offer the ROBERTS SPRAY 33 as a comfortable, long-distance cruiser, capable of carrying adequate stores and equipment and capable of carrying its crew in a degree of comfort not found in a light displacement boat.

SPECIFICATIONS:

L.O.A.	37'8" (11.48 m)
L.O.D.	32'11" (10.03 m)
L.W.L.	26'7" (8.13 m)
BEAM	12'0" (3.66 m)
DRAFT	4'0" (1.22 m)
DISPLACEMENT	22,000 lb. (10,000 kg)
BALLAST	7,500 lbs. (3,400 kg)
AUX. POWER	20—33 hp

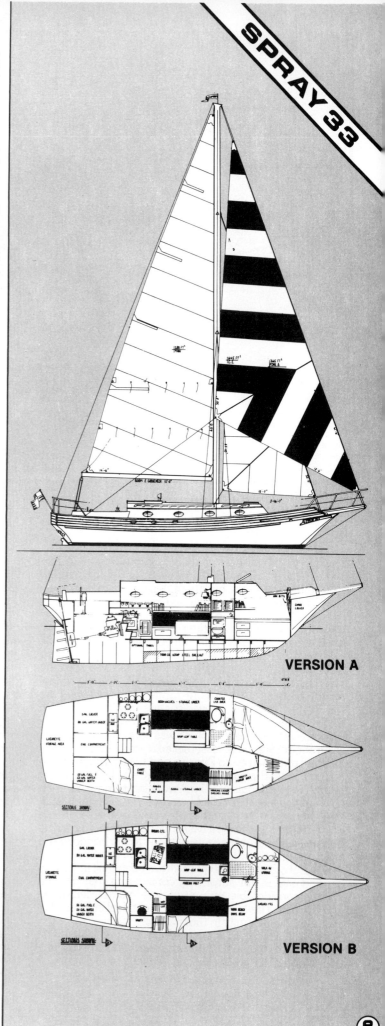

SPRAY 33

VERSION A

VERSION B

200

This Spray may be built in different versions:

A. Center cockpit trunk cabin version
B. Aft cockpit pilot house version.
C. Poop stern center cockpit with pilot house.

You choose between Airex Foam, C-Flex Fiberglass, Steel or Wood/Epoxy.

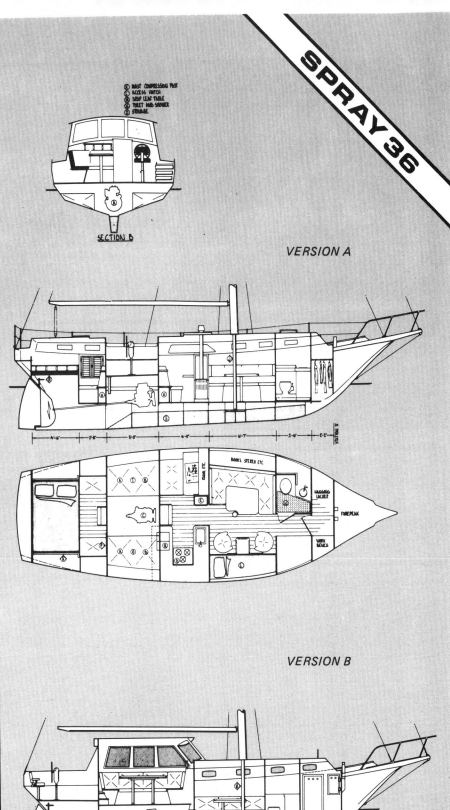

SECTION B

VERSION A

VERSION B

ALTERNATE LAYOUT

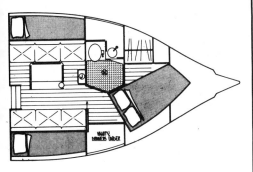

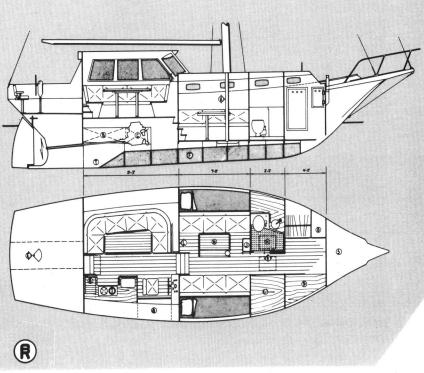

SPECIFICATION:
L.O.A.	36'10"
L.W.L.	30'0"
BEAM	12'0"
DRAFT	4'0"
DISPLACEMENT	24,400 lbs.
BALLAST	8,400 lbs.
CUTTER SAIL AREA	723 ft.
AUX. POWER	20—33 hp

Designed for steel construction this design offers a more compact version of the S40 and larger aft cabin than the S36.

Ketch and cutter rigs are included in large scale plans and full size patterns.

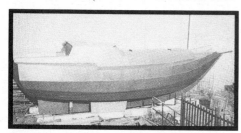

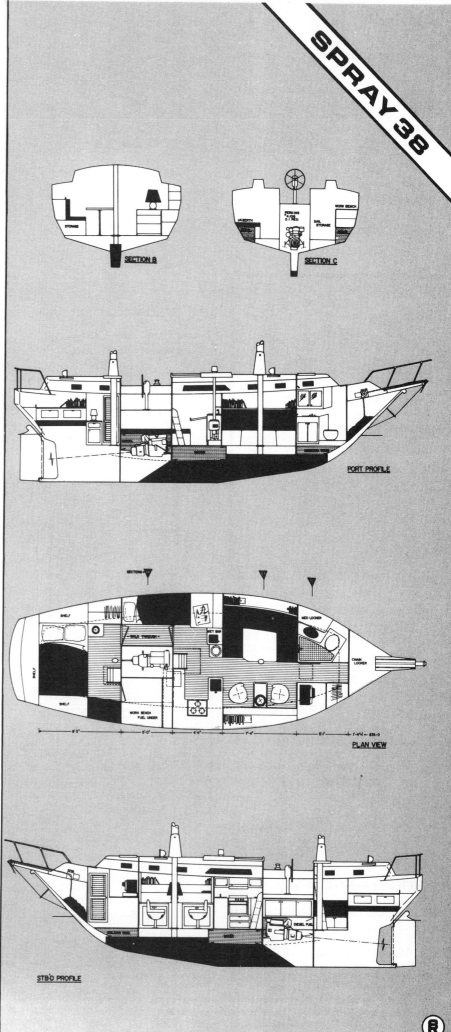

SECTION B

SECTION C

PORT PROFILE

PLAN VIEW

STB'D PROFILE

SPECIFICATIONS:
L.O.W. .... 38'10"
L.W.L. .... 31'8"
BEAM .... 13'0"
DRAFT .... 4'0" or 5'0"
DISPLACEMENT .... 29,000 lbs.

You can build this Spray 40 in Airex Foam, C-Flex Fiberglass, Strip Plank Wood/Epoxy or Steel.

This boat may be rigged as a BMU. Ketch, BMU. Cutter, Gaff Cutter, Gaff Ketch or Gaff Schooner. All rigs included in plans and full size patterns package.

SPRAY hull built by C. Jupp.

Interior framing of SPRAY built by Roger & Riva Palmer.

SPRAY hull is easily beached for bottom painting.

SPECIFICATIONS:

L.O.A. .... 40'0" (12.19 m)
L.W.L. .... 31'11" (9.73 m)
BEAM .... 14'4" (4.37 m)
DRAFT .... 4'2" (1.27 m)
SAIL AREA ...... 927 sq.ft. (86.12 sq. m)
HULL .... Various
SPARS .... Wood or Aluminum
BALLAST .... 15,000 lbs. (6.804 kg)
DISPLACEMENT .... 35,480 lbs.
.... (16,257 kg)
BERTHS 7
AUXILIARY .... 50 to 70 hp Diesel

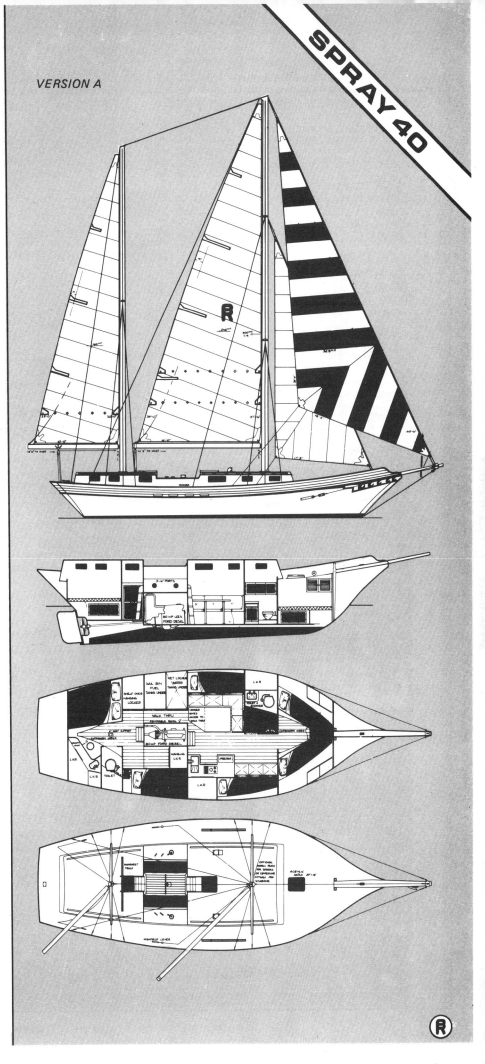

VERSION A

SPRAY 40

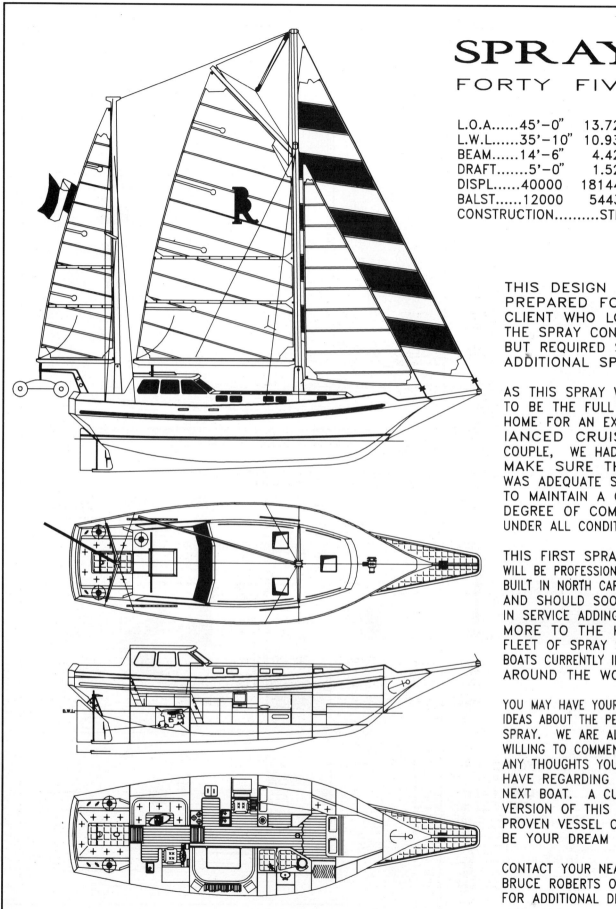

SPRAY
FORTY FIVE

L.O.A......	45'-0"	13.72 M
L.W.L......	35'-10"	10.93 M
BEAM......	14'-6"	4.42 M
DRAFT......	5'-0"	1.52 M
DISPL......	40000	18144 K
BALST......	12000	5443 K
CONSTRUCTION.........STEEL		

THIS DESIGN WAS PREPARED FOR A CLIENT WHO LOVED THE SPRAY CONCEPT BUT REQUIRED SOME ADDITIONAL SPACE.

AS THIS SPRAY WAS TO BE THE FULL TIME HOME FOR AN EXPERIANCED CRUISING COUPLE, WE HAD TO MAKE SURE THERE WAS ADEQUATE SPACE TO MAINTAIN A GOOD DEGREE OF COMFORT UNDER ALL CONDITIONS.

THIS FIRST SPRAY 45 WILL BE PROFESSIONALLY BUILT IN NORTH CAROLINA AND SHOULD SOON BE IN SERVICE ADDING ONE MORE TO THE HUGE FLEET OF SPRAY SAILBOATS CURRENTLY IN USE AROUND THE WORLD.

YOU MAY HAVE YOUR OWN IDEAS ABOUT THE PERFECT SPRAY. WE ARE ALWAYS WILLING TO COMMENT ON ANY THOUGHTS YOU MAY HAVE REGARDING YOUR NEXT BOAT. A CUSTOM VERSION OF THIS WELL PROVEN VESSEL COULD BE YOUR DREAM SHIP.

CONTACT YOUR NEAREST BRUCE ROBERTS OFFICE FOR ADDITIONAL DETAIL.

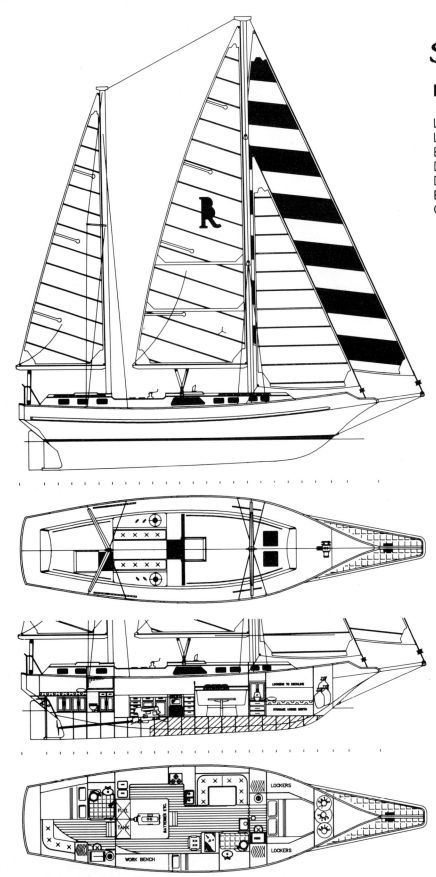

SPRAY
FIFTY

L.O.A......50'-0"	15.24 M
L.W.L......39'-6"	12.04 M
BEAM......14'-6"	4.42 M
DRAFT.......5'-0"	1.52 M
DISPL......45000	20412 K
BALST......12000	5443 K
CONSTRUCTION..........STEEL	

HERE WE HAVE ANOTHER VERSION OF THE EVER POPULAR SPRAY. THE SPRAY 50 WAS DESIGNED FOR AN EXPERIANCED U.K. CLIENT WHO HAS SEEN MANY OF THE SPRAY 40 AND OTHER VERSIONS OF THIS BOAT CURRENTLY IN SERVICE AROUND EUROPE.

THE SPRAY 50 COULD BE BUILT IN ONE OF SEVERAL DIFFERENT VERSIONS AND WE ARE SURE THAT THIS LATEST SPRAY WILL FIND MANY ADMIRERS.

WE ARE PREPARED TO DRAW SEMI—CUSTOM PLANS FOR YOUR OWN ARRANGEMENT FOR THIS OR ANY OTHER OF THE SPRAY RANGE. HAVING A SEMI—CUSTOM PLAN PREPARED FOR YOU IS ONE WAY TO ACQUIRE EXACTLY THE BOAT OF YOUR DREAMS.

CONTACT YOUR NEAREST BRUCE ROBERTS DESIGN OFFICE FOR ADDITIONAL INFORMATION ON THIS OR ANY OTHER OF OUR RANGE OF PLANS AND FULL SIZE PATTERNS.

ROBERTS SPRAY built by Charlie Jupp and sailed single-handed from Australia to England via South Africa.

COASTWORKER 25

- STEEL
- ALUMINUM

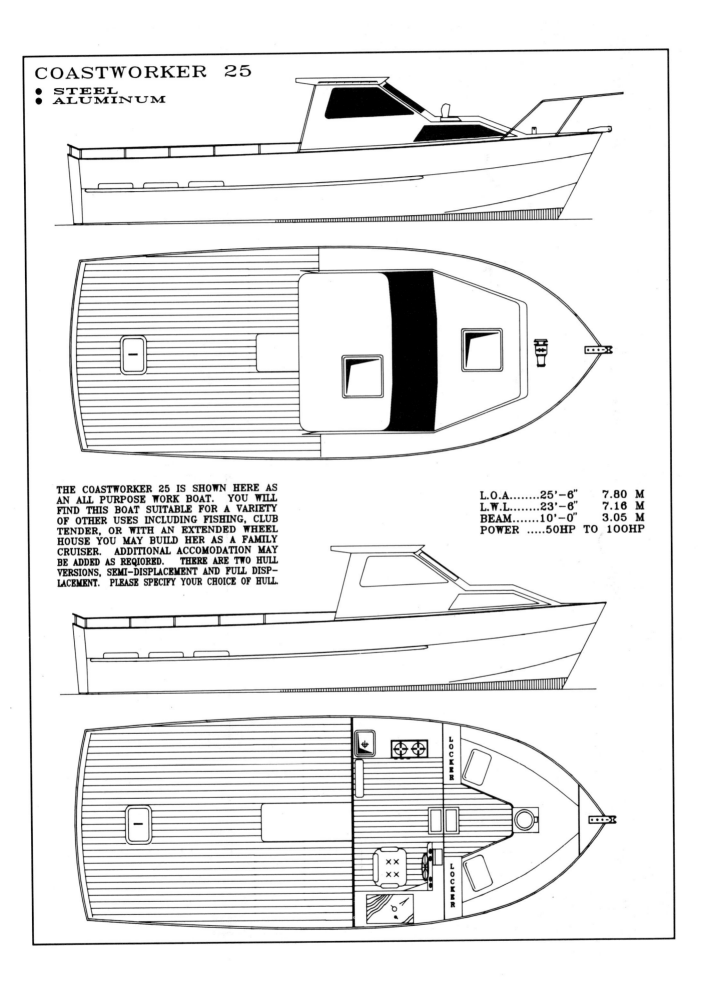

THE COASTWORKER 25 IS SHOWN HERE AS AN ALL PURPOSE WORK BOAT. YOU WILL FIND THIS BOAT SUITABLE FOR A VARIETY OF OTHER USES INCLUDING FISHING, CLUB TENDER, OR WITH AN EXTENDED WHEEL HOUSE YOU MAY BUILD HER AS A FAMILY CRUISER. ADDITIONAL ACCOMODATION MAY BE ADDED AS REQIORED. THERE ARE TWO HULL VERSIONS, SEMI-DISPLACEMENT AND FULL DISPLACEMENT. PLEASE SPECIFY YOUR CHOICE OF HULL.

L.O.A........25'-6"   7.80 M
L.W.L........23'-6"   7.16 M
BEAM.......10'-0"   3.05 M
POWER .....50HP TO 100HP

WAVERUNNER
TWENTY FIVE

L.O.A.	25.9'	....	7.90 M
L.W.L.	23.7'	....	7.21 M
BEAM	10.0'	....	3.00 M
DRAFT	2 — 3.5'	....	.6—1 M

The Waverunner 25 has been designed especially for steel construction and special care has been taken to provide for adequate displacement to build in this material.

Aluminum builders can order special plans, call for details.

Frameless construction and carefully placed bulkheads will provide adequate stiffening for this hull.

We feel that this hull will offer speeds in the high end of the displacement scale provided the builder follows methods described in the plans.

The hull lines were drawn on our computer using our specially developed software that enables us to offer you fully developed FULL SIZE PATTERNS that reflect the true shape of the hull. The plating will literally "DRAPE" over the framework no difficull plate forming with these hulls.

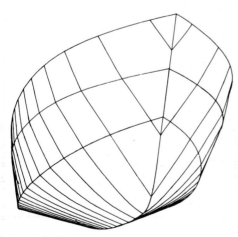

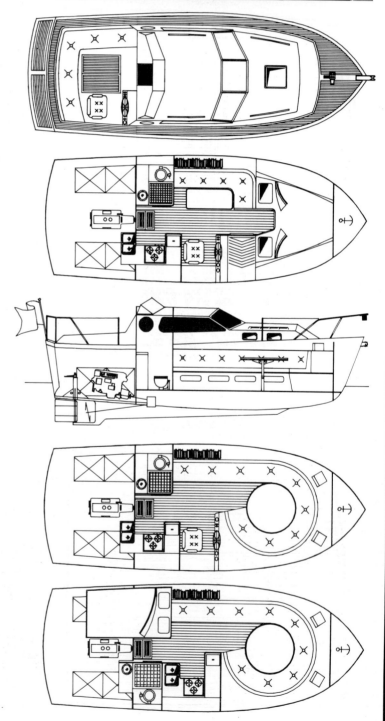

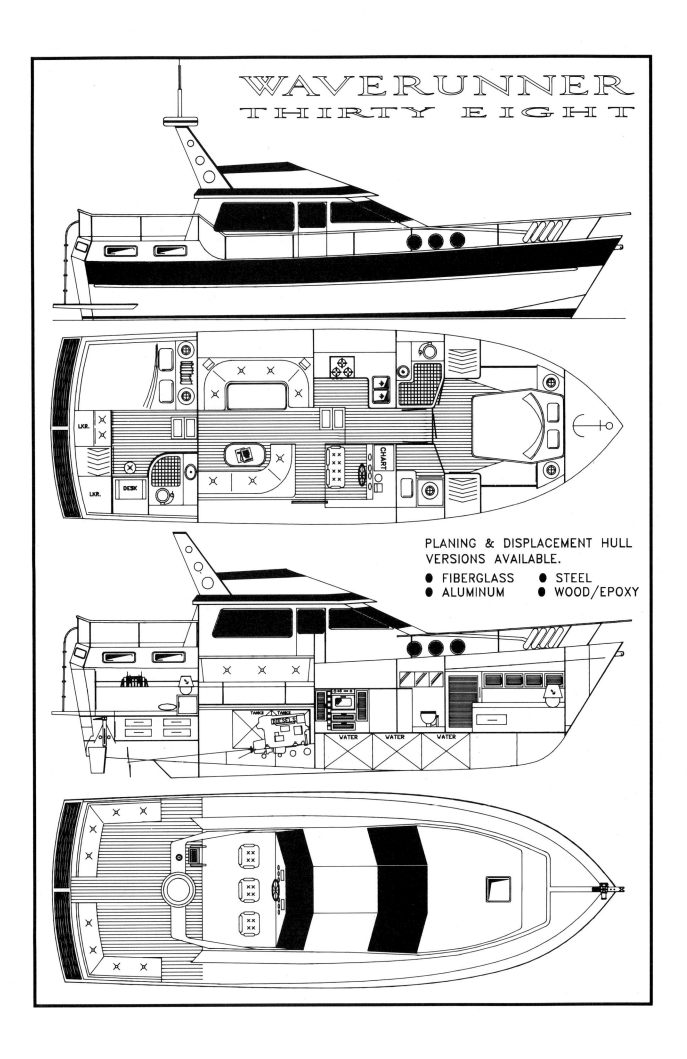

WAVERUNNER
THIRTY EIGHT

PLANING & DISPLACEMENT HULL
VERSIONS AVAILABLE.
- FIBERGLASS   - STEEL
- ALUMINUM   - WOOD/EPOXY

WAVERUNNER 44

The Waverunner Series

The first Waverunner was designed in 1968 and served as a test bed for this increasingly popular range of power boats. Over three thousand Waverunner's, ranging in size from 22'-0" to 70'-0" [6.70 to 21.33 Metres] has been built and cruised successfully throughout the world.

Many of these boats have been built as both commercial or family fishing boats, pilot boats, customs launches, fisheries patrol vessels, and many other commercial uses as well as for family cruising. Waverunners have been designed to be built in fibreglass, steel, aluminum and wood epoxy. The hulls range from pure displacement types, through to high speed planing, luxury cruisers.

When we converted to computer assisted design in the early eighties, we found that it was possible to design boats which not only offered superior performances but were easier, quicker and less expensive to build. The design software has continuously advanced over the past ten years to a point where we can accurately design a hull to perform exactly according to the intending owners requirements. No more guess work on speeds - v - horsepower.

The computer design techniques have made it much easier to control weights and ensure that the finished boat will not exceed its design weight and so impair the performance. We are no lovers of ultra light boats; we recommend that the unnecessary weight be kept to a bare minimum. Computer assisted design allows all those designers who take advantage of its benefits, to spend more time on the actual design process and less time working through pages of calculations. The computer can figure in seconds, what would take the most mathematically literate person, many hours to calculate.

After that reference for computer design, it will come as no surprise when I say that all our Waverunner designs enjoy the benefits of these latest design techniques. Full size patterns for the complete hull framing, deck beams, cabin beams, expanded transom and many other parts of the boat are now so easy for us to produce that we offer these patterns with all our designs at no extra charge. When I remember the many years of crawling around lofting floors, I bless this computer age.

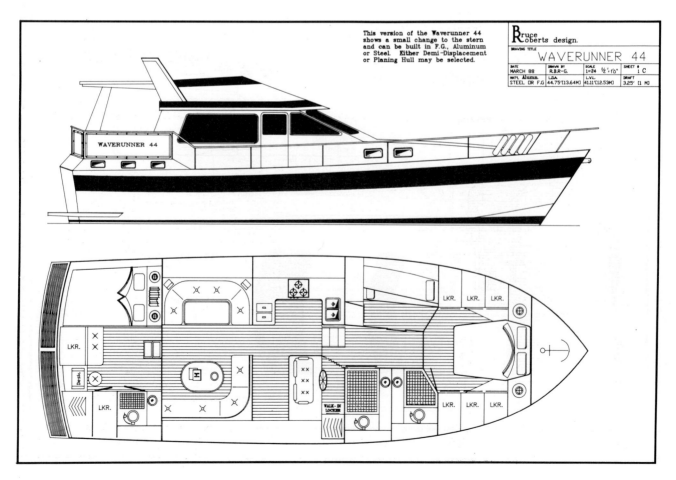

This version of the Waverunner 44 shows a small change to the stern and can be built in F.G., Aluminum or Steel. Either Demi-Displacement or Planing Hull may be selected.

Bruce Roberts design.

DRAWING TITLE: WAVERUNNER 44

| DATE MARCH 88 | DRAWN BY R.B.R-G. | SCALE 1=24 ½"=1'0" | SHEET # 1 C |
| MAT'L. Alumn. STEEL OR F.G | L.O.A. 44.75'[13.64M] | L.W.L. 41.11'[12.53M] | DRAFT 3.25' [1 M] |

WAVERUNNER 52

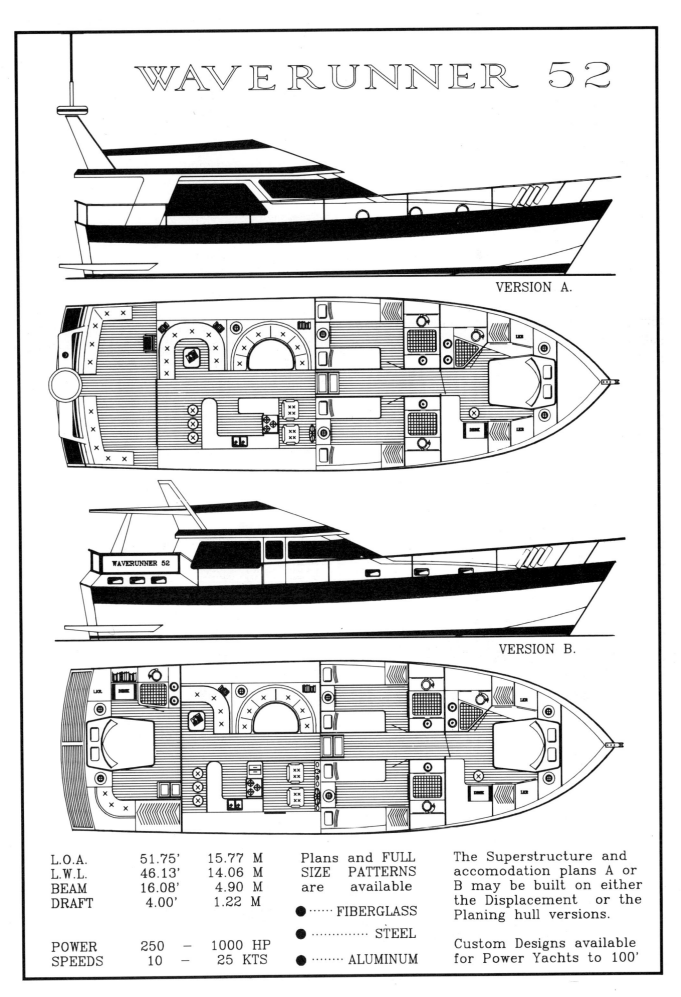

VERSION A.

VERSION B.

L.O.A.	51.75'	15.77 M	
L.W.L.	46.13'	14.06 M	
BEAM	16.08'	4.90 M	
DRAFT	4.00'	1.22 M	
POWER	250	– 1000 HP	
SPEEDS	10	– 25 KTS	

Plans and FULL
SIZE PATTERNS
are available

● ······ FIBERGLASS

● ············ STEEL

● ········ ALUMINUM

The Superstructure and
accomodation plans A or
B may be built on either
the Displacement or the
Planing hull versions.

Custom Designs available
for Power Yachts to 100'

WAVERUNNER 55 & 65

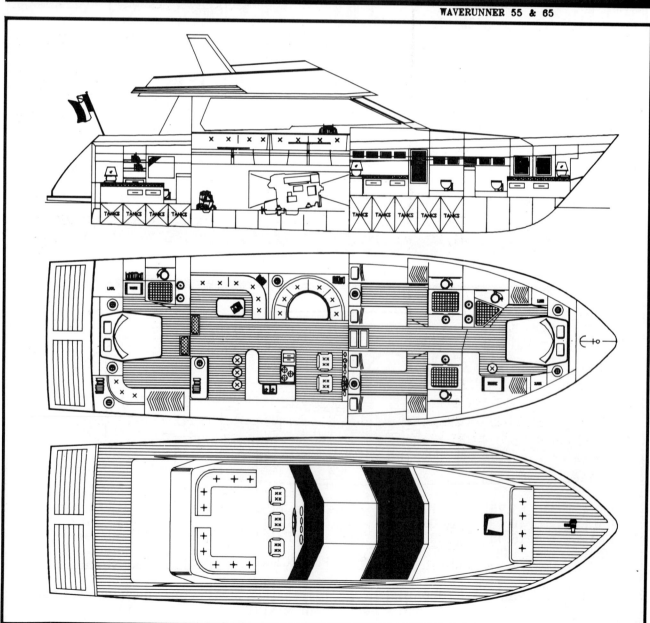

INDEX